FAMILY LOCKET GENEA

Research Like a Pro
with DNA

A Genealogist's Guide to Finding and Confirming Ancestors with DNA Evidence

Diana Elder, Nicole Dyer, and Robin Wirthlin

FOREWORD BY PAUL WOODBURY

FAMILY
LOCKET
BOOKS

Published by:
FAMILY LOCKET BOOKS
an imprint of FAMILY LOCKET GENEALOGISTS LLC
Highland, Utah

All websites were accessed 1 March 2021.
Cover image courtesy of Diana Elder.

To every genealogist who is ready to use DNA in their genealogy research.

Table of Contents

Foreword

Paul Woodbury

When I was still a teenager, I decided that I wanted to become a genetic genealogist. I saw television specials combining genetic evidence with historical research to present groundbreaking discoveries. I saw news stories of exciting finds made possible through the judicious use and application of DNA testing. I knew that I wanted to help unveil similar stories, but there was no clear path forward. In college, I studied genetics. I also studied family history. I would talk to my professors about my goals and none of them knew what to do with me. My genetics professors would look at me blankly and ask if I was talking about some subfield of crime scene investigation. My genealogy and history professors had never met anyone with my specific aims and while they were supportive and encouraging, they could offer little in terms of actionable guidance for pursuing my chosen path. This was my first experience with the chasm that existed between the fields of genetics and genealogy. It was also my first realization that I was in the middle trying to talk to both sides.

Near the end of my college education, I attended the RootsTech conference in Salt Lake City. I soaked up every DNA-related talk I could attend and talked with the presenters to seek their recommendations for future career paths. The advice I received from each one was unanimous—if I wanted to become a genetic genealogist, I should focus on bioinformatics and big data so I could get hired by one of the labs providing genetic testing services for genealogy. I am glad I disregarded that advice. You see, this was another example of the chasm between the fields. At that time, every one of the presenters that I interviewed was a scientist applying their knowledge to their genealogy hobby. Meanwhile, the professional genealogists were hesitant to immediately adopt what these amateur genealogists were claiming as proof for their genealogical work and questioned the reliability of DNA evidence (or at least severely underestimated its potential applications). At that time, the number of professional genealogists with strong academic foundations in historical document analysis who also happened to be utilizing genetic evidence were few and far between. I saw an opportunity, an underrepresented niche, and I pursued it. I set out to bridge the gap between geneticists and genealogists, between scientists and historians. I set out to close the chasm.

Over the ensuing years, I have met many others with the same aim and goal—individuals striving to help geneticists understand genealogical proof and the need for documentary evidence and support individuals striving to help genealogists incorporate DNA evidence into their work. Diana, Nicole, and Robin are among those I have met in this journey, and this book, *Research Like a Pro with DNA*, is part of that effort. If you aim to bridge this gap yourself, this is the book for you. Welcome to the community living in the world between genetics and genealogy! Whether you are coming from the science side and aiming to improve your genealogical research skills or whether you are coming from the genealogy side and are hoping to improve your skills in DNA analysis, correlation, and communication there is something for you here.

If you have set out to close the chasm, whether it be for your own professional development, for pursuit of your own personal research challenges, or both, perhaps you have come to the same realization I have regarding opportunities for growth and learning in genetic genealogy: comprehensive educational opportunities are limited. While there are now a few courses on genetic genealogy taught at institutes and at select colleges, by and large education in this area until recently has mostly been constrained to conferences. If you are lucky, perhaps some of those conferences have dedicated tracks, but even then, you usually get a mix of speakers and perspectives. As a result of this challenge, the perspectives researchers gain regarding the field can be contradictory, confusing, and perhaps slightly imbalanced. While conference presentations may focus on a single methodology, they may not consider the place of that approach or methodology in larger contexts of research strategy and practice. For example, while chromosome mapping is a favorite topic at genealogy conferences, it can be a little overwhelming if you are first getting started, and in reality, it is typically pursued later on in the research process. Meanwhile, clustering and genetic networks are important foundational strategies for the initial organization of DNA test results commonly pursued as a first step in genetic genealogy research which is sometimes overlooked or underrepresented in conference formats. As genetic genealogy is such a new field, it can also be hard in a conference format to discern who is an expert in the field and who is just getting started themselves. When opinions conflict, who should you trust? *Research Like a Pro with DNA* attempts to overcome some of these challenges by providing a birds-eye view of the overall research process. Not only does the book ably review the science, the methodologies, and their applications, but it also provides a framework for efficient prioritization of research strategies, thus helping you to make wise choices as you begin actually applying genetic evidence to your genealogical research or genealogical evidence to your genetics research. This book will help you to develop your process, but it will also help you continually refine it.

Over the years, I have continually refined my own research processes in genetic genealogy. At the same time, I have met other practitioners who are continually refining their own. Throughout this journey, I have found the truth in Abraham Maslow's famous quote that "it is tempting, if the only tool you have is a hammer, to treat everything as if it were a nail." When I am successful with one approach, my first inclination has sometimes been to force every new research problem into the same strict approach. Gradually, I have learned that not every research project is best suited for my hammer du jour—my favorite new tool, approach, or methodology. As I have adopted and mastered new tools, methodologies, approaches, and strategies, my arsenal has grown to the point that I can now consider a research problem on its own merits and select, prioritize, and implement the most appropriate strategies and approaches based on the context of a problem. If you follow the steps of *Research Like a Pro with DNA*, you will get to this point too. The book presents a process for researching, analyzing, and writing about DNA evidence, and while this process is strict enough to reinforce careful and thorough research habits, it is also flexible enough to permit customization for the needs of a particular problem. Rather than presenting you with a hammer that will fail you anytime you face something other than a nail, *Research Like a Pro with DNA* provides you with a toolbox, instruction manual, and resources for regular updates and add-ons.

Genetic Genealogy is a rapidly developing and constantly evolving field. DNA match lists are constantly changing, as are the tools and methodologies for interpreting DNA evidence. For this reason, many other books on genetic genealogy have been obsolete almost immediately off the press. *Research Like a Pro with DNA* is different in that its overall strategies and processes for evidence analysis are evergreen. Meanwhile, its discussions of tools, methodologies, and strategies may be subject to change as the field evolves; however, for these elements, the research Like a Pro podcast series and blog provide a fantastic supplement for continued growth and for staying on top of new developments.

As you close the chasm between genetics and genealogy; as you master the strategies and tools for DNA evidence analysis, interpretation, and writing; as you refine and prioritize your research process and launch (or even just maintain) your genetic genealogy education, *Research Like a Pro with DNA* will help you on the journey. Get ready to *Research Like a Pro with DNA.*

Introduction

Nicole Dyer

Have you been wondering how to use DNA evidence in your genealogy research? Maybe you've tried finding matches that provide evidence of a hypothesized ancestor but came up empty. Perhaps you have already found some evidence that you think may support your theories, but you are not yet confident in your conclusions. Maybe you even have a solid understanding of DNA and how it might be helpful for genealogy, but you haven't yet taken the step of fully applying it in your own genealogy research.

I was in the same boat about five years ago. I knew that DNA evidence was an important way to make discoveries about ancestors, but I wasn't sure how to fully harness its power. I had attended many classes and webinars about using DNA for genealogy and had a pretty good understanding of the basics of genetic inheritance. Even so, I had no practical experience.

After my mother, Diana Elder, received her Accredited Genealogist Professional (AG) credential in 2017, I learned how to perform professional-level research under her tutelage and guidance and eventually started taking on my own client projects. I knew that DNA testing was a next step for many of my clients' brick wall problems, but I wasn't sure how to analyze the test results and apply them.

Enter Robin Wirthlin, a genealogist with a background in molecular biology; Diana met Robin at the Salt Lake Institute of Genealogy, and they began talking about the Research Like a Pro (RLP) book we published in 2018. Robin shared how revolutionary the step-by-step method was for her. Diana thought something similar was needed for genetic genealogy and brought Robin on board to create a Research Like a Pro process that included DNA.

Robin began coaching me on how to use DNA evidence and gave me advice on incorporating it into my own brick wall research. I still remember how illuminating the Lucidchart diagram she drew for my Dyer DNA matches seemed! Everything suddenly became clearer. Robin also mentored me on applying DNA evidence to my client cases. Her advice opened a whole new world to me. I read genetic genealogy books, tried using DNA tools, began testing more relatives, attended two DNA institutes, and practiced applying DNA evidence to all my projects.

Robin studied the steps that were required at the beginning of a DNA project. The Research Like a Pro method laid out in *Research Like a Pro: A Genealogist's Guide* includes seven steps, but Robin reasoned that DNA research requires some additional steps upfront. So, the RLP with DNA process is a little longer than the RLP process.

Diana, Robin, and I regularly collaborated, discussing how documentary research and DNA research could be combined. We charted each step in the process and debated where each step fit most logically. When we nailed down the RLP with DNA process, Robin began writing blog posts to explain the method. We made plans to start an RLP with DNA study group to test the method and launched it in the fall of 2019 with twenty-five participants.

In the RLP with DNA study group, Diana, Robin, and I worked on our own projects along with the other participants. I made huge strides in my Dyer research project when I ordered a network graph during the DNA tools assignment and found a cluster belonging to my brick wall ancestor's hypothesized mother. Writing a report on my Dyer research was gratifying. Just as I made significant progress in my own research through applying the process, so did other members of the group. Many solved their problems or got closer to the answer.

After the first RLP with DNA study group, Diana, Robin, and I made additional tweaks to the process. We moved the citations lesson toward the beginning and improved the efficiency of the research log by switching to Airtable. We started writing the chapters for this book and continued using the process in our own projects and for clients.

The second RLP with DNA study group in the fall of 2020 included forty participants and eight mentors. After seeing fellow study group members apply DNA evidence to their research problems and make progress, we felt ready to publish the process in a book.

Genealogists make headway in their research problems when using the Research Like a Pro with DNA process because it empowers them to organize and focus their efforts on a specific research objective. You begin by gathering the foundational knowledge you need about your matches, the locality, and DNA tools that might help. After planning the research, you follow the plan, log your research, and write a report.

Writing a report is one of the most important parts of the process. Many researchers don't feel like they can go to that step until they have solved their case. However, it's in the writing of the evidence that many cases are solved, especially with indirect evidence. Bringing together the various clues in a narrative format reveals connections and patterns in the evidence. Breaking up your DNA project into phases will allow you to write more as you go along. Another benefit to writing your report based on what you accomplished in one phase is keeping your research hours and report length manageable.

Many genealogists feel their genealogy education has been scattered. They have gathered bits and pieces from various conferences, books, and webinars about courthouse research, land records, Y-DNA testing, and so forth. What's missing is a way to put all the knowledge together into a well-defined procedure that guides you toward achieving a specific goal. If you are like me when I started, you may have learned many things about genetic genealogy without actually applying it. We hope that the Research Like a Pro with DNA method will help you apply what you've learned to a research question in your own family tree.

Each time you repeat the RLP with DNA process, you may wonder if you still need to complete each step of the process. The answer is yes—but some steps will become easier, especially if you are researching in the same locality over and over and have already made your locality guide. Assessing and organizing matches becomes easier when working with the same match list since you have already sorted them into groups. However, you will probably be focusing on a different branch of your family and will need to create a diagram for your new objective. As you become more advanced, you will gain experience with applying tools to your specific project and won't need to spend as much time experimenting with them. When new tools are developed, try them out to learn if they will be useful in future research projects.

We want to thank Paul Woodbury and Alice Childs for their careful review of the entire manuscript and many suggestions on all aspects of the process. We are also grateful for our Research Like a Pro with DNA Study Group members who tested the process on their own projects and provided helpful feedback. Many experts in the genetic genealogy field have laid the foundation for our work by sharing their knowledge in countless ways. We thank each of them. We also appreciate the developers who have created DNA analysis tools to make our work possible.

How to Use This Book

This book is designed to take you from the beginning of a research project to the end. We have provided real-life examples throughout to help you understand the concepts. You'll reap the most benefit if you follow the steps in order, working through your own research project. Because this is an organized method, if you need to take a break, you'll be able to pick up right where you left off.

Throughout the book, we discuss various tools that can help you with each step. You can probably guess that we love Lucidchart, Airtable, and Ancestry trees, but these are not the only tools that will get the job done. We have tried to present the reasoning behind using various types of tools, and we hope you choose the tools you like best. There is a learning curve for any new tool that you decide to use. Be sure to build in extra time for learning Airtable or a diagramming program the first time you use it in a project. To see a list of recommended tools, go to https://familylocket.com/rlpdna. We will be updating this list as time goes on.

We hope that you have already read some of the important books in the field, like Blaine Bettinger's *The Family Tree Guide to DNA Testing and Genetic Genealogy* and *Genetic Genealogy in Practice* which he coauthored with Debbie Parker Wayne. Studying these references will provide a strong foundation in DNA inheritance and testing.

We encourage you to try completing a project and writing a report using the Research Like a Pro process without DNA first. Many of you have experience with this. If you don't, please check out our series of blog posts about how to Research Like a Pro, or our book, *Research Like a Pro: A Genealogist's Guide.*

Some of our examples reference work we have done for clients. You may wonder if the process is different when you are working for yourself versus working for a client. The main difference is the need to be efficient. When working under a time limit, you need to plan for enough time to research *and* write the report. If you are doing research professionally, be sure to read our productivity tips in chapter twelve.

Even when you are working for yourself, you will probably find that setting a time limit will help you make more progress. If you plan to complete a whole phase of research in one month, you will come much closer to your answer than if you research off and on for six months and never write a report.

We have created a list of additional resources to supplement this book on our website at https://familyLocket.com/rlpdna. In the ever-changing world of genetic genealogy, we realized that detailed directions about websites had the potential to become outdated quickly. For that reason, the RLP with DNA webpage will include a list of our blog posts with current tutorials for DNA tools and websites.

With the purchase of this book, you are eligible to join our private RLP with DNA Facebook group. This is a place where you can ask questions, share your progress, and connect with other people using the RLP with DNA process. To join, please email your receipt to info@familylocket.com.

We recommend working through the assignments with a friend or study group. We offer the Research Like a Pro with DNA study group once a year, and our eCourse is always available. Go to https://familylocket.com/services for more information. If you'd like to host your own study group, contact us for more details.

CHAPTER 1

Take a DNA Test

Robin Wirthlin

One of the great discoveries of the nineteenth and twentieth centuries was DNA—deoxyribonucleic acid.[1] DNA consists of a sugar molecule called deoxyribose, a phosphoric acid, and four nitrogen-containing bases called adenine, thymine, guanine, and cytosine. We simplify this by referring only to the four bases using a string of letters, A, T, G, and C. Combinations of these four bases make up the DNA genetic code in each of the cells in our bodies. Over the past 150+ years, human DNA has been described, isolated, and studied. Significant advances in technology and scientific breakthroughs now enable DNA to be used as a genealogical research and discovery tool.[2]

DNA is a biological connection to our ancestors; we inherited our DNA from our parents, who inherited it from their parents, and they inherited DNA from their parents, etc., back through time. We live in an exciting era! Now we can use DNA as evidence to determine and discern family relationships, discover more about our ancestors, and extend our family lines.

---

1. Ral Dahm, "Friedrich Miescher and the Discovery of DNA," *Developmental Biology* 278 (15 February 2005): 274–88; image copy, *ScienceDirect* (https://www.sciencedirect.com/science/article/pii/S0012160604008231). See also J. D. Watson, F.H.C. Crick, "Molecular Structure of Nucleic Acids: A Structure for Deoxyribose Nucleic Acid," *Nature* 171, (1953): 737–738; image copy, *Nature* (https://doi.org/10.1038/171737a0).

2. Ugo A. Perego, et al, "The Science of Molecular Genealogy," *National Genealogical Society Quarterly* 93, (December 2005): 245–59.

Ancestors we seek to identify and confirm do not need to be alive today to test their DNA. We glimpse into the past as we examine our DNA results compared to the DNA results of others who are alive or who have recently passed on. We do not know precisely what happened in the past, but we can use DNA test results in conjunction with genealogical records to confirm or refute family relationships and help us overcome "brick walls" or dead-ends in our family trees. We don't need the DNA from the bodies of specific ancestors to confirm relationships. We just need to compare our DNA to the DNA of other descendants of one of our ancestors to make the connection.

Humans have different types of DNA: nuclear and mitochondrial. The nucleus of most human cells contains nuclear DNA. Nuclear DNA includes 23 pairs of chromosomes, numbered 1–22, and are called autosomal DNA, and the remaining pair are the sex chromosomes, X and Y. One copy of each chromosome numbered 1–22 is inherited from your mother, and one copy of each chromosome 1–22 is inherited from your father. Females have two X chromosomes, and males have one X and one Y chromosome.

All people have mitochondrial DNA, which is found in the many mitochondria in each human cell. Each type of DNA is tested by one or more direct-to-consumer DNA testing companies. The type of DNA you choose to test may depend on the research objective you are seeking to achieve.

Which Kind of DNA Test Should I Take?

Many people wonder, "Which DNA test should I take?" The answer depends on what information you are seeking. The following information will help you choose the type of DNA test that is best for you and learn which companies will help you get the most for your money. The International Society of Genetic Genealogy Wiki (ISOGG Wiki) has excellent ideas on this as well. [3]

Autosomal DNA (atDNA)

The most widely promoted DNA tests on the market today are autosomal DNA (atDNA) tests. These tests focus on the autosomes, which are the 22 chromosome pairs. X chromosome

---

3. "Autosomal DNA testing comparison chart," rev. 18:10, 9 January 2021, *International Society of Genetic Genealogy (ISOGG) Wiki*, (https://isogg.org/wiki/Autosomal_DNA_testing_comparison_chart).

DNA (X-DNA) is also examined in some commercial autosomal DNA tests and has its own unique inheritance pattern.

Most human DNA is the same. There are millions of locations in the human genetic code that are identical from person to person. Direct-to-consumer DNA tests look at approximately 700,000 locations in a person's atDNA, where the DNA code is more likely to vary. The variations are called single nucleotide polymorphisms, or SNPs for short. The nucleotides listed in your raw DNA data are represented by a string of letters, G, A, T, and C. The output from the raw DNA data shows the letter code variations.

When you submit your DNA kit to a testing company, the testing company compares your test results with other test results that are already in their database. A DNA match list is generated from the people that share DNA with you, and the amount of DNA they share with you is listed in centimorgans (cM). A centimorgan is a unit measurement of the likelihood that DNA will recombine.[4] "Recombination [is an] event occurring during meiosis—the formation of sperm and egg cells. One chromosome from the mother and the other from the father break and trade segments with one another."[5]

The number of cM listed with a person on your DNA match list can be compared to a range of cM found in known family relationships. *In general, the higher the number, the closer the relationship.* You do not inherit autosomal DNA from every one of your ancestors on all of your ancestral lines because there is a random element to DNA recombination. Practically speaking, this also means that there is a limit to how far back we can infer genetic relationships. With today's technology, this is approximately 6–8 generations back from you. If you are interested in learning more about your family members, ancestors, or ethnicity, take an autosomal DNA test. And if you have parents, aunts, uncles, grandparents, great-aunts, great-uncles or great-grandparents, etc., still living, seriously consider asking them to take a DNA test too!

Five leading testing companies focus on atDNA. Remember that each company is free to decide how to store and interpret your test results. Periodically, each company offers sales on DNA tests. See the company comparison chart in table 1.1.

AncestryDNA, and 23andMe, do not allow raw data transfers of DNA test results from other companies to be uploaded into their databases. Family Tree DNA, MyHeritage, and Living DNA do allow test results to be transferred from another company. If you think you will want to have your DNA results in more than one company database, it is best to test with AncestryDNA and 23andMe first.

---

4. "CentiMorgan," rev. 22:50, 14 December 2020, *ISOGG Wiki* (https://isogg.org/wiki/CentiMorgan).

5. "Recombination," rev. 11:59, 14 April 2019, *ISOGG Wiki* (https://isogg.org/wiki/Recombination).

Table 1.1. DNA testing company comparison

Company	Transfer From	Transfer To	Autosomal	Y-DNA	Mitochondrial DNA	Sample
AncestryDNA	yes	no	yes	no	no	saliva
Family Tree DNA	yes	yes	yes	yes, multiple test levels	yes, multiple test levels	swab
23andMe	yes	no	yes	Haplogroup given	Haplogroup given	saliva
MyHeritage	yes	yes	yes	no	no	swab
Living DNA	yes	yes	yes	Haplogroup given	Haplogroup given	swab

Raw data results from those two companies may be downloaded to your computer and then uploaded to Family Tree DNA, MyHeritage, and Living DNA for free, where additional analysis tools can be unlocked for a small fee.

When you open your raw DNA data file, you will see a string of letters that report nucleotides at the tested locations in your DNA. DNA information is meaningful in family history research *only* when it is compared with other DNA test-takers, family relationships, and genealogical records. When DNA and family history records are used together, you can learn a great deal about yourself and your family.

Why would you want to have your atDNA test results in multiple DNA companies' databases? *It's all about making connections.* Some companies have databases that are predominantly filled with test results from people who come from certain parts of the world or specific ethnicities. You may find a match with a long-lost cousin who may know more about your ancestors than you currently do, but they may have only had their DNA test done by one company—and it's only in that company's database. The following list in alphabetical order will help you see the value of having your DNA in multiple companies' databases. Additional considerations on which DNA company to test with could include database size, available tools, strengths of ethnicity estimates, number of trees attached to match results, the response rate of matches, collaboration options, etc. The ISOGG Wiki has an extensive comparison chart that lists the major DNA testing companies' features that you can examine in great detail.[6]

- **23andMe** has a reputation for having the best ethnicity estimates. The website also includes a unique ethnicity chromosome browser that indicates sections of your DNA inherited from people with specific ethnic backgrounds. Additionally, 23andMe provides tools to help you see what segments of DNA you share with your relatives.
- **AncestryDNA** has the most family trees associated with DNA matches and the most test results in its database—over 20 million.[7]
- **Family Tree DNA** is best known for having useful analysis tools to compare and understand your DNA data and storing DNA samples for up to 25 years. We can only imagine the significant technological breakthroughs in DNA that will happen in the future. It may be helpful to have your DNA stored so it can be utilized again for new applications.
- **MyHeritage DNA** has a significant European customer base contributing to its database. It offers analysis tools, including an in-house AutoCluster feature that gathers your DNA matches into groups that share DNA with you and with each other.
- **Living DNA** features ethnicity estimates that break down to the sub-regional level in the British Isles, which may help you focus on geographical regions where you can look for genealogical records that may list your ancestors.

Figure 1.1 illustrates the autosomal DNA inheritance pattern. Autosomal DNA is passed from the ancestral couple at the top of the chart to their children, who pass it on to their children, etc.

Y-chromosomal DNA (Y-DNA)

When Y-DNA information in genealogical research, the hope is to learn how two or more male test-takers are related via a common ancestor. It could also help extend the paternal line, give clues for extending a paternal line, distinguish between similarly named

---

6. "Autosomal DNA testing comparison chart," rev. 18:10, 9 January 2021, *ISOGG Wiki*.

7. "Our Story," *Ancestry* (https://www.ancestry.com/corporate/about-ancestry/company-facts).

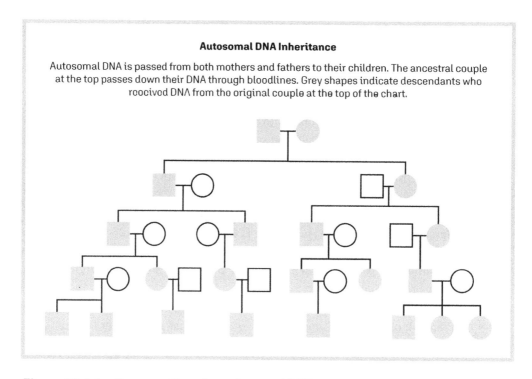

Autosomal DNA Inheritance

Autosomal DNA is passed from both mothers and fathers to their children. The ancestral couple at the top passes down their DNA through bloodlines. Grey shapes indicate descendants who received DNA from the original couple at the top of the chart.

Figure 1.1. Inheritance pattern for autosomal DNA. Created by Robin Wirthlin.

individuals, or evaluate candidates to be a direct paternal ancestor through targeted testing.

A man inherits a Y-chromosome from his father. He inherited a Y-chromosome from his father, which was inherited from his father, and so on, directly along the patrilineal line. If you are a male interested in learning more about your paternal line, or your father's, father's, father's, etc., lineage, take a Y-DNA test. If you are a female, you can ask a male who is descended directly from your father, grandfather, or great-grandfather to take a Y-DNA test.

If you are researching another male ancestor not in your patrilineal line, consider asking a direct paternal descendant of that ancestor to take a Y-DNA test to get more genetic information. This approach is called target testing. The haplogroup and associated surnames reported will provide information and clues about possible ethnicity or family origins. The DNA match list may provide opportunities to connect to other living matches, who may have additional knowledge about the ancestral line.

The Y chromosome is passed down mostly unchanged for many generations, which provides genealogical value in Y-DNA tests. In some cultures, a surname passes from

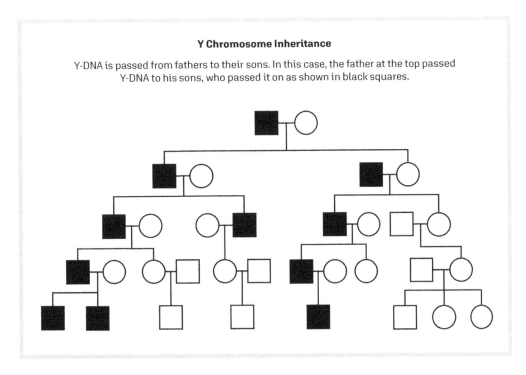

Y Chromosome Inheritance

Y-DNA is passed from fathers to their sons. In this case, the father at the top passed Y-DNA to his sons, who passed it on as shown in black squares.

Figure 1.2. Inheritance pattern for Y- DNA. Created by Robin Wirthlin.

fathers to their children. If a man from one of those cultures takes a Y-DNA test, it may indicate the surname used for generations. It may also show if there has been a misattributed parentage event sometime in the previous generations. Many surname projects are available online where Y-DNA test results can be posted and compared. Members of the projects seek to identify the origin of the surname or how closely people with the same surname are related. This type of test may be beneficial for males seeking to identify unknown fathers.

The DNA inheritance chart in figure 1.2 illustrates how Y-DNA is passed on from father to son through the generations. The black squares show the men who inherit Y-DNA from their paternal line, starting with the ancestral couple at the top of the chart.

In a Y-DNA test, short tandem repeats (STRs) are examined. STRs are regions of DNA where a small motif (typically 2–5 bases in length) is repeated several times in a consecutive sequence in the genetic code. Occasionally when DNA is replicated before being passed on to the next generation, mutations occur. These regions might experience a deletion or addition of the motif causing variation in the general population regarding how many times a particular motif is repeated. DNA locations with STRs tested are called markers. In your Y-DNA results, you will see the tested marker's name and the number of repeats of a motif at that location on the Y-chromosome.

For example, DYS522 is a marker that has four nucleotides that repeat themselves between 8 and 17 times in the pattern [GATA][GATA][GATA][GATA] . . .[8] The genetic distance reported generally indicates how closely individual test takers are related to each other—but it does not mean the number of generations between test takers. It refers to the number of stepwise mutations differentiating the two Y-chromosome haplotypes. The lower the genetic distance (GD), the closer the people are related. There is always a chance that a mutation will occur during the descent from father to son, especially in fast-mutating markers. Some fathers and sons will have a GD of 1 at a particular marker because the mutation happened in their generation. See chapter six for more discussion of fast-mutating or fast-moving markers.

Family Tree DNA offers Y-DNA tests, whose name indicates the number of STR markers that are examined. At first, a 12-marker test was available, then later, 25, 37, 67, and 111 marker tests were added, and finally, the Big-Y-700 test (which looks at STRs and SNPs). Currently, the Y-37, Y-111, and Big Y-700 tests are offered. The higher the number of markers tested, the more refined the results will be.

23andMe, Living DNA, and others examine Y-DNA SNP markers in their tests though not all report them. The more markers, the higher the test's resolution, and the matches you receive will be closer in a genealogical timeframe. If you are a male, 23andMe and LivingDNA tests estimate your Y-DNA haplogroup based on the markers they test on the Y-chromosome, which may help with unknown parentage research. However, the only information given is the haplogroup without the specific number of repeats at the markers tested, which is not detailed enough to achieve genealogical proof.

Mitochondrial DNA (mtDNA)

Both men and women inherit mitochondrial DNA from their mothers, but only women can pass it on to their children. 23andMe and Living DNA report mtDNA haplogroup esti-mates. mtDNA tests, offered by FamilyTree DNA, are genealogically useful and can provide distinctive DNA clues and a set of markers used to create a match list. If you are looking

---

8. U.S. Department of Commerce, National Institute of Standards and Technology, "Summary List of Y Chromosome STR Loci and Available Fact Sheets," *STRBase (SRD-130)* (https://strbase.nist.gov/ystr_fact.htm). See also, John M. Butler et al., "Addressing Y-Chromosome Short Tandem Repeat Allele Nomenclature," *Journal of Genetic Genealogy* 4 (Fall 2008): 125–148; e-journal, (https://jogg.info/pages/42/files/butler.pdf).

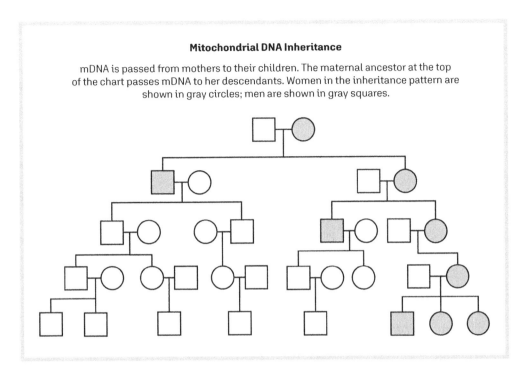

Figure 1.3. Inheritance pattern for mitochondrial DNA. Created by Robin Wirthlin.

for information about your mother's, mother's, mother's genealogical line, take a mito-chondrial DNA test. The results report a mitochondrial haplogroup. People with the same mtDNA haplogroup share a common matrilineal ancestor. See figure 1.3 for an illustration of mtDNA inheritance from mothers to their children.

mtDNA mutates very slowly, and the female ancestor that two DNA matches share may have lived dozens, hundreds, or thousands of years ago. An mtDNA test can show that two individuals are related along the direct maternal line. If they are exact matches at the full mitochondrial sequence level, they may be related within a genealogical time-frame. This result is ideal for testing hypothesized relationships. Imagine the hypothesis that Elizabeth was the daughter of Irinda. We can test a direct maternal descendant of Elizabeth and a direct maternal relative of Irinda, and that should tell us if our hypoth-esis is correct. Still, the defining feature is NOT just a shared haplogroup—instead, it is a shared mtDNA sequence with few (if any) differences. People can belong to the same haplogroup and still have differences between them.

X-chromosomal DNA (X-DNA)

Both men and women have X-chromosomes. Women inherit one X-chromosome from their fathers that was passed on unrecombined. This X-chromosome, in-turn, was inherited from the father's mother. They also inherit an X-chromosome from their mothers—this X- chromosome may be recombined from the X that the mother received from her father and her mother or inherited unrecombined. Men inherit an X-chromosome from their mothers, which may be recombined from the mother's father and mother or inherited unrecombined.

X-DNA has a unique inheritance pattern illustrated in fan charts in figures 1.4 and 1.5. The charts illuminate specific ancestors from whom a whole X-chromosome or X-DNA segments *might be* inherited. It is entirely possible not to inherit X-DNA from some of these ancestors. The X-DNA inheritance pattern is different for males and females. Males are shown in dark gray, and females are shown in light gray. Choose either the male or female inheritance chart for the DNA tester.[9]

For maximum effectiveness, use X-DNA results in conjunction with atDNA results in your research. X-DNA can help you discern if a DNA match is related to your maternal or paternal side only if you are male. If you are female, an X-DNA match could be either maternal or paternal. X-DNA can guide your research and help you focus on the ancestral lines from which it was inherited, which ultimately saves time in your research.

As you can see in the inheritance charts, if you have an X-DNA match and you don't know how they fit into your family tree, you can immediately exclude half or more of your ancestral lines from consideration. Suppose you don't share X-DNA with a match; it doesn't mean that you are not related along a particular ancestral line. Still, if you share a significant portion of X-DNA (at least 10-20 cM) with a DNA match, it indicates that you and the match are related along an X-DNA inheritance path.

X-DNA testing is included in the Illumina OmniExpress and Global Screening Array chips that 23andMe, AncestryDNA, Family Tree DNA, Living DNA, and MyHeritage use.[10] Your raw DNA from each of these companies will report X-DNA results, sometimes listed

---

9. To see more X-DNA inheritance charts, see Blaine Bettinger, "More X-Chromosome Charts," 12 January 2009, *The Genetic Genealogist* (https://thegeneticgenealogist.com/2009/01/12/more-x-chromosome-charts/). Also, Debbie Parker Wayne, "X-DNA Inheritance Charts," Deb's Delvings Blog, posted 25 October 2013 (http://debsdelvings.blogspot.com/2013/10/x-dna-inheritance-charts.html). Also, Debbie Parker Wayne, "Quick Reference Links," *Deb's Delvings Blog* (http://debbiewayne.com/pubs.php#quickref), X-DNA section.

10. "X-chromosome testing," rev. 17:31, 23 November 2020, *ISOGG Wiki* (https://isogg.org/wiki/X-chromosome_testing).

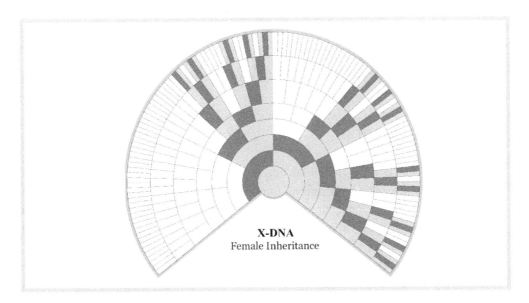

Figure 1.4. X-DNA female inheritance chart, annotated. Courtesy of Blaine Bettinger, "Unlocking the Genealogical Secrets of the X Chromosome," 21 December 2008, The Genetic Genealogist (https://thegeneticgenealogist.com/2008/12/21/unlocking-the-genealogical-secrets-of-the-x-chromosome/).

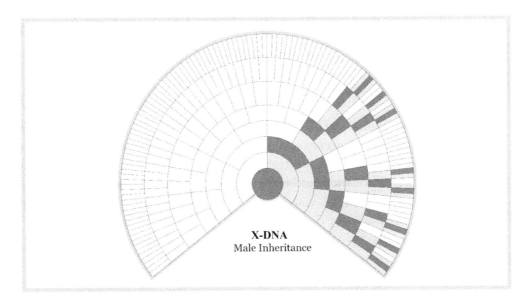

Figure 1.5. X-DNA male inheritance chart, annotated. Courtesy of Blaine Bettinger, "Unlocking the Genealogical Secrets of the X Chromosome," 21 December 2008, The Genetic Genealogist (https://thegeneticgenealogist.com/2008/12/21/unlocking-the-genealogical-secrets-of-the-x-chromosome/).

under chromosome 23, but only 23andMe and Family Tree DNA show the results on a chromosome browser. Additionally, Family Tree DNA tells you on the DNA match page if both you and a DNA match share X-DNA. Be cautious with this information as not all X matches listed share enough X-DNA to be considered pertinent.

Informed Consent

As you take DNA tests yourself and encourage others to test, it is crucial to contemplate genetic testing's long-term implications. Consider the possibility of uncovering unknown information, such as previously unknown relatives, or learning that some family connections are not biological. An informed consent agreement will help you and your family members become aware of DNA testing's positive and possible negative outcomes.

The DNA tester needs to know about these possibilities before agreeing to take a DNA test. If you will be overseeing the DNA test results and working with them in family history research, it is essential to have the tester give permission and learn about the risks involved in DNA testing. Ask the tester to sign an informed consent agreement. This agreement can be sent via email or given in person.

It is also essential to thoroughly review the DNA testing companies' privacy policies. Carefully consider the security of your genetic data. Only utilize companies with which you feel comfortable.

DNA Testing Strategy

With your new understanding of the kinds of DNA tests that exist and the importance of knowing the implications of genetic testing, you are ready to address the question, "What next steps do I take?" The following strategies outline the least expensive testing plan that will deliver the most information quickly. If you already have a specific objective in mind for using DNA evidence in your research, you may want to make a targeted testing plan first, as discussed in chapter six. These options may not be available in all countries.

For Yourself

1. Take an AncestryDNA test.
2. Consider taking a 23andMe DNA test.

3. Transfer the results to other companies to maximize the number of relatives on your DNA match lists.

   a. Download your raw DNA data. For instructions, see "Downloading AncestryDNA® Raw Data"[11] or search for "Download Your Raw Data" on 23andme.com.[12]

   b. Transfer your raw DNA data from AncestryDNA or 23andMe to Family Tree DNA (FTDNA) and unlock the analysis tools for a small fee. Click on "Upload DNA Data" at the top left of the Family Tree DNA website, then choose Autosomal DNA in the drop-down menu for instructions.[13] Another source of instructions is an article called "Autosomal Transfers" found in the Family Tree DNA Learning Center.[14]

   c. Transfer your raw DNA data to MyHeritage and unlock the analysis tools for a relatively small fee. See "Upload DNA data"[15] for instructions.

   d. Consider transferring your raw DNA data to GEDmatch—a 3rd party website. Carefully read the terms and conditions of GEDmatch, which is a public website. *Only transfer your raw DNA data if you agree with the terms and conditions.* After creating an account, on the right side of the main page is a section called "Upload your DNA files:" After clicking on, "Generic Uploads (23andme, FTDNA, AncestryDNA, most others)" detailed instructions are available about how to upload your raw DNA data.[16]

4. Take a Living DNA test or upload raw DNA data from another testing company. See "Upload your DNA for FREE and discover more"[17] for instructions.

5. Take a Y-DNA test at Family Tree DNA if you are a male. Or, if you are a female, ask a male relative to test.

6. Take a mitochondrial DNA test at Family Tree DNA.

---

11. "Downloading AncestryDNA Raw Data," *Ancestry* (https://support.ancestry.com/s/article/Downloading-AncestryDNA-Raw-Data).

12. "Download Raw Data," *23andMe* (https://you.23andme.com/tools/data/download/).

13. Join the world's most comprehensive DNA database!" *Family Tree DNA* (https://www.familytreedna.com/autosomal-transfer).

14. "Autosomal Transfers," *Family Tree DNA Learning Center* (https://learn.familytreedna.com/imports/transfer-autosomal-ancestry/family-tree-dna-family-finder-transfer-program/).

15. "Upload DNA data," *MyHeritage DNA* (https://www.myheritage.com/dna/upload).

16. "GEDmatch raw DNA upload utility," *GEDmatch* (https://www.gedmatch.com/v_upload1N.phpnf).

17. "Upload your DNA for FREE and discover more," *Living DNA* (https://livingdna.com/free-dna-upload).

For others

1. Test the oldest people in your family first, especially those who are generationally closer to shared ancestors.

   a. Parents, grandparents, great-aunts, great-uncles, aunts, uncles, and cousins of parents or grandparents.

2. Test your siblings if *both* parents are not available to DNA test. If both parents have DNA tested, your siblings will not add any more DNA information relevant to your genealogy research. If only one parent is available to take a DNA test, it will be beneficial to your research to ask your siblings to test. The specific segments of DNA inherited by your siblings are different than what you inherited. Each parent randomly gives half of their DNA to each child, so the DNA passed on from their ancestors is unique.

3. Test first cousins, second cousins, or more distant cousins. These relatives inherited some different segments of DNA from your ancestors than you did.

If you test older adults, consider testing directly with FTDNA in addition to AncestryDNA or 23andMe since FTDNA will store the DNA samples for up to 25 years.

Your Task

Take a DNA test and upload the raw data to other DNA websites that accept uploads, following the DNA testing strategy previously outlined. Explore the website of each DNA testing company you chose to use and familiarize yourself with the features in preparation for the next steps in the *Research Like a Pro with DNA* method. The learning center or forums on the DNA company websites answer questions and explain how to best use their tools to work with your DNA test results.

CHAPTER 2

Assess Your DNA Matches and Analyze Your Pedigree

Diana Elder

What did you do when your DNA test results finally arrived? Did you first check your ethnicity results? Did you feel validated to discover the estimated countries of origin? Clicking on your DNA match page, thousands of results likely overwhelmed you. Perhaps you recognized a few close relatives but puzzled over the many unknown cousins appearing on page after page.

As a genealogist, you can use DNA as evidence to discover, confirm, or reject family relationships, but where do you start? Setting up a system to assess your DNA matches will give you control over your test results and help you better understand how to use them to achieve your research goals. Assessing a DNA match includes analyzing the amount of shared DNA against the relationship found in the family tree. For example, does a second cousin share the appropriate amount of DNA? In this chapter, we will discuss each of the following steps needed for this initial assessment.

1. Assess your family tree.
2. Set up a system to track your DNA matches.
3. Cluster your DNA matches into genetic networks.
4. Check the amount of shared DNA.
5. Calculate possible relationships with the Shared cM Project Tool.
6. Contact DNA Matches.

Your Genealogical Family Tree versus Your Genetic Family Tree

When you first began your genealogy journey, how did you start? You probably began to build a family tree, identifying parents and grandparents, then moved back in time. Depending on the family knowledge, localities, and time frame, you may have been able to fill out many generations of your tree, or you may have hit a brick wall ancestor. Beyond that brick wall are several missing branches of your genealogical tree.

Why does this matter? When working with DNA results, how easily you can identify a DNA match will depend on your own tree's fullness. Your goal should be to verify or refute each generation of your family tree and eventually assign each DNA match to a common ancestor or ancestral couple. If you have missing ancestors on your genealogical tree, it will be challenging to determine how you connect with many of your DNA matches. The good news is that you can confirm or reject known relationships by working with your DNA test results. Those results can also provide clues to any unknown ancestors.

For example, my maternal family tree is relatively complete—reaching back to England and Denmark. See figure 2.1. These well-researched ancestral lines make it easier to determine a common ancestral couple for my maternal DNA matches.

On the other hand, my paternal family tree is missing many ancestors. See figure 2.2. I have several unknown ancestors. Because my paternal lines originate in the southern United States, where intermarriage among families was common, determining the common ancestral couple of my paternal DNA matches becomes more complicated.

When you and a DNA match share more than one common ancestor or ancestral couple, that could be a sign of pedigree collapse, a different scenario than endogamy (where intermarriage has occurred among a small group for many generations). Either of these situations can make the DNA analysis more complicated and should be taken into consideration when analyzing your DNA matches.

Your genetic family tree will look different from your genealogical family tree because of DNA inheritance's random nature. You received 50% of your DNA from each of your parents, about 25% from each of your grandparents, and about 12.5% from each of your great grandparents. Figure 2.3 will give you an idea of how much DNA you could share with your close relatives.

With each subsequent generation, the amount of DNA you are likely to inherit from an ancestor is cut in half. Because of DNA inheritance's randomness, some ancestors did not provide you with any DNA and won't be on your genetic family tree. They still make up your genealogical family tree, but you won't have any DNA matches to their descendants.

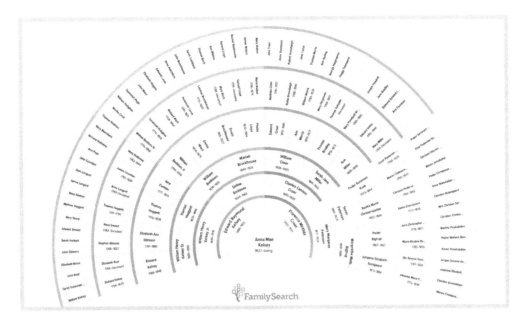

Figure 2.1. Fan Chart for Anna Mae Kelsey.
FamilySearch, https://www.familysearch.org/tree/pedigree/fanchart/LFZX-V49

Figure 2.2. Fan Chart for Bobby Gene Shults.
FamilySearch, https://www.familysearch.org/tree/pedigree/fanchart/KWZM-TKN

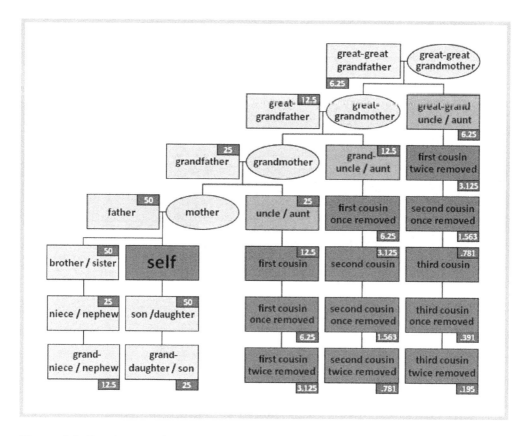

Figure 2.3. Cousin tree showing genetic kinship.
Wikimedia Commons, https://commons.wikimedia.org/wiki/File:Cousin_tree_
[with_genetic_kinship].png.

Whether your genealogical family tree is full, partially full, or missing significant branches, DNA analysis has the power to help you understand your genetic relationships to your relatives. Because autosomal DNA tests yield the most DNA matches, the following steps will be most beneficial for tracking those matches. The testing company databases are large, and you can often have success by "fishing" in each pond of autosomal DNA matches.

If you've taken a Y-DNA or a mitochondrial DNA test, you can also use these steps to evaluate and track your DNA matches. Your match list will typically be smaller because of those tests' narrow focus, but you will still want to work on identifying the matches and possible connections to you. Because these databases are smaller, targeted testing will often yield the best results. Depending on your matches, Autosomal DNA, in conjunction with Y-DNA or mitochondrial DNA (if pertinent to the research question), could give you the most thorough information. See chapter six for more detail on targeted testing.

Tracking your DNA Matches

Before starting any research on your matches, choose a method to record the information you will discover. You'll likely have your DNA data on several testing websites, so you'll want to have a master notebook, document, or spreadsheet to record details about your DNA matches. If you figure out a connection or have a conversation through the company's messaging system, you won't want to lose track of your new knowledge because you didn't record it.

As you work with each match, you'll begin to discover your connection—either a shared ancestor, ancestral couple, or possible family line. A powerful tool for tracking this information is the Airtable DNA research log base (see chapter ten for ideas on setting this up). Airtable is part spreadsheet and part database—enabling you to link information between tables. DNA research is complicated, and Airtable streamlines data entry. The correspondence table within the DNA research log has columns for suggested details to record, such as the date messaged, the DNA matches' contact information, and the messages sent and received. For this chapter's purpose, the term "research log" will be used to refer to whatever record-keeping program you choose.

Each DNA testing company has a notes section to record details about a DNA match. As you fill in the research log, you can also create a note on the website. Because many people use a pseudonym instead of their actual name, it can be easy to forget a previously discovered connection.

I once spent a considerable amount of time corresponding with a DNA match who used a pseudonym not related to her actual name. We found we were second cousins and shared photos and stories. Unfortunately, I failed to put her information into the notes section of the testing company website and messaged her again after a few months. She replied, "This is your cousin, Mary." To keep this from recurring, I now track my DNA matches in my research log and use the DNA testing website note systems to identify the individual and our common ancestral couple.

Notes Protocol
Creating a protocol for the information to include in the notes can help you be consistent and thorough. Useful information includes the amount of DNA shared, the confirmed or possible relationship, the individual's real name once discovered, and the path back

to your shared ancestral couple. Add any other information as desired, such as the date messaged or possible family lines. As your DNA research advances, you may want to note if you've added the match to your chromosome map, family tree, or charting program.

For example, in working with my DNA matches, I wondered about P.H., who appeared in my match list. I sent a message through Ancestry's system with a list of my surnames and was fortunate to receive a response. My match identified herself as Patty and a descendant of my great-grandparents, William Huston Shults and Dora Algie Royston, through their daughter, Lola. I created the following note:

> 2C Pat > Lola Marjorine Jerden Johnson > Lola Shults Jerden > William Huston Shults & Dora Algie Royston, sharing 200 cM across 15 segments.

Using acronyms is an efficient method to note relationships. For example, the 2C in the note is short for second cousin. When charting DNA matches, space is limited, so a shortened description of the relationship is helpful. Once you have discovered the relationship, you could diagram the path in a diagramming program or your chosen family tree organizational system. See chapter three for details about visually organizing your matches.

Suppose you don't know your relationship to the DNA match or the full path back to a suspected ancestral couple. In that case, you can use question marks to indicate a hypothesis rather than a confirmed relationship. You can also use the shared matching system on the DNA company websites to determine a possible common ancestral couple and record that in the notes. Here is another example of a note I created—this time with an unidentified match. Notice my use of the question mark to indicate what I don't know.

> 2C? E. W. > ? > ? > John C. Harris & Malissa Welch, shared matches with Harris/Welch cousins, sharing 224 cM across 13 segments.

Research Logs

As well as creating a note for a DNA match on the company website, you can create an entry in your research log. What is the best way to set up your research log? That will depend on your specific needs and your research project. Following are some suggestions for broad organization. See chapter 10 for specific details.

Master Research Log for Closest Matches

If you don't have a parent's test results in the database and you can't identify any of the close matches to help you determine maternal or paternal lines, you can keep all the DNA matches in one research log and sort them out as you go. This is also a good practice for an adoptee project where maternal lines and paternal lines are unknown.

If your maternal and paternal lines intermarried, you would probably want to have just one research log for all your close matches. You will likely have two sets of common ancestors for some of your DNA matches, and it might be helpful to have all the matches in one research log.

Maternal or Paternal Research Log for Closest Matches

You can choose to have your research log divided into maternal and paternal DNA matches if you've tested a parent. This can help to sort out your closest matches from the beginning. If you have not tested a parent but have sorted DNA matches by paternal or maternal lines based on known relatives such as a first cousin or aunt, you could also use this option. Creating a research log for each grandparent, great-grandparent, etc., could be another way to organize your matches.

I have my DNA results and those of my mother on all the major testing company websites, making it easy to separate maternal and paternal matches. Any DNA match that does not also match my mother is on my paternal line. I chose to create a separate research log for my maternal line and one for my paternal line, which is quite different. My maternal ancestors emigrated from England and Denmark in the mid-1800s coming directly to Utah. My paternal ancestors emigrated in the 1600s and 1700s and eventually found their way to Texas through a southern migration. I have discovered only one overlap in the lines to date, so creating two separate research logs makes sense.

Research Log for an Objective

Suppose you have already identified your close matches and are working on a specific research objective. In that case, the research log can hold the correspondence and match details related only to that objective. The focus will be on a select group of DNA matches from each testing company database used.

Separate DNA Matches into Genetic Networks

After you've recorded the known DNA matches and relationships to you, an efficient next step is to create a genetic network or to separate your matches into groups that cluster around one of your ancestral lines. This will put some order to your DNA match list and aid you in your DNA research. When contacting an unknown DNA match, you can explain that you match on a specific family line.

Dividing your match list into family clusters will let you focus your research on discovering the most recent common ancestor or ancestral couple of that cluster. This knowledge will help you to find, confirm, or reject ancestors on your genetic family tree.

As you gain more information about how you connect to a DNA match, you can record it in the research log: "shared match with Smith relatives" or "in a cluster with the Jones family." You can also record this information in the notes section on each DNA testing company website.

You have two choices when separating your DNA matches into shared match clusters–doing the process manually or using an automatic tool. The following overview will give you an idea of what is available on each website. See chapter eight for an in-depth look at how to use the clustering tools.

Create Shared Match Clusters Manually

What are the advantages of creating shared match clusters manually? You might enjoy working with each match and discovering your shared ancestral lines. Each testing company website enables you to view people that share DNA with you and with your DNA match. Shared DNA match lists and in common with (ICW) lists can help you place a DNA Match in the correct family group. For example, a known first or second cousin would reveal whether a DNA match was on the paternal or maternal line.

Each testing company defines a shared match differently, using unique parameters and approaches to display the information. As you use the features available at each website, you can manually separate your matches into groups.

23andMe: "Relatives in Common"

23andMe uses the term "Relatives in Common" and allows you to see genetic relatives you have in common with a specific DNA match. The website creates a table of relatives in common by looking at your DNA relatives list and checking to see if any other relatives on your list share at least 5cM of identical DNA with your match.[1]

Ancestry: "Shared Matches"

Ancestry uses the term "Shared Matches" and only displays "high confidence" matches (4th cousins and closer to each of you).[2] This generally translates to anyone sharing more

---

1. "DNA Relatives in Common Report Feature," *23andMe* (https://customercare.23andme.com/hc/en-us/articles/221689668-DNA-Relatives-In-Common-Report-Feature).

2. "What are Shared Matches?" *Ancestry* (https://www.ancestry.com/cs/dna-help/matches/shared-matches).

than 20 cM of DNA with you and your DNA match. If you review the more distant matches in your list, you will be able to see those who share at least 20 cM of DNA with your closer genetic cousins, even if they share less with you.

When you click on one of your DNA matches, you will be redirected to the match page that shows more information about your DNA match. If both you and your match have trees that include the same individual, you might see a common ancestor named. You will also be able to compare ethnicity estimates.

Ancestry has the added feature of using colored dots to group people into genetic networks. You can work with the colored dots any way you choose but consider thinking through a system before beginning. A DNA match may have as many dots assigned to it as desired. An initial dot for maternal or paternal could be assigned; then other dots added as you discover more information. Pedigree charts often use blue and green for the paternal line and pink and yellow for the maternal lines. You could follow this practice in assigning the colors to your matches. For an excellent system, see Leah Larkin's article, "Quick Tip: Color Code Your Ancestry Tree."[3]

FamilyTree DNA: "In Common With"

Family Tree DNA defines a shared match when you, your DNA match, and the shared match have at least 20 cM in common. FamilyTree DNA provides two tools for shared matching—"In Common With" and "Matrix." These will help to discover a cluster of individuals who share DNA with you and with each other.

Additionally, if you have a family tree on the website, you can link a known maternal or paternal DNA match using the feature titled "Family Finder—Family Matching." This will phase your DNA test, assigning maternal or paternal icons to each DNA match so you can determine which line a match is on at a glance. See the website for complete instructions on using this feature, which will also be discussed in chapter three.[4]

MyHeritage: "Shared DNA Matches"

My Heritage's shared matching includes anyone sharing DNA with other matches down to 6 cM. MyHeritage provides a chromosome browser to view triangulated segments among shared matches. This capability makes this feature particularly powerful because it lets you identify whether the shared match group of three individuals all share a common

---

3. Leah Larkin, "Quick Tip: Color Code Your Ancestry Tree," *The DNA Geek* (https://thednageek.com/quick-tip-color-code-your-ancestry-tree/).

4. "Family Finder—Family Matching Feature," Learning Center, *FamilyTreeDNA* (https://learn.family-treedna.com/user-guide/family-finder-myftdna/ftdna-family-matching-system/).

segment. If not, that could signal that the three people are related in another way.

Living DNA: "Relatives"

Living DNA reports DNA matches under the term "relatives." When you click on a match, an "in common" list appears, sorted by relationship degree. Living DNA reports shared matches from 9 cM and up. In the future, additional features will be added: "shared map" and "shared DNA."

GEDmatch: "People who match both kits, or 1 of 2 kits"

GEDmatch is a third-party website where you can upload your raw DNA from the DNA testing websites. To cluster your matches, use the tool titled "People who match both kits, or 1 of 2 kits." Enter your kit number and that of a known cousin to find other people related to both of you.

Leeds Method

Dana Leeds created a manual clustering tool in 2018 using a spreadsheet, color coding, and the testing companies' shared matching tools.[5] Initially designed for unknown parentage cases, it also works well for doing an initial sort of your DNA matches. After the method became widespread, others created automated tools to shorten the time it takes to cluster your shared matches.

Create Genetic Networks Using an Automated Tool

If you'd rather not take the time to cluster your DNA matches manually, you can experiment with automated tools to create genetic networks of the DNA matches for analysis. Explore these tools in chapter eight. However you perform clustering, the process will help you make sense of your DNA matches before starting the DNA match analysis.

Analyzing DNA Matches

Can additional information be used for analyzing your shared matches? The amount of shared DNA is vital when it comes to the analysis of possible relationships. Let's look at how that works.

---

5. "The Leeds Method," *Dana Leeds* (https://www.danaleeds.com/the-leeds-method/).

Check the amount of shared DNA

Each testing company lists the amount of DNA you share with a match, reporting it in two ways:

- Centimorgans (cM) as shown at AncestryDNA and Family Tree DNA
- Percentages and centimorgans as shown at 23andMe and My Heritage

Generally, the more DNA you share with a match, the closer the relationship. As you work with your DNA matches, you may discover exceptions to this guideline if you share more than one ancestor with an individual. The testing company will give you an estimate of the relationship you could share with a DNA match. Still, there are usually multiple relationships that can be possible, given the percentage or number of centimorgans of shared DNA.

For example, AncestryDNA estimated a relationship of second to third cousin for my match, Patty. We share 200 cM across 15 segments and are actually second cousins. Don't be surprised if each testing company reports a slightly different amount of shared DNA with the same individual. Each company uses a unique algorithm and different thresholds to evaluate and report the shared DNA.

Calculate possible relationships with the Shared cM Project Tool

Blaine Bettinger created the crowd-sourced Shared cM Project by gathering information from over 60,000 people who reported the amount of DNA they shared with their known relatives. Jonny Perl then created the Shared cM tool and added it to his website, DNA Painter, and added Leah Larkin's probabilities.[6] The collaboration has resulted in a valuable tool for analyzing the amount of DNA you share with a match.

After you've viewed the amount of shared DNA with a match and recorded it in your research log, you can use the Shared cM Project tool (https://dnapainter.com/tools/sharedcmv4) to see what possible familial relationships you might share with that match.

With this free tool, you can see the probabilities of various relationships you might have with your shared DNA match. Access the DNA Painter tool from the link above and enter the number of centimorgans or the percentages from data given by a DNA testing company. The tool will then calculate the probabilities of specific familial relationships based on the amount of shared DNA.

---

6. Jonny Perl, "Introducing the Updated Shared cM Tool," 27 March 2020, *DNA Painter* (https://dnapainter.com/blog/introducing-the-updated-shared-cm-tool/).

For instance, when I entered the 200cM that I share with my DNA match Patty into the tool, I saw many more possibilities than just second to third cousin. Included in the mix were possible relationships of half-second cousin, second cousin once removed, great-great-aunt, etc. The tool suggested over eighteen different relationships.

What if you don't know the relationship to a DNA match? What do you do with the many possibilities? First, don't get overwhelmed—some family tree information may narrow down your relationship. There is not enough information in the amount of DNA shared to determine the exact relationship without looking at known family relationships and family history.

When analyzing a possible relationship, another help is the histogram included for each relationship as part of the Shared cM Project at DNA Painter. See figure 2.4. The histogram allows you to see where the amount of cM you share with a DNA cousin falls in the mix.

Clicking on the 2C for my match with Patty, I saw that 943 people also reported a match of 200 cM as a second cousin. That lets me know that this relationship falls well within the expected range. What if I only shared 50 cM with my second cousin? Only 23 people reported that amount of DNA in a second cousin relationship. It is still possible but could be a cause for re-evaluating the relationship. For more about analyzing DNA matches, including Y-DNA, mtDNA, and X-DNA matches, see chapter six.

Contact DNA Matches

Because you will only recognize your closest DNA matches, you will need to contact more distant matches to see where they fit on the family tree. Using the DNA testing website messaging system or provided email address, you can write to a DNA match and ask them to help you determine the shared common ancestor. Robin shares this example:

> I had three women with whom I shared between 191–315 cM on my DNA match list. I could not figure out who they were from their family tree or lack of a family tree, and I had never heard their names before. I wrote to each of them with a version of the following:
>
> > Hello! [The DNA company] says that we share _____cM of DNA. That puts us in the range of 2nd-3rd cousins. I would love to connect with you and figure out our common ancestor. I have family history information that

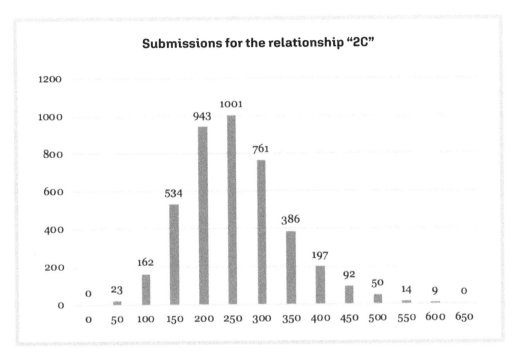

Figure 2.4. Histogram with submissions for the second cousin relationship.
Shared cM Project. Blaine T. Bettinger and Jonny Perl, "The Shared cM project 4.0 tool v4," DNA Painter (https://dnapainter.com/tools/sharedcmv4), licensed under CC BY 4.0 (https://creativecommons.org/licenses/by/4.0/).

> *I would love to share with you. You can contact me through the [DNA company] messaging system or via email at [___@___.com]. I look forward to hearing from you!*

They each responded, and we figured out that our grandparents were siblings. Therefore, our common ancestors are our great-grandparents, which means that we are second cousins. That new information and connection have opened the door for sharing photos, stories, and knowledge about our ancestors."

Keep track of messages or emails sent to unknown DNA matches in your research log. See chapter 10 for ideas on how to set up this portion of your research log. If a match doesn't reply within a reasonable amount of time, you could try again. We never know what might be happening in a match's life that prevents them from communicating with you.

An easy way to help a DNA match see your connection is to include a link to your online family tree. If a match doesn't have an Ancestry subscription, they won't see more than a preview of your Ancestry tree so consider putting a tree in a public place like your website, WikiTree, or FamilySearch.

Some tips for messaging include the following:

- Use exciting message headers to capture their attention.
- Contact new matches as soon as possible as they are more likely to sign into the website to check their results.
- Write out a protocol for a message to reuse.
- Try to determine which family line you match on and include that in the message.
- Offer to share family information.
- Send a direct link to the common ancestor in your online family tree.

Conclusion

Once you receive your DNA test results, some simple steps will help you assess and analyze each match. As you learn more about each match, add that information to your research log.

1. Assess your family tree.
2. Set up a system to track your DNA matches.
3. Cluster your DNA matches into genetic clusters.
4. Check the amount of shared DNA.
5. Calculate possible relationships with the Shared cM Project Tool.
6. Contact DNA Matches.

As you practice, your confidence will grow, and you will learn to assess and analyze your DNA matches effectively.

Your Task

1. Assess your closest DNA matches on each DNA testing website. Use the notes feature to record your relationship following your notes protocol.
2. Start a research log. Choose to create one master log, a log for your maternal line and a log for your paternal line, or a log for a specific project/objective.
3. Record information in the research log for individuals you recognize.
4. Begin clustering your closer DNA matches into genetic clusters either manually or automatically. Add new information to your research log.
5. Analyze the amount of shared DNA with each match using the Shared cM Project tool. Add the information to your research log.
6. Send messages to any matches you don't recognize and track your correspondence.

CHAPTER 3

Organize Your DNA Matches Visually with Diagrams and Family Trees

Nicole Dyer

D o you wonder how a third cousin twice removed fits into your tree? Have you received a message from a DNA match describing how they descend from your common ancestor—but you can't picture the relationship? Now that you have started discovering and assessing your relationship to your matches, you are ready to take your organization to the next level by charting relationships.

In the last chapter, you began organizing your matches by clustering them and taking notes about relationships. You also began logging correspondence with them. Now it's time to organize the relationships you discovered in a visual format. Diagramming your matches in a custom diagram or family tree helps you visualize how you and your matches descend from a common ancestor. Viewing your matches this way helps you make connections and evaluate the DNA evidence.

Visualize Relationships to DNA Matches

In traditional genealogy research, we use a tree or pedigree format to organize our data. Similarly, the tree structure is the most useful way to organize the information we discover in our DNA research. In genetic genealogy, we use descendancy trees frequently. Our DNA matches are descendants of our common ancestors—and diagramming can help us determine the relationships, assess the amounts of shared DNA, and use the matches as evidence in our conclusions.

Visualizing the relationships between you and your DNA matches is crucial to understanding and using DNA evidence. Not only does this help you determine the relationship between you and a match, but it helps you gather your evidence into one place. Combining matches from each testing company into one chart allows you to correlate the information more easily. Choose a central place to diagram the relationships between you and your DNA matches—whether it's an online diagramming tool, a family tree program, or sticky notes on your wall. This will help you stay organized and see the big picture of how you and your DNA matches connect back to common ancestors.

Tracking multiple relationships and data points in our minds is difficult. Plotting this information in a graphical representation frees up our minds to see connections across the data. Imagine you are working on Diana's matches and receive a message from a match named George. The message says he is the great-great-grandson of Richard Frazier. George manages his uncle Dave's kit, who is also Richard's descendant. Diagramming how they both descend from Richard Frazier and Nancy Briscoe helps you see that Diana is a third cousin to George and a second cousin once removed to Dave. As you continue to plot additional DNA matches descending from Richard Frazier, you realize that Dave is the closest descendant of Richard Frazier to take a DNA test. Now you can reach out to George and ask him to share Dave's DNA results with you. Diagramming helps you notice important information!

Relationships Levels

Understanding the exact relationship level between two individuals who share DNA is critical for evaluating the match. First cousins share a grandparent. Second cousins share great-grandparents. But what about half cousins and cousins who are once removed?

Cousins once removed are one generation away from each other. For example, first cousins once removed share the same grandparents, but one cousin is a grandchild, and the other is a great-grandchild. To find the relationship between two DNA matches, diagram their descent from the most recent common ancestors. When counting the generations, I look at the common ancestral couple, then look down one generation and say "siblings," then go down another level and say "first cousins," and so forth until I get to the end of one of their lines. Then I count the number of generations removed and make a note in the box of the DNA match.

Figure 3.1 illustrates Diana's relationship to DNA matches Dave and George. Diana and George are in the same generation, so they are third cousins, shown with the shorthand

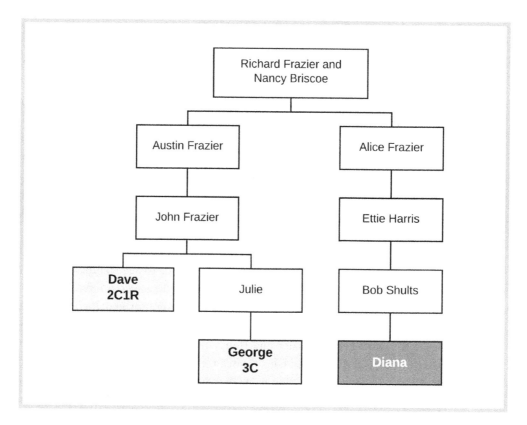

Figure 3.1. Diana's relationship to two DNA matches

3C. Dave is one generation closer to Richard and Nancy, so he is a second cousin once removed, shown with the shorthand 2C1R.

It's important to know the difference between full and half cousins because the expected amount of shared DNA is different. For example, full siblings, who share both parents, will share more DNA than half siblings, who only share one parent. The same is true for half first cousins—they share one grandparent in common instead of two, so the expected amount of shared DNA is less than for a full first cousin.[1] Half relationships include half siblings, half aunt/uncle/niece/nephew, half first cousins, half second cousins, and so forth.

---

1. To learn more about calculating expected amounts of shared DNA for various relationships, see "Autosomal DNA Statistics," rev. 23:35, 8 November 2020, *International Society of Genetic Genealogy (ISOGG) Wiki* (https://isogg.org/wiki/Autosomal_DNA_statistics). Also, "Coefficient of relationship," rev. 11:38, 22 October 2020, *ISOGG Wiki* (https://isogg.org/wiki/Coefficient_of_relationship).

If you and a DNA match descend from different spouses of an ancestor, be sure to show that in your chart and indicate the half relationship. One way to do this is to add the spouses of the common ancestor in separate boxes, as shown in figure 3.2. In shorthand, an 'H' is used to indicate a half cousin relationship, so H1C stands for half first cousin.

Evaluating Evidence

Building diagrams showing DNA matches descending from common ancestors helps you interpret the genetic evidence supporting and confirming your research back to your proposed ancestors. Seeing DNA matches who descend from each generation leading back to a brick wall ancestor can help you confirm that the test taker is a biological descendant of that ancestor. This knowledge provides a good foundation for further investigation of that brick wall.

Charting DNA matches can help you visualize hypotheses about brick wall ancestors. For example, mapping out the DNA matches who descend from a hypothesized ancestor can help you determine the next steps to take with documentary research. Perhaps you have seen several DNA matches with Lewis Tharp in their tree, leading you to hypothesize that he could be the father of your ancestor, Barsheba Tharp. As you create a diagram showing those genetic cousins' descent from Lewis Tharp, you begin to see a trend that

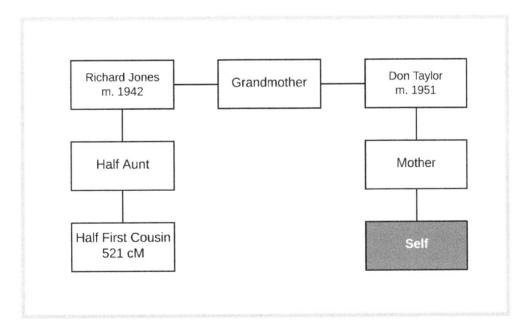

Figure 3.2. Half first cousin relationship

the DNA matches who descend from Lewis' second wife share many more centimorgans of DNA than those who descend from his first wife. Now you have a hypothesis to test with documentary research and possibly mitochondrial DNA testing, if the documentary evidence is unclear.

Many tools are available to genealogists for creating diagrams and family trees. Genetic genealogists love the flexibility of tools like Lucidchart (https://lucidchart.com) to quickly diagram a genetic relationship or build large descendancy trees. Building a family tree with programs made specifically for this purpose, like Ancestry.com's tree-building tool, is also a common practice. You may want to include both diagramming and family tree software in your genetic genealogy toolbox. See chapter six for a discussion of evaluating the evidence in your diagram.

Diagramming Tools

There are many ways to create a diagram ranging from low-tech to high-tech options. A diagramming software tool that allows you to edit and update your diagram as your research progresses will be most beneficial.

Diagram software tools like Lucidchart allow you to use shapes, lines, and text to design specialized charts. They are often used to create floor plans, organizational charts, and flowcharts. Diagram software tools are useful for mapping out descendants from a common ancestor and visualizing relationships of DNA matches.

Although diagram software tools may look complex, they are simple and efficient once you learn a few of the basics. Don't let the word simple fool you—diagramming tools are also powerful and flexible. They provide the freedom to create a chart that looks however you want and includes whatever people you want. You can include multiple sets of common ancestors, double cousins, and multiple spouses. The sky is the limit! In this aspect, tree-building tools are inferior because they limit you to their conventions and preset pedigree views.

Basic DNA Match Diagram

With diagramming software, you can quickly illustrate the relationship between you and your DNA match. Let's say you have found a DNA match and determined she is your cousin's child, a first cousin once removed.

To illustrate the DNA match's relationship to you, draw your line back to the common ancestral couple—your grandparents. Then add another box descending from your grandparents for your aunt, then her child, then her grandchild—your first cousin once

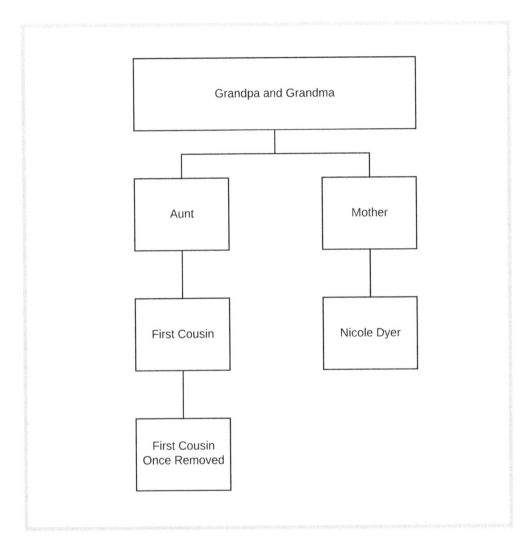

Figure 3.3. Lucidchart diagram showing a first cousin once removed

removed. Figure 3.3 shows a diagram created with Lucidchart that illustrates a first cousin once removed relationship.

When building a chart showing your connection to a DNA match, include only the direct line to the common ancestor, leaving off the spouses until you reach the common ancestral couple. This reduces the number of boxes and people you add and helps visualize the line to the common ancestral couple without distraction.

Adding Details to Boxes

As you add DNA matches to your diagram, you may want to add details about the match to the diagram for quick reference. For atDNA matches, I typically add the amount of shared cM / # of segments, i.e. 34 cM / 2, and the relationship in shorthand, H3C1R (half third cousin once removed). See figure 3.4, where three of Diana's DNA matches, A1, A2, and A3, are shown. Other details like the testing company, GEDmatch kit number, and kit admin can be included, but adding too much to your chart can obscure the information you are trying to draw out. These details are better stored in your research log. For Y-DNA and mtDNA matches, you can add the genetic distance and level of testing. For example, a Y-DNA match at 37 markers and a genetic distance of 2 could be expressed like this: GD 2 / 37. If you are using Lucidchart to make your diagram, use the keyboard shortcut shift+enter to add a line break when typing within a shape. This allows you to add the name of the match on the first line, the shared cM or genetic distance on the next line, and the relationship on the third line.

When adding parents, grandparents, and so forth back to the common ancestor, I often include the years of birth and death. This can help you distinguish same-name descendants. It also helps you check the dates for each generation to see if the proposed relationships (if found in a DNA match's tree) seem accurate. If possible, add the gender of people who are private in DNA matches' trees (i.e. "mother" instead of "private"). This will help you determine if X-DNA, mtDNA, and Y-DNA are applicable to that branch. Another reason to add birth years is to put children in the correct birth order, as shown with Claude, Bob, and Helen in figure 3.4. This can help you identify living descendants who are closer in generations to your research subject by focusing on the youngest children in each family.

Color

Adding colors to the shapes in your diagram can help you keep track of data or see patterns. Coloring the boxes of DNA matches can signify the testing company where the match was found. Coloring branches of the family that descend from various siblings can highlight descent from independent lines. Coloring males blue and females pink can help you quickly see possibilities for patrilineal and matrilineal descendants to take a direct-line test.

Moving Multiple Items

As you create a diagram of DNA matches, you may need to select multiple shapes and lines and move them in order to make space for another branch. This can happen when you add children to some of the children of your common ancestral couple, then later identify a DNA match who descends from one of their children who is not yet in your chart. To insert a line of descent in the middle of the chart, select many shapes in your diagram at once and move them all together. You may want to add the children of the ancestral couple in their birth order when you first start making your chart.

Multiple Pages within a Document

Diagramming tools typically allow you to add multiple pages to your diagram document. This is similar to adding multiple sheets in a spreadsheet. Adding multiple pages is useful if you would like to duplicate your chart to make it private by redacting the names of living individuals. Keeping the original and the private copy together in the same document makes it easy for you to stay organized. You can share the diagram by exporting one page to a PDF or image file.

Additional uses for multiple pages in a diagram document include:

- mapping out different hypotheses for a research question
- exploring multiple clusters that relate to the same research question
- charting matches' relationships to more than one DNA test taker

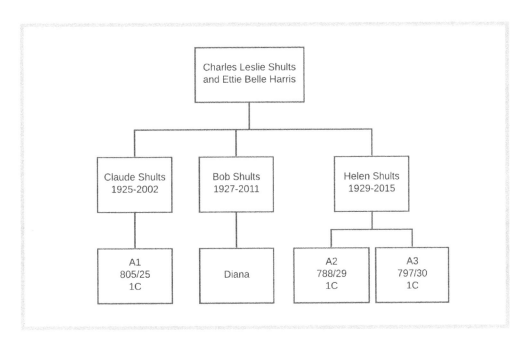

Figure 3.4. Diagram with shared cM, number of segments, and relationship shorthand

Copy and Paste

One of the easiest ways to add new shapes to a diagram is with the copy and paste keyboard shortcuts. Select a shape, then use Ctrl+C for copy and Ctrl+V for paste to quickly duplicate a shape. This ensures that all your shapes are the same size, which is important for keeping the generations lined up in a descendancy diagram. You can also select sections of your chart and use Ctrl +C to copy them onto another page. This makes it easier to build out a particular branch of the family or create an image of part of your diagram that can be used in a report.

Zoom In and Out

Descendancy diagrams may become wide and large with many descendants from a distant ancestral couple. In this case, it's useful to know about the zoom feature. You can zoom in to a particular part of the chart, pan over to the other side with the slider at the bottom, or zoom out to see the whole thing.

Lines

Dotted lines are useful in displaying a hypothesized relationship that hasn't been vetted. When you use a tree from a DNA match but haven't verified each parent-child link through examining sources, it can be helpful to use a dotted line in your diagram to show that a line is unproven.

In a descendancy diagram, lines descending from the bottom of a shape indicate a person's children. Lines coming from the sides of a shape indicate a marriage. You may want to use a double line or an equal sign to indicate a marriage.

Grid and Spacing

The grid feature in typical diagramming tools shows the spacing between objects and can be useful while building your chart. The grid helps you space objects evenly and line up generations in a descendancy diagram. Spacing your generations evenly is important for determining how many generations there are between two individuals.

Advanced Diagrams

Diagramming tools can create McGuire charts. This is a method of comparing multiple test-takers' relationships to DNA matches and a common ancestral couple. This type of diagram was originally created by Lauren McGuire.[2] Figure 3.5 shows a McGuire chart

2. Lauren McGuire and Blaine Bettinger, "GUEST POST: The McGuire Method—Simplified Visual DNA Comparisons," 19 March 2017, *The Genetic Genealogist* (https://thegeneticgenealogist.com/2017/03/19/guest-post-the-mcguire-method-simplified-visual-dna-comparisons/).

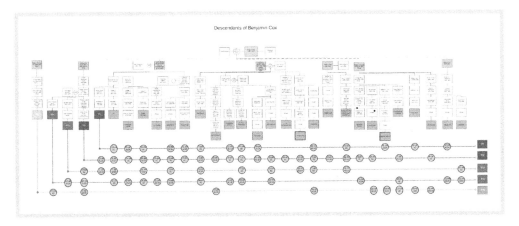

Figure 3.5. Descendants of Benjamin Cox, a McGuire chart. Created by Diana Elder.
See https://familylocket.com/rlpdna for a full-size image.

created by Diana using Lucidchart. The diagram shows the relationships of 5 test takers to 25 DNA matches at Ancestry.com.

PowerPoint and Word Smart Art

The Hierarchy Smart Art template in Microsoft PowerPoint and Word is an easy way to build descendancy trees. If you dread the idea of drawing lines and boxes or learning a new software tool, you may prefer this method. Change the page size in PowerPoint to increase your canvas size. Click Insert > Smart Art > Hierarchy. Adding generations is simple with the text editing pane that pops up. Type a name, press ENTER, then press TAB to add the next descendant. There is not as much flexibility with this tool, but it is a fast way to create professional-looking descendancy charts. See figure 3.6 for a diagram made with Smart Art in PowerPoint.

Hand Drawing a Diagram

Drawing a diagram by hand is an easy and effective method of charting your DNA matches. Be sure to use a pencil in case you need to erase. Draw shapes that are large enough to add names, birth years, and the amount of shared DNA. Consider using a whiteboard with the ability to erase. Be sure to take a photo to refer to later.

Sticky Notes

Moveable sticky notes are another way to diagram in a low-tech way. Use sticky notes with the names of DNA matches and place them on the wall, window, or whiteboard. Rearrange

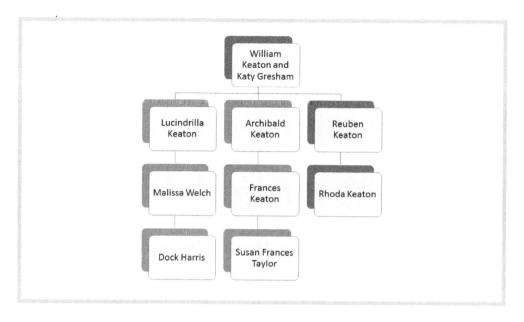

Figure 3.6. Descendancy diagram created with PowerPoint Smart Art Hierarchy Template

them in the configuration of the pedigree as needed. This method gives you flexibility but takes up more space. Other advantages are that you probably already have sticky notes available, you don't have to learn a new program, and you can arrange them any way you like.

What Are The Odds?

The What Are The Odds (WATO) tool at DNA Painter can be used as a diagramming tool as well. It is especially useful for evaluating various hypotheses for where a person with unknown parentage fits into a known descendancy tree. Some people use WATO for building a descendancy diagram and keeping track of DNA matches. See chapter eight for more about WATO.

Family Tree Building Tools

Using a family tree program to organize your DNA matches is useful for several reasons. You can:

- add DNA matches to your tree and link them back to your common ancestor
- include DNA matches from various testing databases in one central location

- check the evidence for each parent-child relationship and add documentation
- build quick trees for DNA matches who haven't shared a full tree
- do descendancy research to find potential test takers
- build out a match's tree, checking for more than one common ancestor

Many of your DNA matches may have small trees that don't go back far enough to find a common ancestor. Genetic genealogists often use tree-building tools like the one available at Ancestry.com to create quick trees for DNA matches. See chapter six for details about building quick trees. Ancestry.com has helpful tree-building tools, like hinting, that assist with building quick trees. However, creating a new tree for each DNA match fills up your list of Ancestry trees quickly. If you don't want to have a long list of Ancestry trees, create one master genetic tree and include all the DNA matches of a test taker or those on a particular side of the family.

Adding a DNA match as a disconnected branch in your tree allows you to build their tree until you discover the common ancestor. Once you find the connection, you can link up their floating branch to an ancestor who was already in the tree. Building trees for matches who share less than 15 cM may be futile because they could be false matches or may not share a common ancestor with you in a genealogical time frame.[3] Work on building trees of closer matches if possible. To read more about how to add a disconnected branch in an Ancestry tree, go to https://familylocket.com/rlpdna.

One benefit of building a DNA match's tree is the ability to compare all branches of their tree to see if you share more than one common ancestor with them. Many have incomplete branches that cannot be extended due to adoption, immigration, or other brick walls. An individual's lack of tree completeness is a consideration when selecting DNA matches to use as genetic evidence in a proof argument. Standard 52 in *Genealogy Standards* says to consider the possibility of more than one common ancestor between two individuals who share DNA as a factor in determining the genetic relationship.[4] Often a problem of tree completeness can be minimized by noting that the unknown ancestors in a genetic cousin's tree came from different regions or countries than the test taker's ancestors. This could mean they are less likely to share more than the one common ancestor already iden- tified. One way to help you find out if a genetic cousin in your tree shares more than one common ancestor with the test taker is to color code all their ancestors. This is possible

---

3. "Identical by descent," rev. 13:08, 6 November 2020, *ISOGG Wiki* (https://isogg.org/wiki/Identical_by_descent).

4. Board for Certification of Genealogists (BCG), *Genealogy Standards,* 2nd ed. (Nashville: Ancestry.com, 2019), 30.

with RootsMagic and Family Tree Maker, software programs discussed later in this chapter.

When choosing a tool for building a master genetic tree, consider choosing one with several of these features:

1. Ability to add living people to the tree
2. Ability to make the tree private (if online)
3. Record hinting and historical record collections
4. Descendancy or family view
5. Ability to create, export, or print custom charts

The collaborative Family Tree at *FamilySearch* is a good place to add conclusions about family relationships but isn't recommended for adding DNA matches to your tree. Living people are private in the Family Tree, but it is recommended that you don't add living people besides yourself and your parents.

Ancestry.com Family Trees

Ancestry.com includes most of the desirable features for including DNA matches in your tree. If you have tested at AncestryDNA, it's a convenient place to build your family tree. Attaching a tree to your DNA results at Ancestry makes it possible for you and DNA matches to more easily find the common ancestor you share with the common ancestor hints. The hinting feature and large collection of records at Ancestry make it possible to expand a DNA match's tree quickly and find a hypothesized common ancestor more efficiently.

Because Ancestry is preferred by many genetic genealogists for tree building, I will share the basic principles for adding DNA matches to your tree using Ancestry as an example. The ideas can be adapted to whatever tree building program you prefer.

Tree Connected to Your AncestryDNA Results

If you already have a tree connected to your AncestryDNA results, you can use this tree to connect DNA matches to individuals in your tree. If you don't have a tree connected to your AncestryDNA results, be sure to add one. It's easy to link your DNA test to an existing tree at Ancestry. To learn how to do it, see the Ancestry Support Article called "Linking an AncestryDNA Test to a Tree."[5] If you manage multiple DNA tests, they can all be linked to the same tree. A DNA test cannot be linked to two trees, so if you have created a separate

---

5. "Linking an AncestryDNA Test to a Tree," *Ancestry Support* (https://support.ancestry.com/s/article/Linking-an-AncestryDNA-Test-to-a-Tree).

maternal and paternal tree, you will need to use a software program like Family Tree Maker to merge your GEDCOM files into one.

Private Research Tree

You may want to create a new, separate tree just for adding DNA matches and hypotheses. You can title it "[Your Name]'s genetic tree. Import a GEDCOM file of your ancestors to begin the tree, then start adding your DNA matches. You may want to keep this research tree private. A private tree is helpful when you are unsure of the relationships you are charting—allowing you to test a hypothesis. You can add your conclusions to a public tree when you're ready. If you want to use ThruLines, you can keep your private tree searchable.

Privacy Settings for Ancestry Trees

Ancestry trees have three levels of privacy: public, private and searchable, and private and unsearchable.[6]

Public trees are viewable by those you invite to collaborate and anyone with an Ancestry subscription. People in your tree who are marked as living are automatically made private for those who are not invited to collaborate on your tree.

Private and searchable trees are shown in search results of the Public Member Tree database, but to click through to view the tree, users must first ask for your permission. You may want to make your tree private so that others don't copy unproven relationships into their trees. For Ancestry ThruLines to work, your tree must be set to either public or private/searchable.

Private and unsearchable trees do not appear in search results and are not used in Ancestry ThruLines. To set this high level of privacy, go to tree settings > privacy settings. From there, select "Private Tree" and then check the box below that says "also prevent your tree from being found in searches."

If you want to keep the names of your private, unsearchable trees from being found by anyone, don't save images to your tree that other Ancestry users have added, or your tree will show up in a list of trees that include that item. You may want to keep your tree at this high level of privacy if you are working on a sensitive case.

Adding DNA Matches to Your Ancestry Tree

Now that you have your Ancestry tree set up and have chosen the privacy settings, you

---

6. "Family Tree Privacy," *Ancestry Support* (https://support.ancestry.com/s/article/Family-Tree-Privacy).

can start adding DNA matches. Add your DNA matches as descendants of the ancestors you have already identified in your tree by building the lineage down to the present day. Be sure to mark your DNA matches and their parents as living unless you know them to be deceased. Anyone who is marked living will be kept private when others view your tree unless you have added the viewer as a collaborator.

I typically add DNA matches to my tree who I think will be useful in proving a certain case. I then attach sources and citations to document each parent-child relationship back to the common ancestor. When it's time to write a proof argument, I can cite this tree for documentation of the relationships in my descendancy diagram. You can also add the documentation for each parent-child link directly to the proof argument if space is not an issue.

After adding a profile for the genetic cousin to your tree, you can link their DNA match page to that profile. To do this, go to the DNA match page for the genetic cousin and find the pedigree icon. Click the icon to find them in the tree and link them. After doing this, an icon shows on the genetic cousin in your tree, indicating they are a DNA match. From the tree, you can click the icon to go to their match page. You can also click on the icon in your DNA match list to go to their profile in your tree. This is a helpful way to visualize DNA matches in your family tree, especially when viewing it in the family/descendancy view.

You may want to add additional data about the match that will be visible in the family/descendancy view. Here are some suggestions:

- Add the number of shared cM in the suffix box. This will allow you to see amounts of shared DNA when you view descendants of a common ancestor.
- If you are working with Y-DNA and mtDNA, you may want to add the haplogroup as a middle name, so it's displayed in the pedigree chart, as one genetic genealogist does.[7]

After you have added several DNA matches to your tree, you can view them in the family tree using the family view (instead of the pedigree view). The family view allows you to see descendants, spouses, cousins, aunts, and uncles, and so forth. It won't show all the descendants of a couple at once, but it does show some branches and then allows you to click and expand other branches. Ancestry's family view is not as flexible as a Lucidchart diagram but is still a useful way to view descendants and DNA matches.

---

7. Roberta Estes, "Confusion: Family Tree Maker, Family Tree DNA and Ancestry.com," 13 December 2015, *DNA Explained—Genetic Genealogy* (https://dna-explained.com/2015/12/13/confusion-family-tree-maker-family-tree-dna-and-ancestry-com/).

Label DNA Matches with MyTreeTags

After adding a DNA match to your tree, consider adding the "DNA Match" tag to help you sort and filter matches in your tree. Ancestry's MyTreeTags allows users to label people in their tree and filter searches by tag.

Ancestry has three default DNA tags that you can use to help identify people in your tree. They are defined as follows:

1. **Common DNA Ancestor:** This person is a common ancestor between yourself and at least one of your DNA Matches.
2. **DNA Connection:** This person is a relative on the path between a DNA Match and a common ancestor.
3. **DNA Match:** This person is on your DNA Match List.

MyTreeTags also allows you to create custom tags. Custom tags could include the shared match group (i.e. maternal, paternal, Grandpa Jones, Ross/Silvius), matches you have contacted, or anything that might be useful to you. If you need to search within your family tree, you can use these tags to quickly find just the people with a certain tag. To learn how to add tags to people in your tree, go to Ancestry's support article about MyTreeTags.[8]

Adding People to Your Tree with Ancestry ThruLines

Ancestry ThruLines show how you may be connected to DNA matches through a common ancestor. If you have a public or private searchable tree connected to your DNA results, you will be eligible to receive ThruLines. ThruLines are not proven conclusions about ancestors but suggestions that may lead to a conclusion. Ancestry uses the public and private searchable trees in their database to generate ThruLines suggestions for you and your DNA matches. ThruLines does not evaluate the amount of shared DNA between you and a match before suggesting a particular common ancestor. If you are seeing a ThruLines suggestion with all the DNA Matches descending from just one child, it may not be accurate. Look for ThruLines about an ancestor who has descendants through multiple children who are DNA matches to you.

To evaluate a ThruLines hypothesis for accuracy, consider taking the following steps:

- Check to see if DNA matches descend from more than one child of the proposed ancestor.
- Review the documentation for parent-child links.

---

8. "MyTreeTags," *Ancestry Support* (https://support.ancestry.com/s/article/MyTreeTags).

- Check to see if people with similar names have been merged by the system.
- Look at the shared matches to see if most DNA matches in the ThruLines hypothesis are in the same shared match cluster.
- Look at the amount of shared DNA to see if they share too much or too little DNA for the proposed relationship.

If the documentary evidence looks possible, no same-name individuals have been merged, and the DNA matches are mostly in the same shared match cluster, then the ThruLines hypothesis may be worth pursuing.

If a ThruLines hypothesis looks accurate, you may want to add those matches to your tree. ThruLines makes it easy to add DNA matches to your family tree. While you can't add the DNA matches themselves to your tree using ThruLines, you can add their line of descent from the suggested common ancestor. The tree attached to your DNA results is the tree that will be updated when you add people from ThruLines.

If there is a dotted line around a person in ThruLines with the "evaluate" label it means they are not in your tree. For example, ThruLines showed me two possible siblings for my ancestor, Elam Hollingsworth. See figure 3.7. I have not added these proposed siblings to my tree yet, so have dotted lines around them. These new siblings for Elam have several descendants who are DNA matches to me.

If you have a ThruLines suggestion and would like to evaluate the suggested relatives, click on the relative's box to open the side panel and review their sources. If everything looks right, click next and add them to your tree. Continue adding the relative's descendants until you get to the DNA match. You will have to add the DNA match to your tree manually.

Common Ancestor Hints

In your list of DNA matches, you may see common ancestor hints. If you click on a match with a common ancestor hint and go to the match page, you'll see potential ancestors or common ancestor hints on the left side panel. Click on a potential ancestor to evaluate them in ThruLines and then add them to your tree.

Other DNA Testing Companies' Tree-Building Tools

If you have tested your DNA at Family Tree DNA, MyHeritage, or Living DNA, you may want to investigate their tree-building tools to see if they will help you organize matches. However, if you have matches across several testing companies, it will be more efficient to choose just one central place to build a family tree for all your matches. If you decide to do this, choose the company that has more record collections and sharing features.

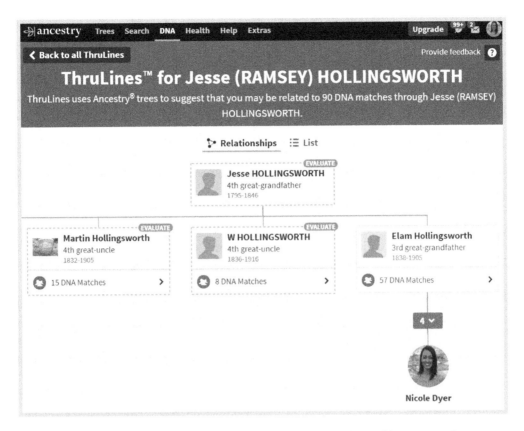

Figure 3.7. Ancestry ThruLines suggestion showing the dotted box around potential siblings of a known ancestor

There are advantages to adding a least a basic tree at each DNA testing company's website that allows it. The main advantages include receiving computer-generated hypotheses from the testing company like common ancestor hints, Ancestry ThruLines, and the MyHeritage Theories of Family Relativity. Another advantage is helping your matches find out how they are related to you and increase the chance that they will collaborate with you. If you add a tree for each kit you manage at each site, just think how much easier it will be for everyone to find their connections!

Family Tree DNA myFamilyTree and Family Matching

Family Tree DNA (FTNDA) has a tree-building feature called myFamilyTree that allows you to link your DNA matches directly to your family tree. You can start by building the tree manually or importing a GEDCOM file. From there, you can select the parent of your DNA match and add your DNA match to the tree. Once you link a match to your tree, you can view your relationship in the DNA match list.

Family Tree DNA does not include any historical record collections, so it's not an ideal place for your working tree. However, a helpful part of FTDNA's tree feature is family matching. The phased family matching system separates matches into paternal and maternal groups after you link DNA matches to your tree.

For example, let's say you find a paternal first cousin in the FTDNA database, and you add them to your tree. Next, you link their DNA results to this profile in your tree. Once you do this, the family matching system detects segments over the 9 cM threshold and assigns the paternal icon to other matches who share these segments with you and the match.[9] When you return to the match list, the family matching system will show a paternal icon on matches who share that segment. Linking a parent, aunt/niece, uncle/nephew, or 1st cousin is a good way to begin, but the system works with matches as distant as 3rd cousin. Full siblings will show both maternal and paternal icons.

In an FTDNA Family Finder kit that I manage, I linked nine DNA matches, about half maternal and half paternal, ranging from 1C1R to 3C1R, to the family tree tool. Now, out of 7,434 matches, 607 are bucketed to the paternal side, and 679 are bucketed to the maternal side. Adding matches to your FTDNA tree is an enjoyable and efficient way to sort your matches.

MyHeritage Family Trees

MyHeritage has a large collection of historical records to help you build your tree. You can add DNA test results directly to a relative's profile in your family tree as an attachment to their profile. On each person's profile, there is an option to either upload DNA data or purchase a DNA test. If you manage multiple tests, this is a useful feature. In your MyHeritage tree, a DNA badge is added to relatives whose DNA tests you manage. You cannot link DNA matches found in the MyHeritage DNA match database to your tree like in Ancestry and FTDNA, but you can add DNA matches to your MyHeritage tree manually.

In your MyHeritage DNA match list, you can filter to see just people who have Smart Matches with you. Smart Matching is the MyHeritage technology for finding people in your tree who match people in other users' trees. By narrowing your DNA match list by just those who have Smart Matches, you can focus on people who are more likely to have information you can add to your tree.

---

9. "Family Finder—Family Matching Feature," *Family Tree DNA Learning Center* (https://learn.family-treedna.com/user-guide/family-finder-myftdna/ftdna-family-matching-system/).

Desktop Software Programs for Family Tree Building

Many desktop programs for building family trees are suitable for creating a central place to record relationships to DNA matches. The best way to choose one is to read about its features and try the free version of the program (if available). Most of the programs offer all the features you'll need for genetic genealogy and some support adding Y-DNA and mtDNA markers, as well as the ability to add a custom fact with a link to the DNA match page.

Legacy Family Tree

Legacy Family Tree is a favorite program among professional genealogists. It includes a wide array of printed reports and an extensive chart creation feature. You can create Y-DNA inheritance charts, mtDNA inheritance charts, and all kinds of ancestor, descendant, fan, and hourglass charts. Legacy even has a color scheme for fan charts highlighting X-DNA inheritance.

Legacy allows you to add unlimited hashtags to people in your tree. A hashtag is simply a way of categorizing people in your tree so that you can sort and find them later. Some examples include #DNATested or #MRCASmithPeterson for descendants of a common ancestral couple.

RootsMagic

RootsMagic can sync with your Ancestry Tree and the FamilySearch Family Tree. It also allows you to search based on mtDNA and Y-DNA lines. Rootsmagic also has a color-coding feature that can be used in a variety of ways. When you are comparing family trees of genetic matches, it can be useful to color code all ancestors of a particular genetic cousin to see if there are multiple shared ancestors between them and other genetic cousins. This is particularly helpful for endogamy cases. RootsMagic has fourteen colors that you can apply to a person's ancestors or descendants or other criteria.[10]

Family Tree Maker

Family Tree Maker (FTM) is a good desktop program for those who have tested at AncestryDNA because it syncs with your Ancestry tree and shows hints to Ancestry's extensive record collections. It has a color-coding feature that allows you to select up to eight colors per individual. You can also apply color coding to an individual's ancestors or

---

10. "Tip: Never Get Lost in Your Tree with Color Coding," 6 June 2014, *RootsMagic Blog* (http://blog. rootsmagic.com/?p=1994).

descendants. Family Tree Maker can be used in conjunction with Charting Companion, a DNA plugin, to generate a DNA matrix chart showing the relationships and shared DNA of several test takers to each other. The DNA matrix chart is similar to a McGuire chart. The FTM Charting Companion plugin also helps you group potential cousins in your DNA Match list into branches of the family and set priorities for your DNA research.

Charting Companion Plugin

Progeny Genealogy offers a program called Charting Companion which can be used as a plugin with most tree-building programs. A plugin is a piece of software that "plugs into" or goes along with existing programs. Charting Companion creates several types of DNA charts, including:

- DNA matrix (looks like a McGuire chart)—only available with the FTM plugin
- DNA simulation
- DNA matches
- X-chromosome fan chart showing ancestors you could have inherited the X from
- X-chromosome fan chart showing descendants who inherited the X from an ancestor
- Mitochondrial DNA chart

Be sure to purchase the Charting Companion plugin from the same website where you purchased your family tree program. For example, RootsMagic sells their own Charting Companion plugin, as does Family Tree Maker.

Diagrams in Assembled Research Results

Diagrams and family trees are important tools to help you stay organized throughout the research process. Keeping your family tree up to date with the documentation for each parent-child link of DNA matches back to the common ancestor will make writing your proof argument easier. You may even choose to cite your online family tree for documentation if publishing in a journal with limited space.

Diagrams are important parts of written conclusions and show the reader how the DNA matches are evidence for a conclusion. Standard 65 in *Genealogy Standards* suggests using tools that help present relationships clearly in assembled research results.[11] The

---

11. BCG, *Genealogy Standards*, 2nd ed., 37.

diagrams you create during your research will be useful as you write reports and other written conclusions. Keeping your diagram up to date with matches relevant to your case will increase your efficiency in selecting and using DNA matches as evidence as you write.

Your Task

Create a diagram showing you and your closest DNA matches using Lucidchart or your preferred diagramming tool. For a list of diagramming tools, see https://familylocket.com/rlpdna. After you have chosen your research objective in the next chapter, you will expand your diagram or create a new one by focusing on matches on the relevant side of the family.

Choose a tree-building tool to keep track of important DNA matches, documentation of parent-child links, and pedigree evaluations. Add some of your DNA matches to the tree.

CHAPTER 4

Create a Research Objective

Diana Elder

You've tested your DNA and possibly that of several relatives. Looking at the thousands of DNA matches generated by the testing companies, you've begun to contact the closest relatives. In organizing your matches by building trees and charting connections, you've started to make sense of your DNA results. Now what?

All research begins with a question, and perhaps you are wondering if DNA could help answer the many questions lurking in your family tree. Focusing on a definitive and answerable question will help you move ahead on the dead ends in your pedigree. Although documentary research can answer many questions, some will benefit from using DNA. Once you've determined a research question involving DNA, you can formulate an objective to frame and guide the research process. Without a clear objective, you'll find yourself continually spinning your wheels, working here and there among your match list, but not making any real progress. A research objective will keep you efficient and moving ahead on a focused research path.

Types of DNA Research Objectives

Research objectives for document-based research projects generally center on identity, actions, or relationships. When adding DNA as a source, an objective can best test a hypothesis on an ancestor's identity or relationship. DNA analysis could also help answer the question of possible family connections or discover an unknown DNA match's identity. DNA would not lend additional knowledge to an ancestor's military service if he weren't first identified as the John Smith who served in the Revolutionary War from a specific location.

What types of research questions can be answered with DNA, and how do you form an objective for each one to guide your research? Let's take a look.

Identify an Individual

People of the same name have always posed a problem in genealogy. Often the original settler of a new location had several descendants named after him, each residing in the same area, then slowly spreading out. With the ease of creating online trees from suggested records, unique identities have been merged then multiplied. How can you discover which John Smith is your John Smith? Enter the unique source of DNA. Each ancestor gave a particular piece of DNA to you, which can help you identify your ancestor out of the field of many with the same name.

For example, when I first began my research, I had traced my Royston ancestry back to a John Royston of Oglethorpe County, Georgia. He first appeared in Georgia records in 1803, and I had hypothesized that he belonged to the Virginia Royston's of Gloucester County. He would have been born about 1750. The only problem was that the Maryland Royston's also had a John Royston born about the same time. In 2004 another Royston researcher invited me to join a Y-DNA project to determine if my line matched the Virginia family. I located a proper candidate, a male with an unbroken paternal Royston line. His Y-DNA test results matched other Royston men who had also traced their lines to Gloucester County, Virginia. The additional evidence the Y-DNA testing provided confirmed my hypothesis that my Royston line descended from the original settler, Thomas Royston, of Virginia.

Your research question about identity could be similar to the following fictional examples:

EXAMPLE: Which of the four Isaac Normans found in the 1840 Greene County, Virginia, census is my ancestor?

EXAMPLE: Which John Adams is the father of Mary Adams, who was born on 9 March 1825 in Dover, Kent, England?

Discover or Confirm/Reject a Biological Family Relationship

Family relationships that could only be hypothesized in the past can now be confirmed or rejected using DNA as a source. In the case of unknown parentage, an entire family tree branch can be discovered and added. DNA can break down brick walls in our genealogy that have stood for years because of record loss. The most effective approach will be to research each parent-child relationship separately because you'll be separating clusters of matches for each parent.

Identifying a specific research question regarding your pedigree is the first step. Here are some examples of research questions involving family relationships.

> *EXAMPLE:* Who was the biological mother of Fern Smith, born on 11 December 1911 in Chicago, Illinois?

> *EXAMPLE:* Who was the biological father of Jack Kenneth Shaffer, born in 1928 in Oklahoma City, Oklahoma?

> *EXAMPLE:* Was Benjamin Cox of Texas the biological father of Rachel Cox, married 1848 to William Henderson Shults in Navarro County, Texas?

> *EXAMPLE:* Was Nancy Bullard the biological mother of Susannah Clanton, born in 1817 in South Carolina?

Discover a Collateral Relationship

Do you have a family story that you are related to a famous individual such as Daniel Boone? Perhaps an unknown close relative appeared on your DNA match list, and you'd like to discover your connection. With a focused objective, DNA can sometimes answer these types of questions. Some examples of research questions involving collateral relationships follow.

> *EXAMPLE:* What is the relationship of my Boone ancestor to Daniel Boon, who was born 2 November 1734 in Pennsylvania, and died 26 September 1820 in Defiance, Missouri?

> *EXAMPLE:* How am I connected to my DNA match, Jane Smith, with whom I share 583 cm?

Choosing an Ancestor to Research Using DNA Evidence

An understanding of DNA inheritance is key to formulating a research question that can be answered using DNA evidence. Review the concepts discussed in chapter one to ensure that you have sufficient test results from yourself or other individuals for the research project. Without enough DNA matches, you may not be able to make significant progress. To increase the odds of connecting with pertinent genetic cousins, you can test or upload raw DNA to each testing company.

For example, if you're working on a family line centered in Germany, but you only have a handful of matches on Ancestry DNA, you might consider transferring your raw DNA to MyHeritage, where there could be additional matches. MyHeritage often has more users of recent European descent.

Can DNA be used to solve every genealogical question? No, when creating a research objective, take into consideration the limitations for each type of test.

Limitations of Autosomal DNA

Most DNA projects will use autosomal DNA (atDNA) because of its broad scope. Even Y-DNA and mitochondrial DNA (mtDNA) projects could benefit from using autosomal DNA simultaneously. However, atDNA may not be the answer to every brick wall question. Because of the predictable average amount of DNA passed from a parent to a child, close biological relationships can be confirmed or rejected with atDNA. Those easiest to determine include aunts, uncles, nieces, nephews, half-siblings, first cousins, and second cousins. You should share significant amounts of DNA with these relatives, and identifying common ancestors will be doable.

As the relationships move back generationally, less DNA will be shared, and it will be more challenging to identify a common ancestor. Due to recombination, you won't share atDNA with all your 3rd cousins. Beyond six to eight generations, the amount of DNA inherited from a specific ancestor may be too small to identify its origin definitively.

Limitations of Y-DNA

As discussed in chapter one, Y-DNA is passed down from father to son throughout time virtually unchanged. This inheritance pattern makes Y-DNA useful for connecting to a group of individuals sharing a surname, but it won't identify an exact ancestor. You might be able to connect to a specific family, but be unable to determine which son would be your ancestor.

Locating testers for a Y-DNA test can be another limitation. Because only males inherit a Y chromosome, it may be challenging to find a direct male descendant of the ancestor in question to test. Some ancestral lines die out, and no males carrying the Y chromosome have survived.

Once you find someone to take the test, there may be few, if any, matches in the testing pool. Additionally, if there was a surname change or misattributed parentage event, Y-DNA test results may reveal matches of different surnames. Additional research in the records and utilizing the autosomal DNA will be needed to discover the genetic line.

Limitations of mitochondrial DNA

Just as Y-DNA is passed along the patrilineal line, mitochondrial DNA (mtDNA) is passed only along the matrilineal line. A mother passes mtDNA to all her children, so both males and females can have their mtDNA tested. However, only the females will pass it on to their children. Mitochondrial DNA changes very slowly over time and will show inheritance for distant relationships. Although it can show where a matrilineal line originated in the world thousands of years ago, it may not yield information for your third great-grandmother if none of her other descendants have tested their mtDNA. You can best use this type of test to compare the mtDNA of a woman's possible descendants. For example, if your third great-grandfather had three wives, you could test each of the wives' descendants to determine each child's mother.

Practice with Evaluating DNA Research Questions

Before identifying a DNA research question of your own, evaluate the following scenarios and determine if DNA can be used to answer the question.

Scenario #1

Katherine has taken an autosomal DNA test. Her research question is: Who is the father of my 2nd great-grandfather, Patrick McKell? Patrick was born about 1825 in Ireland and immigrated to Michigan. He married Hannah, maiden name unknown, born about 1840 in Ireland.

The diagram in figure 4.1 illustrates this line of Katherine's family tree.

Can Katherine's autosomal DNA results be used to help answer her research question? Why or why not?

Answer: Katherine's ancestor, Patrick McKell, is well within the range of using autosomal DNA to help answer her research question. However, the number of DNA matches on this line could limit the project.

Scenario #2

Steve Bingham Jr. and his father, Steve Bingham Sr., have taken autosomal DNA tests. Steve's research question is: I want to research my father's side. I have traced my ancestry back to my 4th great grandfather, Ralph Bingham, born in 1760 in North Carolina. I want to find Ralph Bingham's father and eventually trace the Bingham line back several more generations. Figure 4.2 illustrates this scenario.

Can Steve and his father's autosomal DNA results be used to help answer his research question? Why or why not?

Answer: Steve's ancestor, Ralph Bingham, is within the range of six to eight generations of using autosomal DNA to help answer his research question. The research should

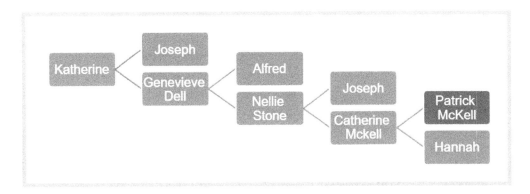

Figure 4.1. Katherine's line from Patrick and Hannah McKell

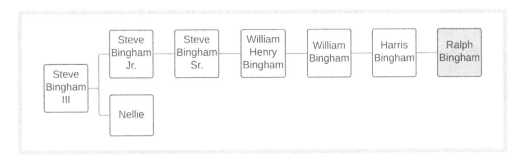

Figure 4.2. Steve's patrilineal descent from Ralph Bingham

use the senior Steve Bingham's atDNA results as he inherited more DNA from his ancestor Ralph Bingham than did his son.

Steve Bingham also asks this question: *Who is the original Bingham ancestor who immigrated to the United States?*

Can DNA help answer this research question? Why or why not?

Answer: Identifying the original Bingham immigrant with DNA help will be pushing the limits of autosomal DNA testing. If Ralph Bingham were the 4th great-grandfather and was born in 1760, the Bingham immigrant could be within eight generations, and autosomal DNA could help identify the ancestor. However, a severe limitation is that Steve Bingham Sr. may not have inherited DNA from the immigrant ancestor. Testing other known descendants could increase the ancestor's DNA coverage and give more data points to utilize. When identifying an ancestor further back than six generations, using Y-DNA testing and autosomal testing increases the likelihood of success. Y-DNA testing could lead to connecting with other Bingham descendants and possibly point to an immigrant ancestor.

Scenario #3

Denise has taken a mitochondrial DNA test. Denise's question: *Who is the mother of my fourth great-grandmother, Sarah Graves, born about 1795 in North Carolina?*

Can mitochondrial DNA help answer this question? Why or why not?

Answer: Because mitochondrial DNA traces the maternal line back for many generations, Denise will likely have DNA matches of various surnames with no clue how they connect. If she can identify a possible fifth great-grandmother and trace her female descendants forward, she could compare mitochondrial DNA with one of those descendants. If it is a positive match, that could help confirm her hypothesis. She could seek autosomal DNA evidence as well to further test the theory.

What Brick Wall Can You Overcome with DNA Evidence?

Now that we've explored the basics of DNA inheritance, the limitations of DNA, and some of the possibilities for using DNA in genealogy, you're ready to choose a research question of your own. Examine your pedigree chart and consider what brick wall you could overcome with DNA evidence. Several DNA testing companies' tools can help you explore your family tree and provide clues for potential research questions. The tools can also help you evaluate whether there would be enough DNA evidence for a research project.

Surname Searches

A useful tool for formulating DNA research questions is the surname search feature on the DNA testing websites. Searching by surname allows you to narrow down your matches to specific family lines quickly. If you consider researching a brick wall ancestor, a surname search can reveal if there is enough information for a viable DNA project. Experiment with this feature on each website to discover the capabilities and limitations.

For example, one of my brick walls is Mary "Clemsy" Cline, born in 1818 in Missouri. Doing a surname search on AncestryDNA identified a small group of DNA matches with the surname CLINE in their family tree. Viewing the trees, I noticed similar locations to my family. Working with these DNA matches would be a good start in discovering my ancestor's mother or father.

Tree Comparisons

Two testing companies have created a way to view a path to a common ancestor between you and your shared matches: Ancestry ThruLines and MyHeritage Theory of Family Relativity. Use both with caution because they are based on user-created family trees. With that said, they can be excellent tools to explore possible research projects.

If you have connected a family tree to your DNA results on Ancestry, the system will generate ThruLines for you. Any shared DNA match who has some of the same relatives listed in their tree as you will appear as part of the descendancy tree generated by ThruLines. Some of the connections are correct, but not all. A suggested ancestor may appear in your list based on a shared DNA match's tree and become an excellent subject for a DNA research project.

For example, I have done extensive research on Benjamin Cox of Texas and hypothesized that he was the father of my third great-grandmother, Rachel Cox. I added him to my Ancestry tree, and he appeared in my ThruLines with over seventy shared DNA matches. Most of these were small segments of ten cM or less. Knowing the danger of small segments, I decided a complete project was in order. I needed to analyze the DNA evidence in conjunction with documentary research. See chapter six for more about small segments.

Similar to Ancestry ThruLines, MyHeritage offers the Theory of Family Relativity. Based on user-submitted family trees and sometimes documentary evidence, the technology will suggest the most recent common ancestor and show a proposed line back to that ancestor from both you and your DNA match. To see any proposed theories, view your DNA match list and look for the purple "View theory" at the bottom of each DNA match's summary. If the match has no tree associated with their DNA, no theory will appear.

Unique to this tool is the feature that may depict various paths through which you and your shared DNA match are related depending on the user-submitted trees. The program suggests the connection, but you need to do the research and analysis to confirm the relationships.

Ancestry DNA Common Ancestors

Ancestry DNA features a unique tool—Common ancestors. If you and a DNA match both link to the same ancestor, that DNA match will appear in a list when you select "Common ancestors" at the top of your match page. Not included are those DNA matches without an attached family tree. If you plan to confirm a generational link in your family tree, evaluating the shared DNA of descendants of a common ancestor is essential. This tool provides a quick way to isolate those specific DNA matches that you can then evaluate as part of a DNA research project.

Writing the Research Objective

After determining a research question with enough DNA evidence to use, you can write an objective. What if your research question does not have sufficient DNA evidence to explore the question? Consider targeted testing to generate additional DNA evidence. You may need to perform further descendancy research to identify candidates for a DNA test. See chapter six for more information on targeted testing.

When considering your objective, it can be concise or complex. A project that could be completed in 20 hours, such as a client project, requires a concise objective. Alternately your objective might be complex and need to be broken into phases to focus on gathering information step by step.

For example, in researching the mother of a female ancestor born in the early 1800s, several phases might be necessary to come to a conclusion. Each phase would be a separate project and have its own objective. The overarching research question of "Who was the mother of Elsie born 1820?" could have the following phases.

Phase 1 Objective: Perform documentary research for the mother of Elsie.

Phase 2 Objective: Research the descendants of Elsie for potential DNA test-takers.

Phase 3 Objective: Explore the genetic networks of DNA testers for possible hypotheses.

Phase 4 Objective: Test a specific hypothesis for the mother of Elsie.

Phase 5 Objective: Test additional hypotheses for the mother of Elsie.

If you have already thoroughly researched your ancestor in question and already have adequate DNA results to use, you may be ready to start with phase 3. Each research project is unique, and a thoughtful approach to an objective ensures you won't tackle a too large project.

When ready, you can use key identifying information about the ancestor to create your research objective. Key identifiers include full names, spouses, birth, marriage, and death dates and places.

These facts serve to uniquely identify the person of interest from any other with similar information. Also, when writing a DNA objective, we are generally seeking to test, confirm, or reject a hypothesized identity or biological relationship, so using those specific terms can clarify the research's purpose.

For example, I formulated this objective from the following research question: Is Benjamin Cox the biological father of Rachel Cox? Starting with that basic premise, I added in the details that would guide the documentary research. Several Ben Coxes appear in the records. Adding unique identifiers such as birth and death will help me analyze each document I locate.

Example Objective

The objective of this research project is to confirm the hypothesized relationship of Benjamin Cox as the biological father of Rachel Cox through autosomal DNA evidence and documentary research. Benjamin Cox was born about 1791 in Ohio and died between 1870 and 1880 in Bell County, Texas. Rachel Cox was born about 1828 in Indiana and died between 1870 and 1880 in Falls County, Texas. Rachel married Hickman Monroe Shults on 4 July 1848 in Navarro County, Texas.

Practice writing an objective for each of the following fictional research questions, then check your answers at the end of this chapter.

Question 1

I have traced my ancestor George Harris to Licking County, Ohio, in 1850. He married Elizabeth Morris in 1843 and died in Crawford County, Missouri, in 1892. George was born about 1817 in Ohio. His death certificate states his father's name as Henry Harris. Three men named Henry Harris lived in Licking County. *Which is the father of George?*

Question 2

My ancestor William Holloway immigrated from England to Sussex County, New Jersey, in 1852. Who was his father? William married Margaret Jackson in 1859 in Sussex County, New Jersey, and died in Clark County, Kansas, in 1902. Neither his death certificate nor immigration record named a father. *Who were his parents?*

Question 3

My brick wall ancestor is Nancy Bailey, born about 1800 in North Carolina. She is my direct maternal line, and I have both mitochondrial and autosomal DNA test results. I'd like to know her parents. She married Robert Taylor in Rowan County, North Carolina, about 1822 and died in Greene County, Georgia, in 1861.

Your Task

Examine your family tree and choose two to three questions that could be answered using existing DNA test results. Consider the limitations of DNA evidence in answering each question, then select one question. Determine whether a research project answering that question would be concise or complex. If the project would be too complicated, consider breaking it into phases. Write a research objective based on that question using the key identifiers of full names, spouses, birth, marriage, and death dates and places.

Objective Answers

Question 1

I have traced my ancestor George Harris to Licking County, Ohio, in 1850. He married Elizabeth Morris in 1843 and died in Crawford County, Missouri, in 1892. Who was his father? George was born about 1817 in Ohio. His death certificate states his father's name as Henry Harris. Three men named Henry Harris lived in Licking County. Which is the father of George? I have my autosomal DNA at Ancestry as well as that of my sister.

Incomplete objective: Which of the three men named Henry Harris was the father of George Harris?

Complete objective for identity: The objective of this research project is to utilize documentary research and autosomal DNA evidence to identify which of three men named Henry Harris of Licking County, Ohio, was the biological father of George Harris, born about 1817 in Ohio. George married Elizabeth Morris in 1843 and died in Crawford County, Missouri, in 1892.

Question 2

My ancestor William Holloway immigrated from England to Sussex County, New Jersey, in 1852. Who was his father? William was born about 1832 in England and married Margaret Jackson in 1859 in Sussex County, New Jersey. He died in Clark County, Kansas, in 1902. Neither his death certificate nor immigration record named a father. Who were his parents? I have both autosomal and Y-DNA testing completed.

Incomplete objective: Who were the parents of William Holloway?

Complete objective for a relationship, narrowed down: The objective of this research session is to discover the biological father of William Holloway, born about 1832 in England and died in Clark County, Kansas, in 1902. William married Margaret Jackson in 1859 in Sussex County, New Jersey. Documentary research and autosomal DNA will be used to discover probable candidates for the father of William Holloway. Utilize Y-DNA testing to find additional connections to Holloway men in England.

Question 3

My brick wall ancestor is Nancy Bailey, born about 1800 in North Carolina. She is my direct maternal line, and I have both mitochondrial and autosomal DNA test results. I'd like to know her parents. She married Robert Taylor in Rowan County, North Carolina, about 1822 and died in Greene County, Georgia, in 1861.

Incomplete objective: Who were the parents of Nancy Bailey?

Complete objective for a relationship, divided into segments: This research project aims to identify a possible biological mother for Nancy Bailey using autosomal DNA. Nancy was born about 1800 in North Carolina and died in Greene County, Georgia, in 1861. She married Robert Taylor in Rowan County, North Carolina, about 1822. The subsequent project will be to identify descendants of the identified candidate for Nancy Bailey's mother and ask them to take a mitochondrial DNA test to compare with the descendant of Nancy Bailey.

CHAPTER 5

Write Source Citations for DNA and Documentary Sources

Diana Elder

How do you cite DNA evidence? When and where do you incorporate it into your research? As genealogists, we create source citations for our personal use in research logs, notes, and genealogical software. When we are ready to share our conclusions in a research report, family history, blog post, proof argument, journal article, or lineage society application, we use citations to document each genealogical fact. Source citations also lend credence to our presentations, syllabus material, charts, and forms.

As the second element of the Genealogical Proof Standard, "complete and accurate source citations" demonstrate our research scope and our sources' quality.[1] Whenever we state any fact that is not common knowledge or need to give attribution to a statement or image not created by us, we use a citation. Informative citations help prove our conclusions, allowing a fellow researcher to follow each citation to its source and independently evaluate the information.

Like all genealogy sources, DNA evidence gains credibility when backed with a source citation describing the source, allowing independent evaluation. A common saying in the genetic genealogy world is, "DNA doesn't lie, but the analysis could be wrong."

---

1. Board for Certification of Genealogists (BCG), *Genealogy Standards,* 2nd ed. (Nashville: Ancestry.com, 2019), 2.

Documenting DNA sources and information in enough detail allows us to meet genetic genealogy standards, ensuring that others can follow our research and either agree or disagree with our conclusions.[2]

You create source citations throughout a research project, beginning with the initial analysis of existing documentary research. During the research phase of your project, you will create a source citation for each search performed. When you have completed your DNA research project, you will share your conclusions in a written report complete with source citations for both the documentary and genetic research. Whether you have proven a genetic relationship or not, thorough documentation raises your research quality and enables others to follow your analysis and reasoning.

A documentary source can be anything or any person providing information that becomes evidence in proving a fact or relationship. Commonly used sources are birth, death, and marriage certificates, census records, gravestones, interviews, letters, published histories, etc. Stating that a birth date came from the family bible gains credibility when backed with a source citation that describes the Bible's provenance—the original owner, date of publication, and the path to the current owner. The citation could also include an evaluation of the handwriting.

Typical DNA sources include DNA matches, reports created by the testing companies, family trees of DNA matches, and references explaining DNA inheritance patterns. Mastering the art of citation for documentary and DNA research provides you with an important tool to help prove your work. This chapter will discuss the principles of citation with a focus on DNA sources.

Creating DNA Source Citations

Two steps will help you create a citation for DNA sources: understanding the source and identifying the five elements needed for a clear and complete citation.

Understand the Source

When using documentary sources, we learn about the source before we create a citation. We look at the beginning of the microfilm. We read the information in the catalog entry. We uncover the origins of the family bible. With DNA source citations, we also need a clear understanding of the sources we are using. Like documentary genealogical sources, DNA

---

2. BCG, *Genealogy Standards,* 2nd ed., 31.

sources can be original, derivative, or authored. Chapter six provides greater detail on analyzing DNA sources. Use those concepts as a resource to understand each DNA source.

Elements of Source Citations

When looking at a source, you may feel overwhelmed at the prospect of forming a citation from either a large amount of data or the lack thereof. To simplify the process, *Genealogy Standards* defines five questions a source citation should answer.[3]

- Who created the source?
- What is the source?
- When was the source created or accessed?
- Where is the source?
- Where in the source is the item of information used?

Creating a source citation depends upon answering these five questions. A variety of examples will provide ideas for how to answer each question for typical DNA sources. In each example, the bolded citation element illustrates the answer to the question.

WHO Created the Source?

Book, Article, or Blog Post

Because genetic genealogy contains many new concepts, when writing a report to share with a client or family member, you may choose to quote a sentence or short paragraph from a book, article, or blog post. Answering the question "Who created the source?" is relatively easy, naming the author or authors as shown in the first and third examples. Because the *ISOGG Wiki* article in the second example was created by several contributors, no single author is listed. Instead, the creator of the article is the same as the title of the website and is omitted.

- **Blaine T. Bettinger and Debbie Parker Wayne**, *Genetic Genealogy in Practice* (Arlington, Virginia: National Genealogical Society, 2016), 23.
- "Y chromosome DNA tests," rev. 4 September 2019, ***International Society of Genetic Genealogy (ISOGG) Wiki*** (https://isogg.org/wiki/Y_chromosome_DNA_tests : accessed 21 October 2019), para. 2.

---

3. BCG, *Genealogy Standards,* 2nd ed., 7.

- **Robin Wirthlin,** "Understanding and Using Your DNA Results—4 Simple Steps," blog post, 22 February 2019, *Family Locket* (https://familylocket.com/understanding-and-using-your-dna-results-4-simple-steps/ : accessed 8 February 2021).

Reports and Company Tools

Since working with DNA involves our genetic cousins, we may be using a report generated by them in our conclusions. In that case, the question "Who created the source" is answered by their name. We address privacy issues by always seeking permission to include their name in a citation shared publicly. The example below highlights my genetic cousin, Donald Robert Royston, as the report's creator for a Y-DNA Royston project. I used this report to help prove the connection between my California Royston family and their Virginia Royston origins.

- **Donald Robert Royston,** "The Results of the 46 Marker DNA Male Y Chromosome Tests," Y-DNA Royston project, showing matches for Bill Gene Royston & Donald Robert Royston matching 100% in all 46 markers, 24 October 2009 (revised 21 June 2010), report prepared for Diana Elder, Highland, Utah, privately held by Diana Elder, 2017.

We rely heavily on the online reports and tools generated by DNA testing companies and third-party websites as we analyze cousin matches, amount of shared DNA, segment data, ethnicity results, etc. The examples below highlight a DNA testing company or website as both the creator and the source's publisher. When the website and the author are the same, there is no need to cite both.

- "Coon/Koontz/Kuhn/Coonts, etc. DNA/Genealogy Website—Y-DNA Classic Chart," Y-Chromosome DNA STR surname project results, *FamilyTree DNA* (https://www.familytreedna.com/public/Coon?iframe=yresults : accessed 22 October 2018).
- "Review DNA Match for Robin Wirthlin," database report, *MyHeritage* (https://www.myheritage.com/dna/match : accessed 10 September 2019), estimated 2nd Cousin Once Removed relationship with [Private] sharing 2.3% DNA (165.7 cM) across 8 shared segments (largest segment 51.1 cM), DNA managed by [Private], (MRCA: J. E. Taylor and M. A. Ollerton).
- "AutoCluster Visualization for Robin Wirthlin," database report, *Genetic Affairs* (https://www.geneticaffairs.com : accessed 13 September 2019), 23andMe data showing 5 members in Cluster 8, (MRCA E. Taylor and W. A. Spafford).

▪ "Ethnicity Estimate report for Diana Elder," ***AncestryDNA*** (https://www. ancestry.com/dna/origins : accessed 21 October 2019), 81% England, Wales & Northwestern Europe, 11% Ireland & Scotland, 8% Norway.

Online Family Tree

Because our genetic genealogy relies heavily on tracing generational links, we will often refer to an online tree to verify a specific family line. State the name of the tree's creator as shown on the website.

▪ **Diana Elder,** "Shults_Kelsey family tree," public member tree, *Ancestry* (https://www.ancestry.com/family-tree/tree/58419748/family? : accessed 17 June 2020), sourced data for the family of William Huston Shults and Dora Algie Royston.

▪ **M. Romine,** "Elkins-Cox Family Tree," profile for William Thomas "Billy" Cox (1827–1912), public member tree, *Ancestry* (https://www.ancestry.com : accessed 11 June 2019).

Digital Diagram

To answer the question of "who" for a diagram or graph, state the name of the creator.

▪ **Jane Doe,** "Doe-Smith Descendant Diagram," digital diagram created with *Lucidchart* (https://lucidchart.com), DNA matches from MyHeritage AutoCluster Report for Jane Doe, cluster 8, generated 8 February 2021, privately held by Jane Doe, Anywhere, USA.

▪ **Jane Doe**, "Gephi network graph for John Smith using Ancestry DNA data," digital diagram created with *Gephi,* files gathered with *DNAGedcom Client* using 25–250 cM shared DNA, gathered 18 October 2020, privately held by Jane Doe, Anywhere, USA.

WHAT is the Source?

Book, Article, or Blog Post

When citing a published book, article, or blog post, the question "What is the source" is answered by the title. Following general citation rules, italics set off publications such as a book, magazine, or website, and quotation marks enclose chapters within a publication.

- Blaine T. Bettinger and Debbie Parker Wayne, *Genetic Genealogy in Practice* (Arlington, Virginia: National Genealogical Society, 2016), 23.
- **"Y chromosome DNA tests,"** rev. 4 September 2019, *International Society of Genetic Genealogy (ISOGG) Wiki* (https://isogg.org/wiki/Y_chromosome_DNA_tests : accessed 21 October 2019), para. 2.
- Robin Wirthlin, **"Understanding and Using Your DNA Results—4 Simple Steps,"** blog post, 22 February 2019, *Family Locket* (https://familylocket.com/understanding-and-using-your-dna-results-4-simple-steps/ : accessed 8 February 2020).

Reports and Company Tools

When citing a report or tool, quotation marks inserted around the title or website's description signal to the reader the specific report. Add additional information as necessary as part of the "What," such as the term "database report."

- Donald Robert Royston**, "The Results of the 46 Marker DNA Male Y Chromosome Tests," Y-DNA Royston project,** showing matches for Bill Gene Royston & Donald Robert Royston matching 100% in all 46 markers, 24 October 2009 (revised 21 June 2010), report prepared for Diana Elder, Highland, Utah, privately held by Diana Elder, 2017.
- **"Ethnicity Estimate report for Diana Elder,"** *AncestryDNA* (https://www.ancestry.com/dna/origins : accessed 21 October 2019), 81% England, Wales & Northwestern Europe, 11% Ireland & Scotland, 8% Norway.
- **"X-DNA Comparison" database, vers. 2.1.0(a)," database report,** *GEDmatch* (https://www.gedmatch.com : downloaded 19 January 2019), kits A480154 (Nicole Dyer) and A279720 (Diana Elder), chromosome X, start-stop points 2321–154886292, 196.1 cMs.
- **"Coon/Koontz/Kuhn/Coonts, etc. DNA/Genealogy Website—Y-DNA Classic Chart," Y-Chromosome DNA STR surname project results,** *FamilyTree DNA* (https://www.familytreedna.com/public/Coon?iframe=yresults : accessed 22 October 2018).
- **"Review DNA Match for Robin Wirthlin," database report,** *MyHeritage* (https://www.myheritage.com/dna/match : accessed 10 September 2019), estimated 2nd Cousin Once Removed relationship with [Private] sharing 2.3% DNA (165.7 cM) across 8 shared segments (largest segment 51.1 cM), DNA managed by [Private], (MRCA: J. E. Taylor and M. A. Ollerton).

■ **"AutoCluster Visualization for Robin Wirthlin," database report,** *Genetic Affairs* (https://www.geneticaffairs.com : accessed 13 September 2019), 23andMe data showing 5 members in Cluster 8, (MRCA E. Taylor and W. A. Spafford).

Online Family Tree

Answering the question "What is the source" for an online family tree will include both the description of the broad collection and the family tree's exact name. A short analysis of the tree can follow the description and location of the tree. A specific ancestor's profile could also be referenced and identifying information included as part of the "what."

■ Diana Elder, **"Shults_Kelsey family tree," public member tree,** *Ancestry* (https://www.ancestry.com/family-tree/tree/58419748/family? : accessed 17 June 2020), **sourced data for the family of William Huston Shults and Dora Algie Royston.**

■ M. Romine, **"Elkins-Cox Family Tree,"** profile for William Thomas "Billy" Cox (1827–1912), **public member tree,** *Ancestry* (https://www.ancestry.com : accessed 11 June 2019).

Digital Diagrams

When we create a diagram or graph to illustrate connections between DNA matches, we can title the visual and include the title in quotation marks to set it apart in the citation. Additional information can be added, such as the program used to create the visual representation.

■ Jane Doe, **"Doe-Smith Descendant Diagram," digital diagram created with** *Lucidchart* (https://lucidchart.com), DNA matches from MyHeritage AutoCluster Report for Jane Doe, cluster 8, generated 8 February 2021, privately held by Jane Doe, Anywhere, USA.

■ Jane Doe, **"Gephi network graph for John Smith using Ancestry DNA data," digital diagram created with** *Gephi,* files gathered with *DNAGedcom Client* using 25–250 cM shared DNA, gathered 18 October 2020, privately held by Jane Doe, Anywhere, USA.

WHEN was the Source Published, Created, or Accessed?

Book, Article, or Blog Post

With the field of DNA changing rapidly, the date of publication is essential. Are we citing the latest developments? A citation for an article from a wiki should always include both the revision date and the access date. Similarly, a blog post citation would include the date published and the access date. A blog author may revise or update a post as well, and you could note that date.

- Blaine T. Bettinger and Debbie Parker Wayne, *Genetic Genealogy in Practice* (Arlington, Virginia: National Genealogical Society, **2016**), 23.

- "Y chromosome DNA tests," **rev. 4 September 2019**, *International Society of Genetic Genealogy (ISOGG) Wiki* (https://isogg.org/wiki/Y_chromosome_DNA_tests : **accessed 21 October 2019**), para. 2.

- Robin Wirthlin, "Understanding and Using Your DNA Results—4 Simple Steps," blog post, **22 February 2019**, *Family Locket* (https://familylocket.com/understanding-and-using-your-dna-results-4-simple-steps/ : **accessed 8 February 2020**).

Reports and Company Tools

Cite the date a DNA match report was created and downloaded. Although the information is not likely to change, the date will be necessary if the database updates the algorithm used to calculate the report.

- Donald Robert Royston, "The Results of the 46 Marker DNA Male Y Chromosome Tests," Y-DNA Royston project, showing matches for Bill Gene Royston & Donald Robert Royston matching 100% in all 46 markers, **24 October 2009 (revised 21 June 2010)**, report prepared for Diana Elder, Highland, Utah, privately held by Diana Elder, **2017**.

- "Ethnicity Estimate report for Diana Elder," *AncestryDNA* (https://www.ancestry.com/dna/origins : **accessed 21 October 2019**), 81% England, Wales & Northwestern Europe, 11% Ireland & Scotland, 8% Norway.

- "X-DNA Comparison" database, vers. 2.1.0(a)," database report, *GEDmatch* (https://www.gedmatch.com : **downloaded 19 January 2019**), kits A480154 (Nicole Dyer) and A279720 (Diana Elder), chromosome X, start-stop points 2321–154886292, 196.1 cMs.

- "Coon/Koontz/Kuhn/Coonts, etc. DNA/Genealogy Website—Y-DNA Classic Chart," Y-Chromosome DNA STR surname project results, *FamilyTree DNA* (https://www.familytreedna.com/public/Coon?iframe=yresults : **accessed 22 October 2018**).

- "Review DNA Match for Robin Wirthlin," database report, *MyHeritage* (https://www.myheritage.com/dna/match : **accessed 10 September 2019**), estimated 2nd Cousin Once Removed relationship with [Private] sharing 2.3% DNA (165.7

cM) across 8 shared segments (largest segment 51.1 cM), DNA managed by [Private], (MRCA: J. E. Taylor and M. A. Ollerton).

- "AutoCluster Visualization for Robin Wirthlin," database report, *Genetic Affairs* (https://www.geneticaffairs.com : **accessed 13 September 2019**), 23andMe data showing 5 members in Cluster 8, (MRCA E. Taylor and W. A. Spafford)

Online Family Tree
Cite the specific day and year you accessed the tree, as online trees can change often.

- Diana Elder, "Shults_Kelsey family tree," public member tree, *Ancestry* (https://www.ancestry.com/family-tree/tree/58419748/family? : **accessed 17 June 2020**), sourced data for the family of William Huston Shults and Dora Algie Royston.
- M. Romine, "Elkins-Cox Family Tree," profile for William Thomas "Billy" Cox (1827–1912), public member tree, *Ancestry* (https://www.ancestry.com : **accessed 11 June 2019**).

Digital Diagram
DNA information changes continually as new matches become available, so note the date of creation for a digital diagram or graph.

- Jane Doe, "Doe-Smith Descendant Diagram," digital diagram created with *Lucidchart* (https://lucidchart.com), DNA matches from MyHeritage AutoCluster Report for Jane Doe, cluster 8, **generated 8 February 2021**, privately held by Jane Doe, Anywhere, USA.
- Jane Doe, "Gephi network graph for John Smith using Ancestry DNA data," digital diagram created with *Gephi*, files gathered with *DNAGedcom Client* using 25–250 cM shared DNA, **gathered 18 October 2020**, privately held by Jane Doe, Anywhere, USA.

WHERE is the Source?

Book, Article, or Blog Post
When citing a published source, the question "Where is the source" is answered by the place of publication. Because the book could be physically located in many locations or could be out of print, you use the place of publication rather than the location you viewed the source.

For an article published online, cite the complete URL. In case the website disappears online, you can use the Internet Archive Wayback Machine to relocate the original article. Because the URL is part of the publication information, parentheses set it apart from the other citation information.

▨ Blaine T. Bettinger and Debbie Parker Wayne, *Genetic Genealogy in Practice* (**Arlington, Virginia:** National Genealogical Society, 2016), 23.

▨ "Y chromosome DNA tests," rev. 4 September 2019, *International Society of Genetic Genealogy (ISOGG) Wiki* (**https://isogg.org/wiki/Y_chromosome_DNA_tests** : accessed 21 October 2019).

▨ Robin Wirthlin, "Understanding and Using Your DNA Results—4 Simple Steps," blog post, 22 February 2019, *Family Locket* (**https://familylocket.com/understanding-and-using-your-dna-results-4-simple-steps/** : accessed 8 February 2021).

Reports and Company Tools

The location of a privately held report generally states only the city and state with the specific address withheld for privacy. A citation for a company report or tool should cite the complete URL only if it is a publicly accessible page, as in a surname project hosted by FamilyTree DNA. A match report should use the generic URL as the specific URL would only work if logged in to the DNA account.

▨ Donald Robert Royston, "The Results of the 46 Marker DNA Male Y Chromosome Tests," Y-DNA Royston project, showing matches for Bill Gene Royston & Donald Robert Royston matching 100% in all 46 markers, 24 October 2009 (revised 21 June 2010), report prepared for Diana Elder, **Highland, Utah**, privately held by Diana Elder, 2017.

▨ "Ethnicity Estimate report for Diana Elder," *AncestryDNA* (**https://www.ancestry.com/dna/origins** : accessed 21 October 2019), 81% England, Wales & Northwestern Europe, 11% Ireland & Scotland, 8% Norway.

▨ "X-DNA Comparison" database, vers. 2.1.0(a)," database report, *GEDmatch* (**https://www.gedmatch.com** : downloaded 19 January 2019), kits A480154 (Nicole Dyer) and A279720 (Diana Elder), chromosome X, start-stop points 2321–154886292, 196.1 cMs.

▨ "Coon/Koontz/Kuhn/Coonts, etc. DNA/Genealogy Website—Y-DNA Classic Chart," Y-Chromosome DNA STR surname project results, *FamilyTree DNA* (**https://www.familytreedna.com/public/Coon?iframe=yresults** : accessed 22 October 2018).

- "Review DNA Match for Robin Wirthlin," database report, *MyHeritage* (**https://www.myheritage.com/dna/**match : accessed 10 September 2019), estimated 2nd Cousin Once Removed relationship with [Private] sharing 2.3% DNA (165.7 cM) across 8 shared segments (largest segment 51.1 cM), DNA managed by [Private], (MRCA: J. E. Taylor and M. A. Ollerton).
- "AutoCluster Visualization for Robin Wirthlin," database report, *Genetic Affairs* (**https://www.geneticaffairs.com** : accessed 13 September 2019), 23andMe data showing 5 members in Cluster 8, (MRCA E. Taylor and W. A. Spafford).

Online Family Tree

When citing an online tree, consider using the full URL for ease of access. If a tree is private, the generic URL would be sufficient.

- Diana Elder, "Shults_Kelsey family tree," public member tree, *Ancestry* (**https://www.ancestry.com/family-tree/tree/58419748/family?** : accessed 17 June 2020), sourced data for the family of William Huston Shults and Dora Algie Royston.
- M. Romine, "Elkins-Cox Family Tree," profile for William Thomas "Billy" Cox (1827–1912), public member tree, *Ancestry* (**https://www.ancestry.com** : accessed 11 June 2019).

Digital Diagram

The question of "where" for a diagram you create is answered by your physical residence.

- Jane Doe, "Doe-Smith Descendant Diagram," digital diagram created with *Lucidchart* (https://lucidchart.com), DNA matches from MyHeritage AutoCluster Report for Jane Doe, cluster 8, generated 8 February 2021, privately held by Jane Doe, **Anywhere, USA.**
- Jane Doe, "Gephi network graph for John Smith using Ancestry DNA data," digital diagram created with *Gephi,* files gathered with *DNAGedcom Client* using 25–250 cM shared DNA, gathered 18 October 2020, privately held by Jane Doe, **Anywhere, USA.**

WHERE IN is the Item of Information?

When working with documentary sources, we cite specifics such as a page or image number to point to the specific information item. Many of the sources used for genetic genealogy can be accessed only by the user, such as DNA matches and ethnicity reports. We can add specific details about the report, such as segment data, haplogroups, or ethnicity percentages in these cases.

Book, Article, or Blog Post

When citing a specific detail within a book or article, identify the page or paragraph where the information is found. If you are citing the whole book or article, no specific page is needed.

- Blaine T. Bettinger and Debbie Parker Wayne, *Genetic Genealogy in Practice* (Arlington, Virginia: National Genealogical Society, 2016), **23**.
- "Y chromosome DNA tests," rev. 4 September 2019, *International Society of Genetic Genealogy (ISOGG) Wiki* (https://isogg.org/wiki/Y_chromosome_DNA_tests : accessed 21 October 2019), **para. 2.**
- Robin Wirthlin, "Understanding and Using Your DNA Results—4 Simple Steps," blog post, 22 February 2019, *Family Locket* (https://familylocket.com/understanding-and-using-your-dna-results-4-simple-steps/ : accessed 8 February 2021).

Reports and Company Tools

Citing a user report or a specific DNA match on a testing company website requires adding specific information because the match can only be accessed by the user. If you are trying to relocate a match, this will help you find the match more easily because most DNA companies allow you to sort by shared DNA and search by name. Also, if a DNA match deletes their test results, the citation preserves the details.

For a public site such as GEDmatch or Y-DNA projects that anyone can access, cite the specific kit numbers used in the comparison and other particular data. When citing an ethnicity report, add the percentages and regions, creating a record to compare with any future company updates to the ethnicity results.

- Donald Robert Royston, "The Results of the 46 Marker DNA Male Y Chromosome Tests," Y-DNA Royston project, **showing matches for Bill Gene Royston & Donald Robert Royston matching 100% in all 46 markers,** 24 October 2009 (revised 21 June 2010), report prepared for Diana Elder, Highland, Utah, privately held by Diana Elder, 2017.
- "Ethnicity Estimate report for Diana Elder," *AncestryDNA* (https://www.ancestry.com/dna/origins : accessed 21 October 2019), **81% England, Wales & Northwestern Europe, 11% Ireland & Scotland, 8% Norway.**

- "X-DNA Comparison" database, vers. 2.1.0(a)," database report, *GEDmatch* (https://www.gedmatch.com : downloaded 19 January 2019), **kits A480154 (Nicole Dyer) and A279720 (Diana Elder), chromosome X, start-stop points 2321–154886292, 196.1 cMs.**
- "Coon/Koontz/Kuhn/Coonts, etc. DNA/Genealogy Website—Y-DNA Classic Chart," **Y-Chromosome DNA STR surname project results,** *FamilyTree DNA* (https://www.familytreedna.com/public/Coon?iframe=yresults : accessed 22 October 2018).
- "Review DNA Match for Robin Wirthlin," database report, *MyHeritage* (https://www.myheritage.com/dna/match : accessed 10 September 2019), **estimated 2nd Cousin Once Removed relationship with [Private] sharing 2.3% DNA (165.7 cM) across 8 shared segments (largest segment 51.1 cM), DNA managed by [Private], (MRCA: J. E. Taylor and M. A. Ollerton).**
- "AutoCluster Visualization for Robin Wirthlin," database report, *Genetic Affairs* (https://www.geneticaffairs.com : accessed 13 September 2019), **23andMe data showing 5 members in Cluster 8, (MRCA E. Taylor and W. A. Spafford).**

Online Family Tree

A citation for an online tree could point to the entire tree with no specific "where in" item noted or to a specific profile within the tree.

- Diana Elder, "Shults_Kelsey family tree," public member tree, *Ancestry* (https://www.ancestry.com/family-tree/tree/58419748/family? : accessed 17 June 2020), sourced data for the family of William Huston Shults and Dora Algie Royston.
- M. Romine, "Elkins-Cox Family Tree," **profile for William Thomas "Billy" Cox (1827–1912),** public member tree, *Ancestry* (https://www.ancestry.com : accessed 11 June 2019).

Digital Diagram

The citation for a digital diagram could include details about the specific matches or amount of cM used in gathering the data.

- Jane Doe, "Doe-Smith Descendant Diagram," digital diagram created with *Lucidchart* (https://lucidchart.com), **DNA matches from MyHeritage AutoCluster Report for Jane Doe, cluster 8,** generated 8 February 2021, privately held by Jane Doe, Anywhere USA.
- Jane Doe, "Gephi network graph for John Smith using Ancestry DNA data," digital diagram created with *Gephi,* **files gathered with *DNAGedcom Client* using**

25–250 cM shared DNA, gathered 18 October 2020, privately held by Jane Doe, Anywhere, USA.

Citation Formats, Styles, and Standards

Layered Citations

DNA sources typically are viewed only online, but many of the documentary sources we use in our research are digitized original images. We create layered source citations that reflect both the physical information for that source and the digital information.[4] The example below demonstrates a source located by browsing digitized microfilm on FamilySearch. The physical information is listed first, followed by the digital information separated by the semicolon, with the film numbers listed last. A third layer cites the original microfilm number and the new digital film number, important for quickly locating the document through the FamilySearch Catalog.

- Montague County, Texas, "Delayed Birth Certificates, Event Date Ca. 1870–1933," entry for Alice Frazier, certificate 6–54, 1886 (1949), arranged alphabetically; digitized image 210 of 1926, *FamilySearch* (https://www.familysearch.org/ ark:/61903/3:1:3QS7-89VD-G42M? : accessed 31 May 2020); citing DGS Film 007611604, FHL microfilm 1,435,324.

For an indexed record collection that also includes images, reference the digital information first, then the physical information as shown in the following example from Find My Past.

- "Ireland, Petty Sessions Court Registers" entry for Patrick Savage, 8 February 1854, digital image, *Findmypast* (https://www.findmypast.com : accessed 10 June 2020); County Court, Ireland, Kerry, Tralee, Petty Sessions Order Books, National Archives of Ireland, Dublin, CSPS 1/9609.

---

4. Elizabeth Shown Mills, "Fundamentals of Citation," *Evidence Explained: Citing History Sources from Artifacts to Cyberspace*, 3rd ed. (Baltimore: Genealogical Publishing Company, 2015), 58, specifically 2.3 "Citation Layers."

Citation Formats

Depending on the project, we may use various citation formats: the full reference note, shortened reference note, or source list entry.

The most common format we will use in our DNA research is the full reference note. Either inserted throughout the report as footnotes or included after the report as endnotes, the reference notes provide proof for each specific assertion of a relationship or genealogical fact. Cite subsequent references to the same source using a shortened reference note.

We may need to provide a source list for our reader at the end of the report or book, citing each general source used in the project. Entries for a source list do not refer to a specific page or image number, rather the source as a whole. A source list entry uses slightly different formatting: periods instead of commas to separate the elements, no parentheses around publication information, and authors listed by their last name. The alphabetical arrangement groups titles by author and makes it easy to see the sources at a glance. See Appendix B for the source list for this book.

Examples:

Full Reference Note

- Blaine T. Bettinger and Debbie Parker Wayne, *Genetic Genealogy in Practice*, (Arlington, Virginia: National Genealogical Society, 2016), 23.
- "Review DNA Match" for Robin Wirthlin, database report, *MyHeritage* (https://www.myheritage.com/dna/match : accessed 10 September 2019), estimated 2nd Cousin Once Removed relationship with [Private] sharing 2.3% DNA (165.7 cM) across 8 shared segments (largest segment 51.1 cM), DNA managed by [Private], (MRCA: J. E. Taylor and M. A. Ollerton).

Shortened Reference Note

- Bettinger, *Genetic Genealogy in Practice*, 23.
- "Review DNA Match" for Robin Wirthlin, *MyHeritage,* September 2019, estimated 2C1R relationship with [Private] sharing 2.3% DNA (165.7 cM) across 8 shared segments (largest segment 51.1 cM).

Source List Entry

- Bettinger, Blaine T. and Debbie Parker Wayne. *Genetic Genealogy in Practice*. Arlington, Virginia: National Genealogical Society, 2016.

- "Review DNA Match for Robin Wirthlin." Database report. *MyHeritage.*
  https://www.myheritage.com/dna/match : 10 September 2019.

Style Standards

Many source citation styles exist in the world of publishing. Each journal, magazine, or book may use a slightly different way of presenting the essential citation elements. In genealogy, we follow the *Chicago Manual of Style* because it works well for the type of sources we use.[5] Elizabeth Shown Mills' *Evidence Explained* adapts the principles for a wide variety of genealogical sources.[6] Use these excellent works for reference but remember the best resource we have is our common sense. After creating a citation, evaluate it for clarity and readability.

Would a reader be able to evaluate your evidence by considering the information in the source (if it is privately held and generally inaccessible) or accessing the source? Would someone be able to find this source quickly?

Using the following style standards will help you formulate clear citations. Punctuation in a paragraph aids the reader in understanding the content. Punctuation in a source citation serves the same purpose. Once you have conquered the basics, creating a clear, informative citation will become second nature.

- Italicize titles of publications such as a book, blog, or website.
- A website is often the publisher and the creator of the report or record collection, no need to cite it twice. Italicize the website and place it before the specific publication information, which is set off by parentheses.
- Use quotation marks to set off the title of a record collection, article, report, or chapter title in a book (if the chapters are authored separately).
- Separate each citation element with a comma.
- Use parentheses to set off publication details such as the place and date of publication or URL and access date.
- When citing a physical record viewed online, use a semicolon to separate the physical information from the digital information.
- Anonymize names or obtain written permission to include full names of living individuals for a citation published or shared with others besides a client.

---

5. *The Chicago Manual of Style: The Essential Guide for Writers, Editors, and Publishers,* 17th ed. (Chicago: University of Chicago Press, 2017).

6. Elizabeth Shown Mills, *Evidence Explained : Citing History Sources from Artifacts to Cyberspace,* 3rd ed. (Baltimore: Genealogical Publishing, 2015).

Your Task

S tart a citation template and practice writing citations for a variety of DNA and documentary sources. Use table 5.1 to guide you in identifying each element to include in a citation.

Table 5.1. Citation Element Examples

Citation Element	DNA Source Examples	Documentary Source Examples
WHO created the source?	• DNA testing company • Third-party DNA company • Author of a DNA report	• Author of a book, article, or blog post • Government entity • Church entity • Informant
WHAT is the source?	• Ethnicity estimate • DNA Match • Haplogroup • Segment triangulation • Online family tree	• Book, article, or blog post title • Record collection title • Description of the item of interest (name of the individual(s) and type of record)
WHEN was the source created or accessed?	• Date a DNA report was created • Date a DNA match or online family tree was accessed	• Date of publication for a book or microfilm • Date a website was accessed. • Date of the event
WHERE IS the source?	• URL for an online DNA report • Address of the creator of a DNA report	• Publication location for a book • Physical location of the repository • URL for a record viewed online
WHERE IN the source is the item of information?	• Specific details about a DNA match or ethnicity report	• Volume, page number in a book • Image number for a digitized film • Identification of an order for unpublished materials

CHAPTER 6

Analyze Your Sources and Evaluate Your DNA Matches

Robin Wirthlin

Are you hoping to use DNA test results to break down a long-standing brick wall in a family tree? After creating a research objective, the next step is to obtain documentary sources, then analyze them and their information. As you continue on the journey of Research Like A Pro with DNA, you will use information in your documentary and DNA sources as evidence to go back in time and overcome brick walls. Source analysis helps you determine the reliability of a source's contents. The more reliable a source's information, the more confident you can be in making sound and logical conclusions about your research.

The quality and quantity of documentary and DNA sources are central to the success of research projects involving genetic evidence. Documentary sources play a vital role in genealogical research by verifying key events in a person's life. The records also help establish an ancestor's unique identity and ensure that we are following the correct person. By correctly identifying the time and location our ancestors lived, the movements, and important events in their lifetimes, we build connections to them. When we identify these anchor points in our ancestors' lives, we understand their experiences better and see their world in a historical context.

Remember that for DNA to be useful in genealogical research; it needs to be used in combination with known or newly discovered familial relationships. DNA can validate that relationships proposed through sound documentary research are genetically correct.

Create a Timeline

Organizing your sources in a timeline will help you see if some events or records are missing. You will learn if you need additional documents to establish your ancestor's unique identity. As you add information to your timeline, you can also track additional questions and ideas.

Create a timeline page in your research log for the family or person in the research objective. Enter the following headings at the top of the columns:

- Event
- Date
- Place
- Source Citation
- Authored, Original, Derivative Source
- Primary, Secondary, Undetermined Information
- Direct, Indirect, Negative Evidence
- Notes

Make a chronological list of events and documents that verify the actions experienced in your research subject's lifetime. Include the dates and places where events took place and the sources of the information. Consider color-coding events such as births, residences, moves, marriages, and deaths to differentiate them from one another.

In addition to the sources you have gathered in your research, several automated resources can help you create a chronological timeline. Use the "Time Line" feature found in a person's entry in the FamilySearch Family Tree. The Time Line tab is located near the top of the page under an individual's name. Turn on the map element to view where important events in an ancestor's life took place.

Ancestry.com provides a timeline on the "Facts" page of an ancestor's profile page in a family tree. The "Life Story" page also has a chronological list of events. Also, your personal genealogy software may provide a timeline or chronology feature that lists events and actions for an ancestor's life based on the sources you've added.

After using the information from the documents to compile the timeline, examine the list and the dates when significant events in the research subject's life occurred. Ask yourself if the information makes sense. Think about the timing of the events. Some questions to consider are the following:

- Was each child born during the mother's childbearing years? Was a child born after their mother died?

- What major historical events occurred in your ancestor's lifetime that may have generated records? Have you searched for, obtained, and included all the possible records that pertain to an ancestor?
- Look for inconsistencies. Was your ancestor in two places at once? Are there conflicting records? Note any discrepancies in your research log.
- What records might help resolve conflicting information? Make a list of additional documents to search.

After you have gathered all the documentary sources that outline and highlight your ancestor's life, examine the documents. Look at each piece of information, assess the credibility of the information, and evaluate how it illustrates your ancestor's life. Go to https://familylocket.com/rlpdna for an example of a timeline for my research objective to identify the father of Sparks Shifflet, born 15 May 1877 in Greene County, Virginia, to Francis A. Shifflet & died 18 April 1966, in Ponca City, Kay, Oklahoma.

Why do we need to do this? If we don't carefully examine and analyze records, we may miss important clues or even draw the wrong conclusion about our ancestors. You may even find through your thoughtful examination that the documents you have already found contain the information you need to answer your research question!

Analyzing both documentary and DNA sources helps us understand the sources so we can use them correctly and create correct citations. DNA sources will be examined in this chapter in detail. To learn more about the analysis of documentary sources, information, and evidence, see *Research Like a Pro: A Genealogist's Guide* by Diana Elder and Nicole Dyer.

Source Analysis

Learning how to understand and analyze sources helps you recognize precisely what you are working with. Understanding a source's quality also helps you know if you should look for additional sources to achieve your research objective. Sources are classified into three categories: original, derivative, and authored narratives.

- **Original Source:** The first recording of the information.
- **Derivative Source**: A copy or summary of another record. The source is derived from another document.
- **Authored Works:** A source produced by gathering records, analyzing them, and creating a new piece of work. Often a narrative that contains a discussion of both original and derivative sources.

Original DNA Sources

After you test your DNA, you have an additional original source to help you research your family history. You cannot see your DNA to evaluate it directly, but you can see the results of SNP (Single Nucleotide Polymorphism) testing for autosomal and mitochondrial DNA and STR (Short Tandem Repeats) for Y-DNA. The sources that you *can* see are reports based on raw DNA data. These reports are original sources. In addition to your downloadable raw DNA data results, you can also see databases of DNA matches and other DNA reports on the DNA testing company websites.

The raw data does not mean anything genealogically until it is compared with other people's DNA data stored in a company's database. When you receive your DNA results, you are given access to reports or lists. These are classified as original sources. These sources provide DNA information that will help you verify and build your family tree.

In the interest of privacy, DNA testing companies have taken measures to ensure that a test taker can only access raw data for their own kit and for other kits they manage. The limitations effectively eliminate the opportunity to compare raw DNA data with a DNA match.

Each DNA testing company has a proprietary algorithm used to interpret DNA data and compare your DNA to other test takers' DNA in their databases. The companies test many of the same SNPs, and they also test many SNPs that the companies select by customizing their own DNA testing chips. Even if the company is looking at the same locations in the genome as another company, they have different thresholds for the size of DNA segments reported to the test taker, different ways of determining a genetic match, and which matches are included in a match list. For example, AncestryDNA reports shared DNA segments that are 8 cM and above.[1] As science and technology advance DNA analysis, DNA companies' algorithms and criteria will continue to change. For a current list of DNA company criteria for matching segments, see the Autosomal DNA testing comparison chart found at the *International Society of Genetic Genealogy (ISOGG) Wiki.*[2]

MyHeritage automatically sets the matching parameters in AutoCluster reports; however, they can be adjusted in other Genetic Affairs reports and network graphs—particularly for companies where data on the amount of shared DNA between shared matches is known. Even when there is no ability to adjust these parameters (as is the case

1. Catherine A. Ball, et al, "AncestryDNA Matching White Paper," updated 15 July 2020, *AncestryDNA* (https://www.ancestrycdn.com/support/us/2020/08/matchingwhitepaper.pdf), 20.

2. "Autosomal DNA testing comparison chart," rev. 18:10, 9 January 2021, *International Society of Genetic Genealogy (ISOGG) Wiki,* (https://isogg.org/wiki/Autosomal_DNA_testing_comparison_chart).

with Ancestry), it is helpful to understand that a "shared match relationship" between genetic cousins indicates that they share at least 20 cM with each other.

Each DNA testing company has reports that are variations on themes of the following:

- **DNA match lists** provide the names and estimated relationships of people with whom you share DNA. Also included is the amount of DNA you share with DNA matches given in centimorgans (cM) or a percentage.
- **Ethnicity estimates** list the countries or regions your ancestors may have come from. These estimates vary over time as the reference populations grow and the science of evaluating the meaning of raw DNA data improves.
- **Chromosome browsers** compare DNA segments on the various chromosomes that you and one or more of your DNA matches have in common. The information shown in chromosome browsers can help you identify the common ancestor(s) you share with your DNA matches.
- **Shared matches or AutoClusters** are reports or tools that show groups of DNA matches related to you and to each other. These tools help you discern through which lines of the family your DNA matches are connected.

Derivative DNA Sources

Derivative sources are created from an original source to extract and consolidate information in a new document. Derivative DNA sources are excerpts or partial DNA reports from a DNA testing company. An example of a derivative DNA source is an email message from a person who has taken a DNA test describing some of their matches. We can verify the information in a derivative source by viewing the original document or report. If we only record information from derivative sources, we risk incorporating errors in our research.

Authored DNA Sources

An authored source is a compilation of information from other sources into a final product. These sources may contain both original and derivative sources. The following are examples of authored sources that include DNA information:

- **A family tree belonging to a DNA match**—Trees are comprised of the names of ancestors and records verifying events in their lives. The creator of the tree decided which information and documents to include to establish their ancestors' identities. The tree's information may be correct, but an important step for DNA research is verifying each generational link. A tree may give hints about the DNA match's ancestry and these can guide you to documentary records for verification. Throughout your research, you may need to build trees for some or many of your matches. This is especially true in adoption or unknown parentage research.

- **DNA Research reports**—Reports written by a genealogist explain the information found and summarize the conclusions based on evidence from original DNA reports and documentary records.
- **AncestryDNA ThruLines**—ThruLines are based primarily on family trees that are correlated with DNA match information. To be included in a ThruLines report, the individual must share at least some DNA with the test subject. ThruLines gives suggestions about research that you can pursue.
- **MyHeritage Theory of Family Relativity**—These theories estimate a relationship between you and a DNA match. The system searches family trees, historical records, and DNA connections and suggests one or more pathways of how you and a DNA match may be related. Use clues from the theories to confirm the path to the DNA match through research.

Information Analysis

Each source contains many pieces of information. When examining documents, seek to identify the informant or person who gave each information item in the record. Information comes in three types:

- **Primary Information:** Information given by a person who witnessed the event firsthand.
- **Secondary Information:** Information provided by someone who obtained the information secondhand, then reported it.
- **Undetermined:** Information given by an unknown informant.

Primary DNA Information

Reports about the results of DNA testing are primary information with the DNA testing company as the informant. The company creates DNA reports for the customer. Examples of primary information from DNA reports include raw DNA data, the amount of cM shared between two matches, the haplogroup, the number of STRs at a particular marker, start and stop points for a shared segment of DNA, and so forth.

Secondary DNA Information

Secondary information is the reporting of information first received elsewhere. A genealogist's report of DNA matches from a testing company or family tree information that DNA test takers attach to their results would be considered secondary information. The testing company does not have firsthand knowledge of all the information in a family tree.

Undetermined DNA Information

The informant for DNA information is not typically undetermined, unlike documentary sources where the informant is often unknown.

Evidence Analysis

Evidence is the meaning we assign to information to answer a research question. Genealogists use three types of evidence.

- **Direct Evidence:** The information clearly states the answer to the research question.
- **Indirect:** The researcher must deduce the answer to the research question by combining two or more facts.
- **Negative:** Negative evidence occurs when the ancestor is not found in the expected time and place.

Direct Evidence

Answering a research question about an exact relationship with direct DNA evidence is possible, but not likely because there are multiple possible relationships for each amount of shared DNA. DNA evidence is almost always indirect when trying to determine a specific relationship. Even for parent-child relationships, you can't determine which tester is the parent and which tester is the child without more information. Consider a research question of "who is Ben's biological father?" Ben's DNA test results report a parent-child relationship with a male tester. This is direct evidence of a very close relationship, but until more information is known, like the ages of the testers, it doesn't directly answer the question of "Who is Ben's father?" The match could be an unknown son of Ben or the identical twin of Ben's father.

In contrast, documentary sources often provide direct evidence. If you are looking for evidence of a parent-child relationship, many sources can provide that. A birth record lists the parents of the child. A man declares the names of his children in his will. Recent U.S. census records list relationships of household members to the head of household. Each of these sources has the potential to answer a research question about the parents of your research subject. Whether or not the direct answer is correct or not is another story. Sometimes indirect evidence can provide a more accurate answer to your question, even if it's not as obvious initially.

If your research question involves testing a hypothesis, often Y-DNA or mitochondrial DNA test results can provide direct evidence. For example, Nicole's husband's third great-grandfather's parents are unknown. She found several autosomal DNA matches descending from Robert Daugherty and Sarah Taylor and asked, "Was John Robert Dyer the biological son of Robert Daugherty?" A patrilineal descendant of John Robert Dyer had already tested. Nicole added him to the Doherty surname project, and he was grouped under the heading, "Testers likely not from an O'Dochartaigh Patriline." Nicole talked with the Doherty surname project managers and found out that a descendant of Robert Daugherty had already tested as well.

These two descendants of John Robert Dyer and Robert Daugherty had different haplogroups and were not a match. All of this provided direct evidence that John Robert Dyer was not the biological son of Robert Daugherty. If the two descendants were a match, the question would not be directly answered. Robert Daugherty could have been that father or another male relative of John Robert Dyer–a brother, uncle, grandfather, or cousin. Additional documentary and DNA evidence would be required to determine if the hypothesized father-son relationship existed.

Indirect Evidence

A piece of indirect evidence does not provide the answer to our research question by itself—it provides a clue. When combined with other evidence, this clue becomes part of the case we build to answer the question. The combination of DNA evidence and documentary evidence can help build a powerful case for relationships in our family tree.

For example, a researcher asks, "who was the father of Alice Frazier, born 1885 in Montague County, Texas?" The great-great-granddaughter of Alice took an autosomal DNA test and found three DNA matches who trace their pedigree to Richard Frazier and Nancy Briscoe who were married in McDonald County, Missouri in 1863. The researcher puts these clues together and deduces that Richard Frazier could have been the father of Alice. Building this case would require including evidence from documentary sources and checking the accuracy of the DNA matches' trees.

Indirect evidence from documentary sources also requires building a case. For example, the relationship between a child and the head of household was not reported in the 1850 census, but the child's residence with a man could be a clue that he was the child's father. Other types of indirect evidence that could indicate familial relationships include proximity, land transfer, legal association, and so forth.

Negative Evidence

Negative evidence is the absence of expected information. It is a type of indirect evidence and must be combined with other clues to determine the answer to a research question. An example of negative DNA evidence is when oral tradition claims a particular ethnicity for your grandparent, but it is not identified in DNA test results. Another example is the absence of a biological relationship between people who are expected to share DNA. You won't always share autosomal DNA with more distant cousins due to recombination, but first cousins and second cousins will always share DNA.[3]

For example, your research objective is to confirm the biological connection to your grandparents. You test your first cousin and find that you don't share any DNA with them. Now you have a piece of negative evidence that either you or your cousin is not biologically related to your grandparents. Further research could reveal a misattributed parentage event in either of your lines. Your research objective was not fully met by comparing test results with only one first cousin. Additional research and possibly additional testing are required to determine if the relationship between you and your grandparents is biological.

In documentary sources, negative evidence can be found when your research subject is absent in a time and place he was expected to be. Negative evidence is often found in tax and census records. If a man paid taxes on a property for ten years and suddenly disappeared from the tax list, he may have moved or died. For example, negative evidence helped answer the research question, "When did William Keaton die?" William Keaton was listed on census records in Pendleton District, South Carolina, from 1790–1820. He was absent from the 1830 census, which provided negative evidence that he died. He also could have moved or begun living in a relative's household, but his estate file was found in 1828, providing direct evidence of his death.

Negative evidence is not the same as negative search results. In the William Keaton case, the fact that he was missing in the 1830 census did not become negative evidence until the researcher knew that he lived in Anderson county from 1790–1820 and was

---

3. "Cousin Statistics," *ISOGG Wiki*, rev. 8 November 2020, (https://isogg.org/wiki/Cousin_statistics); also, "The Probability of Detecting Different Types of Cousins," *23andMe* (https://customercare.23andme.com/hc/en-us/articles/212861317-The-Probability-of-Detecting-Different-Types-of-Cousins).

expected to be there in 1830. If you search your DNA match list for the surname of your fourth-great-grandparent and don't find it, that is not evidence that you have the incorrect ancestor in your tree. It could be that your matches who descend from that ancestor just don't have a family tree built out that far. Negative search results should be logged in your research log, as discussed in chapter ten. Perhaps your negative search results can provide evidence for your research question at some point.

Evaluate Your Matches

As you work with your DNA, continue to analyze the evidence found in your sources. Chapter three focused on diagramming your DNA matches—now it is time to evaluate and analyze them. See what evidence the matches provide for your research objective. After writing your research objective in chapter four, you have a defined goal and focus for your research. To concentrate on your research objective, you may need to make a second diagram that includes just the relevant DNA matches and ancestors. You can use your original diagram to help you with your next research objective.

If you are using Lucidchart or Diagrams.net, you can copy your diagram by clicking on "File" on the page's top-left side under the current file name. Then click on "Make a Copy;" a box will open and ask you to enter a new title for the copy. In the new diagram, you can delete some information and leave just those relatives who will help you achieve your research objective.

Focusing on the most pertinent family members will keep your diagram more manageable. If there are siblings of the ancestor you are seeking to verify, include them in the diagram. You may find that there are descendants of the siblings that will help you achieve your research objective. Consider including color-coding or another designation for X-DNA, mtDNA, and Y-DNA matches. If you don't have X-DNA, mtDNA or Y-DNA matches yet, use color coding to designate possible testing candidates that may help you achieve your research objective.

Evaluating the source, information, and evidence for your DNA matches will be simple. DNA matches will usually be original sources, providing primary information, and indirect evidence of a specific relationship. What else is required to analyze the matches? Standard 52 of *Genealogy Standards* suggests many factors to consider when analyzing DNA matches, especially those that affect determining the relationship.[4]

---

4. Board for Certification of Genealogists (BCG), *Genealogy Standards,* 2nd ed. (Nashville: Ancestry.com, 2019), 3–31.

In the next section, we will discuss factors to consider in your analysis of DNA matches. It's vital to look carefully at each DNA match and understand what the data means. This may involve researching the terms used by the testing company so you understand the meaning of the test results.[5] You don't need to be an expert, but you should do your best to analyze the data and understand it properly. Asking for feedback on your work is an effective way to see if you have missed something important in your analysis. Continuing education can also help you learn how to better analyze DNA matches. See chapter twelve to see ideas for additional genetic genealogy education.

Autosomal DNA Match Analysis

The main method for analyzing autosomal DNA matches is to compare the amount of shared DNA with the Shared cM Project by Blaine Bettinger, look for the most likely relationship, then compare trees and find common ancestors. See chapter two for a discussion of using the Shared cM Project tool at DNA Painter.[6] While looking at your diagram, ask yourself the following questions to help you evaluate each DNA match:

1. Do the autosomal DNA matches seem to fall within the expected total cM or percent range and associated probabilities for known relationships?
2. If not, are there alternative relationships besides those that have been proposed with that DNA match?
3. Does this DNA match help verify the proposed family relationships?

If the amount of shared DNA between the tester and the match seems high, consider that they might be related in more than one way. If they share less than expected, consider that they could be descending from the common ancestor through different spouses.

Pedigree Collapse and Endogamy

As you analyze your DNA matches and their family trees, you may notice that they descend multiple times from the same family; this is called *pedigree collapse*. Additionally, you may learn that some ancestors lived in isolated areas or had religious practices that involved families intermarrying for generations; this is known as *endogamy*. If the family line you are researching has pedigree collapse or endogamy, the amount of DNA shared with

---

5. BCG, *Genealogy Standards,* 2nd ed., 17, standard 24, "Understanding meanings."

6. Blaine Bettinger and Jonny Perl, "The Shared cM Project 4.0 tool v4," last updated 26 March 2020, *DNA Painter* (https://dnapainter.com/tools/sharedcmv4).

matches in that genetic cluster will be higher than expected. Also, if other lines of your family tree originate from the same area or endogamous population, you may have a cluster composed of members of a population rather than relatives from a specific ancestral line.

If both parents of a test taker may have come from an endogamous community, use the tool "Are your parents related?" at GEDmatch. It looks for pieces of DNA that are identical on both maternal and paternal chromosomes, called runs of homozygosity (ROH).[7] If a match seems to share more than the expected amount of DNA, you may want to check their kit for high ROH as well.[8]

Meiosis Groupings

The meiosis groupings in the Shared cM Project PDF provide additional data for evaluating shared DNA and possible relationships.[9] A meiosis grouping is a set of similar relationships. Each grouping of relationships has the same number of separating meiosis or recombination events. Because of this, it is expected that the minimum, average, and maximum amount of shared DNA for the relationships in the group will be the same. Bettinger combined the submissions for each relationship in the meiosis grouping to calculate average, minimum, and maximum values for that grouping.[10]

You may want to use the meiosis groupings to better understand the range of shared DNA for relationships that have a small number of submissions in the Shared cM Project. Half relationships and cousins 2–3 times removed often have less than one hundred submissions, while more common relationships have over one thousand submissions.

For example, the Shared cM Project tool at DNA Painter does not show the half fourth cousin relationship. The Shared cM Project PDF does include data for the half fourth cousin relationship, but there are only eighty-nine submissions. The range for half fourth cousins is 0–74 cM, with an average of 30 cM.[11] How reliable is this data when it comes

7. Brianne Kirkpatrick, ""High ROH" in your DNA - what is it and what can you do next?" blog post, 2 February 2017, updated 29 December 2018, *Watershed DNA* (https://www.watersheddna.com/blog-and-news/highrohinfosheet).

8. Kimberly Powell, "The Challenge of Endogamy and Pedigree Collapse," Debbie Parker Wayne, ed., *Advanced Genetic Genealogy: Techniques and Case Studies* (Cushing, Texas: Wayne Research, 2019), 133.

9. Blaine Bettinger, "The Shared cM Project Version 4.0 (March 2020)," PDF document, *The Genetic Genealogist* (https://thegeneticgenealogist.com/wp-content/uploads/2020/03/Shared-cM-Project-Version-4.pdf), esp. p. 5 titled "Using the Shared cM Project."

10. Bettinger, "The Shared cM Project Version 4.0 (March 2020)," p. 6, "Meiosis Groupings."

11. Bettinger, "The Shared cM Project Version 4.0 (March 2020)," p. 41, "Half 4C."

from only eighty-nine submissions? This is a good time to look at the meiosis groupings in the Shared cM Project to better understand the minimum and maximum for half fourth cousins. Meiosis grouping ten includes 2,633 combined submissions of half 3C2R, 3C3R, half 4C, and 4C1R relationships. The range is 0–126 with an average of 28. Using this range and average will help you more accurately evaluate half fourth cousin relationships. Of note is the possibility of sharing up to 126 cM with anyone in meiosis grouping ten. This is quite different from the range for half fourth cousin submissions.

You can also use histograms from the Shared cM project to evaluate shared cM and possible relationships, as discussed in chapter 2. The Shared cM Project tool at DNA Painter makes it easy to see histograms for each relationship. Just click on a relationship box to see the histogram for a that relationship. The histogram shows the distribution of the submissions with the amount of shared DNA in a known relationship. To see the histograms for meiosis groupings, go to the Shared cM Project PDF at Blaine Bettinger's website.

Small Segments

If you come across a DNA match who shares less than 7–10 cM of autosomal DNA with you, be wary. Small matches are often false positive matches and do not share common ancestors with you. A false match often occurs when the testing company's matching system zigzags back and forth between the maternal and paternal copy of the chromosome to form a pseudosegment.[12] Current technology used for autosomal DNA testing does not provide the exact sequence of DNA transmitted by each parent. Testing companies see unordered pairs of the nucleotides A, T, G, or C.[13] AncestryDNA attempts to phase the data and separate it into maternal and paternal chromosomes using their genotype phasing algorithm called Underdog.[14] However, this process is not perfect and does not eliminate the possibility of false matches.[15] The best way to avoid errors caused by false matches is to avoid using segments less than 7–10 cM.

Another consideration when analyzing small shared segments is the age of a segment.

---

12. Blaine T. Bettinger, *The Family Tree Guide to DNA Testing and Genetic Genealogy*, 2nd ed. (Cincinnati: Family Tree Books, 2019) 70–71, "Troubleshooting: False Positives and Small Segments." See also "A Small Segment Round-Up," blog post, 28 December 2017, *The Genetic Genealogist* (https://thegeneticgenealogist. com/2017/12/29/a-small-segment-round-up/).

13. Catherine A. Ball, et al, "AncestryDNA Matching White Paper," updated 15 July 2020, *AncestryDNA* (https://www.ancestrycdn.com/support/us/2020/08/matchingwhitepaper.pdf), 4.

14. Catherine A. Ball, et al, "AncestryDNA Matching White Paper," updated 15 July 2020, *AncestryDNA* (https://www.ancestrycdn.com/support/us/2020/08/matchingwhitepaper.pdf), 7.

15. Bettinger, *The Family Tree Guide to DNA Testing and Genetic Genealogy*, 71.

Small segments can be very "old," meaning they were passed down from a very distant ancestor—possibly more than twenty generations ago.[16] Because most of our trees are incomplete at that level, we probably won't be able to find the common ancestral couple who contributed a very old segment. Tim Janzen created a table for the *ISOGG Wiki* article "Identical by Descent (IBD)" to help assess small segments. The table shows that two individuals sharing a 6–12 cM segment have a 5% likelihood of sharing a common ancestor within six generations.[17] This means that we may not want to spend hours researching DNA matches who share less than 12 cM. Prioritizing matches who share larger segments is wise.

Pile-up Regions

Some small segments of our DNA are shared with many other people and may not be due to recent common ancestors. This is called excess IBD sharing.[18] These segments in pile-up regions are sometimes called population segments because scientists believe they are shared due to shared ethnic history rather than recent common ancestry. Ancestry's Timber algorithm removes population segments from matches sharing less than 90 cM.[19] Most segments filtered out by Timber are under 10 cM.[20]

Other autosomal DNA testing companies do not remove pile-up regions, but you can see them on DNA Painter's chromosome mapping tool. Striped segments on the chromosome map indicate areas that have been identified by *ISOGG Wiki* as prone to excessive IBD sharing.[21] Analyzing a segment of DNA in a pile-up region might not be fruitful because it may not lead to common ancestors in a genealogical timeframe.

---

16. Blaine Bettinger, "Losing Distant Matches at AncestryDNA," blog post, 17 July 2020, *The Genetic Genealogist* (https://thegeneticgenealogist.com/2020/07/17/losing-distant-matches-at-ancestrydna/), section titled "The (In)Validity of Small Segments," paras. 7–8. See also Steve Mount, "Genetic Genealogy and the Single Segment," blog post, 19 February 2011, *On Genetics* (http://ongenetics.blogspot.com/2011/02/genetic-genealogy-and-single-segment.html).

17. "Identical by descent," rev. 13:08, 6 November 2020, *ISOGG Wiki* (https://isogg.org/wiki/Identical_by_descent).

18. Ibid.

19. Catherine A. Ball, et al, "AncestryDNA Matching White Paper," updated 15 July 2020, *AncestryDNA* (https://www.ancestrycdn.com/support/us/2020/08/matchingwhitepaper.pdf), 19–20.

20. J. Granka, "Filtering DNA matches at AncestryDNA with Timber," blog post, 8 June 2015, *Ancestry Corporate* (https://www.ancestry.com/corporate/blog/filtering-dna-matches-at-ancestrydna-with-timber/)

21. Jonny Perl, "Frequently Asked Questions," *DNA Painter* (https://dnapainter.com/help/faq), "What are those little stripey segments that appear on some of the chromosomes?"

X Match Analysis

Each person has an X chromosome that they inherited from their parents. Men (XY) inherit an X chromosome from their mother and a Y chromosome from their father. Women (XX) inherit one X chromosome from their father and one X from their mother.

The X chromosome is SNP tested as part of the autosomal DNA test. 23andMe and Family Tree DNA (FTDNA) provide X-DNA match information. Additionally, if you transfer your DNA results from any testing company to GEDmatch, you can see the people with whom you share X-DNA. Sisters who share the same father also share the X chromosome he passed on to them. The X passed from fathers to their daughters is virtually the same as the one inherited from the father's mother. The X passed from mothers to their children may be a recombination of the mother's two X chromosomes. This explains why some full siblings may not match on the X chromosome inherited from their mother.

A key point to remember is that lack of X-DNA sharing doesn't disprove any ancestral lines except in close relationships such as parents to children and maternal grandparents to grandchildren.[22] If you have an autosomal DNA match that also shares X-DNA with you, it doesn't necessarily mean that the atDNA *and* the X-DNA segments came from the same common ancestor. It could suggest that your relationship is limited to a particular subset of possible ancestral connections (assuming that there is only one common ancestor or common ancestral couple between you). However, this is not always the case, and having a genetic cousin with shared X-DNA and autosomal DNA does not necessarily mean that both atDNA and X-DNA segments came from the same common ancestor. This is particularly true in endogamous populations or situations of pedigree collapse.

The X chromosome's unique inheritance pattern means that you can eliminate part of the pedigree that in consideration for finding the MRCA. However, there are challenges with analyzing X-DNA matches. Testing companies test a small number of SNPs on the X chromosome, so false matches are more common. It is recommended that you only analyze longer X-DNA segments that are over about 15 cM.[23]

Only 23andMe, FTDNA, and GEDmatch report X-matches. Individuals tested at MyHeritage or Ancestry and who might be X-DNA matches could transfer their raw DNA data to Family Tree DNA and GEDmatch to determine if there is shared X-DNA.

---

22. "X-DNA Techniques and Limitations," Kathryn J. Johnston, MD, *Advanced Genetic Genealogy: Techniques and Case Studies,* Debbie Parker Wayne, Editor, (Cushing, Texas: Wayne Research, 2019).

23. Bettinger, *The Family Tree Guide to DNA Testing and Genetic Genealogy*, 145.

If you share X-DNA with a match, do the following:

1. Focus on X-DNA segments that are *a minimum* of 10 cM—20 cM.
2. Look on X-DNA fan or pedigree charts to identify ancestors who may have contributed to your X-DNA.
3. Examine the family trees of your X-DNA matches. You are seeking ancestors that both you and the DNA match share along your respective X-DNA inheritance paths.

Y-DNA Match Analysis

Y chromosomal DNA is passed from father to son and so on through time. In cultures where a surname passes from father to son, the surnames of DNA matches may affirm your patrilineal surname or give new information about others whose great-grandfathers have similar origins with surname changes. If you are an adoptee or know of a misattributed parentage event in the past, DNA match information may help you identify surnames to watch for as you research. You may not have any Y-DNA matches who share your surname. This could mean that not many people from your surname have tested, or it could mean that there was a misattributed parentage event in your line. You may need to target test men who you think could be patrilineally related.

Y-STR Tests

Standard Y-DNA tests for genealogy report results based on the Short Tandem Repeats (STR) in Y-chromosomal DNA. After taking a Y-DNA test, you will receive results that tell you your "Predicted Y-DNA Haplogroup." A haplogroup is a classification that indicates your distant ancestral origins that date back thousands of years to a common ancestor.

Haplogroups have names that start with a letter and end in numbers, such as R-M269 or T-M184. The Y chromosome locations where a nucleotide has mutated or changed to another nucleotide determine the haplogroup. The mutation is known as a single-nucleotide polymorphism (SNP). The haplogroup prediction can guide you toward discerning between two historical men with the same name, surname research, or unknown parentage.

Exercise great caution when using predicted haplogroups at 23andMe and Living DNA to draw genealogical conclusions. Each company may report slightly different haplogroups for the same tester. The reason for these differences is that the reported haplogroups (clades or branches of the Y chromosome tree), are actually subclades - a branch of the Y chromosome tree that occurred later in time than a clade. Also, exercise caution when reviewing matches' haplogroups at Family Tree DNA. You may notice differences between DNA matches who have taken the Big Y-700 test and have their terminal haplogroup and those who just have the predicted haplogroup. Men who have not tested at the Big Y-700 level will have an estimated haplogroup clade much further upstream of the terminal clade. Also, GEDmatch's haplogroups are self-reported and therefore not as reliable.

Haplotypes in Y-DNA tests refer to the group of marker values that a test taker has. The markers are always inherited together—differences in the markers are due to mutations—and are useful in genealogy to compare how a test taker is related to others. When men have similar numbers of STR repeats, they are listed as matches. When you look at your Y-DNA match list at FTDNA, you will first see the list of matches that tested at the same marker level that you did. You can change the number of markers to see matches that tested at 12, 25, 37, 67, and 111 markers. Some people may have tested at a lower number of markers, and if you have tested at a higher number, you may not see those DNA matches unless you change the marker level to a lower one.

Family Tree DNA explains genetic distance for Y-DNA and mtDNA matches: "Genetic distance is the number of differences, or mutations, between two sets of results. A genetic distance of zero means there are no differences in the results being compared against one another, i.e., an exact match."[24]

For example, if there is one difference in the number of repeats between a tester and a Y-DNA match, the genetic distance is one. If there are four differences, the genetic distance is 4. This is a composite across all tested markers and not necessarily an individual marker location. Mutations or changes in the number of repeats occur as the Y-chromosome passes from a father to a son. The more mutations, the greater the genetic distance, which indicates that a DNA match is more distantly related than a match with a genetic distance of zero. This is a general rule, but a mutation can occur at any time. Sometimes, a mutation will occur between two very closely related men, like a father and son.

To analyze a Y-STR match, first look to see how many markers they have tested. If they have not tested as many markers as you, remember that only the smaller number of markers will be compared. Also, someone who is not a match with you on 37 markers may show up as a match on 67 or 111 markers because more markers are compared and the system's threshold for matching increases. You can use the Family Tree DNA Time Predictor (TiP) tool for an estimate of the time to the common ancestor. This tool uses STR matching and STR mutation rates.[25] Some markers mutate quickly and are known as fast-moving markers. An analysis of mismatching fast-moving markers for two men can

---

24. Learning Center, *Family Tree DNA,* (https://learn.familytreedna.com/faq-items/genetic-distance/).

25. "Y-DNA Matches—FTDNATiP Tool," *FamilyTreeDNA Learning Center* (https://learn.familytreedna.com/y-dna-testing/ftdna-tip/ftdnatip-different-matching-tools/).

provide evidence that they are more closely related.[26] See chapter eight for more about the TiP calculator.

Some of your Y-STR matches may appear to be very close, but because of convergence, they may actually be very distant.[27] Convergence is when "two different genetic signatures (usually Y-STR based haplotypes) have mutated over time to become identical or near identical resulting in an accidental or coincidental match."[28] Convergence is more common when less markers are compared, like 12, 25 and 37 marker tests. Matches at 12 and 25 markers are typically related thousands of years in the past.[29] Upgrading your test to include more markers can reduce the number of matches who are a result of convergence.

Y-SNP Test Results

Analysis of Y-SNP test results is an advanced task and you may want to talk with an expert, like a Y-DNA haplogroup project administrator.[30] The Big-Y 700 test at FTDNA provides the tester with a confirmed haplogroup and a specific place on the haplotree. Testers also receive a list of matches who share 30 or fewer differences. Because relatively few men have taken the Big-Y test, you may receive few to no matches.

To analyze Big-Y matches, use the haplotree to help you estimate the timeframe you and your matches are related. You may want to transfer your results to YFull (https://www.yfull.com/) which provides age estimates of SNPs on the Y-DNA haplotree.[31] Family Tree DNA provides the Block Tree as a representation of the haplotree. The gray blocks on the left represent SNPs. Count the number of blocks until the birth of the SNP you share with the match. Once you know how many SNPs separate you and the SNP, multiply that by the average age of a SNP: about 80–140 years.[32] This estimate is an

26. Blaine T. Bettinger and Debbie Parker Wayne, *Genetic Genealogy in Practice* (Arlington, Virginia: National Genealogical Society), 31.

27. Maurice Gleeson, "Convergence—What is it?" blog post, 20 May 2017, *The Gleason/ Gleeson DNA Project* (https://gleesondna.blogspot.com/2017/05/convergence-in-practice.html).

28. "Convergence," rev. 15:19, 6 December 2018, *ISOGG Wiki* (https://isogg.org/wiki/Convergence).

29. James M. Owston, "Y-DNA Analysis for a Family Study," in Debbie Parker Wayne, editor, *Advanced Genetic Genealogy: Techniques and Case Studies* (Cushing, Texas: Wayne Research, 2019) 84.

30. "Y-SNP Testing," rev. 11:33, 4 September 2019, *ISOGG Wiki* (https://isogg.org/wiki/Y-SNP_testing).

31. David Vance, *The Genealogist's Guide to Y-DNA Testing for Genetic Genealogy* (Middletown, Delaware: David Vance, 2020), 133.

32. Roberta Estes, "Family Tree DNA's New Big Y Block Tree," blog post, 24 January 2019, *DNAeXplained— Genetic Genealogy* (https://dna-explained.com/2019/01/24/family-tree-dnas-new-big-y-block-tree/).

approximation and may change when more men take the Big-Y test and identify new SNPs on the haplotree.

Mitochondrial DNA Match Analysis

After taking an mtDNA test at Family Tree DNA, you receive a report that tells you your haplogroup, which specifies a location on the mtDNA Haplotree. People with the same mitochondrial DNA (mtDNA) haplogroup are descended from the same matrilineal ancestor either recently or in the distant past—hundreds of thousands of years when we are working at the haplogroup level. Haplotype, meanwhile, may be closer. Men and women inherit mtDNA from their mothers, but only women can pass it on to their children.

A mitochondrial DNA match only indicates you that you and the match are have a common matrilineal ancestor at some point in the past. It can't tell you how close you are related. Originally, Family Tree DNA only tested the hypervariable control regions (HVR) of mitochondrial DNA. Now, most people take the full mitochondrial sequence test (FMS), which includes HVR1, HVR2, and the coding region. At FTDNA, you can view your matches at three testing levels:[33]

- HVR1
- HVR1, HVR2
- HVR1, HVR2, Coding Regions (FMS or mtFullSequence)

FTDNA predicts with 50% confidence that the time to the common ancestor with an exact match at the HVR1 level is 1,300 years; and an exact match at the HVR1 and HVR2 level is 700 years. They predict with 95% confidence that the time to the common ancestor with an exact full sequence match is 550 years.[34] Only exact matches on HVR 1 and HVR1, HVR2 testing levels are shown. At the mtFullSequence level, matches with up to three differences are shown.[35]

Heteroplasmy is "the co-existence of multiple mitochondrial DNA variants in a single source."[36] If a person's mtDNA is heteroplasmic, it may cause matches to look more distant

33. "mtDNA—Matches," *FamilyTreeDNA Learning Center* (https://learn.familytreedna.com/user-guide/mtdna-myftdna/mt-matches-page/).

34. "How do I tell how closely I am related to a mitochondrial DNA (mtDNA) match?," *FamilyTreeDNA Learning Center* (https://learn.familytreedna.com/mtdna-testing/tell-closeness-relationship/).

35. "mtDNA—Matches," *FamilyTreeDNA Learning Center* (https://learn.familytreedna.com/user-guide/mtdna-myftdna/mt-matches-page/).

36. "Heteroplasmy," rev. 17:47, 22 April 2018, *ISOGG Wiki* (https://isogg.org/wiki/Heteroplasmy).

than they are, or not show up as a match at all (if they have only tested the HVR regions). Family Tree DNA's Learning Center provides a table with symbols that you can look for in your test results to find heteroplasmic mutations.[37]

Evaluate Shared Match Clusters and Find Common Ancestors

To find more DNA matches to analyze as evidence for your objective, continue dividing the people in your DNA match list into genetic groups or clusters. Use the shared matches of a known match who descends from your research subject to identify additional matches who are likely related through the same ancestral line. Assign your common ancestors' names to the genetic cluster you share with the known DNA matches. Another tip is to use the AncestryDNA ThruLines feature, as discussed in chapter three.

Find Common Ancestors

To start identifying common ancestors in a shared match cluster, check for family trees associated with the DNA matches in the cluster. If a DNA match has no family tree attached to their account, check for an unlinked tree. Unlinked trees could include a match's family tree, or that of their spouse, or trees they have made for friends, so use caution. Sometimes you can tell who the tree is for by looking at the title of the tree.

Build Quick Trees

If your DNA match has no tree, you may need to build a quick tree (sometimes called a "quick and dirty" or "quick and speculative" tree) for the match to identify shared common ancestors. To build a quick tree, look for obituaries that mention the DNA match, online trees, and documents that can quickly verify the connection to the generations going up the tree. Additional sources are public record websites, social media, newspapers, vital record indexes, and other sources for identifying the living.

When building quick trees, you do not need to study the people in-depth. You *do* need some concrete evidence that the generations are linked together. If you decide to use a DNA match as evidence in your report or proof argument, you can then revisit the quick tree and solidify each parent-child connection with additional documentation.

---

37. "How do I know if I have an mtDNA (mitochondrial DNA) heteroplasmy? What is the nomenclature?" *FamilyTreeDNA Learning Center* (https://learn.familytreedna.com/mtdna-testing/heteroplasmy-nomenclature/).

Additional Strategies

Another clue for determining how a match is related to you is the shared match or "in common with" list. Often the shared matches have a family tree that you can use for clues about common ancestors. Some companies apply a maternal or paternal label to your matches if you have tested one of your parents. For example, AncestryDNA applies the "mother's side" and "father's side" labels to matches who also match one of your parents who have tested, but only for matches who share more than 20 cM with you.[38] Those who share less than 20 cM with you will not be given the mother's side or father's side labels.

You may be able to use segment information to help you figure out where a match belongs in your tree. Comparing the segments of an unknown match with segments previously mapped with DNA Painter's chromosome mapping tool can reveal a specific family line to focus on. (See chapter 8 for more details on chromosome mapping.) This is most useful when you already know if the match is maternal or paternal. If these strategies don't identify your common ancestors, set the match aside and move on to the next DNA match in the cluster.

Once you have identified the cluster with DNA matches who descend from the person in your research objective, add the matches in the cluster to your diagram. These are the people who point to the common ancestor. You will use the amount of DNA shared with the people in the cluster to help you make progress on your research objective. You will be able to confirm genetic connections and link generations going up the shared ancestral line to the ancestors you seek.

Additionally, these DNA matches may have more information than you do about your shared ancestors. They may have well-documented family trees that go beyond the ancestor you are researching. The documents and information the DNA matches have can help you verify the family connections and gather the evidence needed to confirm your hypothesis. You can also share records, photos, and ideas with your newly identified genetic cousins.

Example of Evaluating an atDNA Match

For an example of evaluating a match and finding the common ancestor, I will tell you about Gary. When I saw a 675 cM DNA match in my AncestryDNA account with an unknown

---

38. "Grouping and Filtering AncestryDNA Matches," *Ancestry Support* (https://support.ancestry.com/s/article/Grouping-and-Filtering-AncestryDNA-Matches).

relative named, Gary Robertson, I wanted to discover possible relationships.[39] In the Shared cM Project tool found at DNA Painter, I entered 675 cM in the filter box and saw the possibilities.[40] The results indicated a 60% probability that Gary could fit into the following relationships: Great-Grandparent/Great-Grandchild, Great-Aunt/Uncle, Half-Aunt/Uncle, 1C, Half Niece/Nephew, Great Niece/Nephew, Great Grandchild. There was a 40% probability that Gary fit into these other relationships: Half Great-Aunt/Uncle, Half Great-Niece/Nephew, Great-Great-Aunt/Uncle, Half 1C, 1C1R, or Great-Great Niece/Nephew.

Next, I wrote the following to Gary:

"I saw in my DNA match list that we are related. I'm not exactly sure who our common ancestor is, but we match over 600 centimorgans, which places us in the range of first cousins or first cousins once removed. If you are interested, I'd love to be in contact with you and figure out how we are related."

He replied,

"I would appreciate any information you can give me! I, too, do not know who our common ancestor would be. I found out at a late age that I was adopted and have not had much success in tracking down my birth family . . . "

I was intrigued and excited to help my newly found relative. I started comparing the amount of DNA he shared with other family members. Gary shared 645 cM with one sibling, yet only 392 cM and 274 cM with other siblings. These numbers led me to believe that we were not as closely related as my initial DNA results indicated. It is expected that a cousin will share differing amounts of DNA with family members because of the randomness of DNA inheritance, so that wasn't startling. Still, the 400 cM difference shared with me versus the amount of DNA he shared with my siblings did surprise me.

As Gary and I continued to communicate, I learned that he was 18 years older than me. I realized that it was unlikely (but not impossible) that Gary was a great-grandparent,

39. "DNA Matches for Robin Wirthlin," database report, AncestryDNA (https://ancestry.com/dna), Gary Robertson 675 cM match; also Gary Robertson (Glendale, Arizona) telephone interview by Robin Wirthlin, March 2020, transcript privately held, Robin Wirthlin, Robin@FamilyLocket.com, 2021, Gary granted permission to use his name.

40. Blaine Bettinger and Jonny Perl, "The Shared cM Project 4.0 tool v4," DNA Painter (https://dnapainter.com/tools/sharedcmv4), relationship probabilities for 675 shared cM, 1C relationship: 60% probability.

great-uncle, or great-nephew. I knew that I didn't have any grandchildren, so I ruled out a great-grandchild relationship. After setting those relationship possibilities aside, I focused on the greater likelihood that Gary was a first cousin or half-uncle.

I compared the amount of DNA he shared with my siblings, and I could see that the amount he and I shared was an outlier—he shared less with each of my siblings. When I averaged the amount of DNA each of my siblings and I shared with Gary (582 cM), it was closer to the average amount of cM reported for a half first cousin or first cousin once removed (1C1R). This example demonstrates the importance of viewing the amount of shared DNA in context with other genetic relationships.

After more research, including family tree building and documentary research, we eliminated other possible biological parent candidates by identifying their descendants in Gary's DNA match list. We discovered that Gary is my first cousin once removed (1C1R). His father and my grandfather were brothers. We have shared photos and had some fantastic reunions. Our family is delighted to connect with our newly found cousin!

This example shows how a combination of indirect evidence helped me determine my relationship with Gary. I needed the amount of shared DNA, the probabilities of certain relationships, Gary's age, and information about Gary's relationships to other people in my known family tree. I eliminated other possible hypotheses for how we were related, until there was only one possibility left.

Targeted Testing

Once you have analyzed each DNA match in the diagram, ask yourself these questions about the diagram as a whole:

1. Do you have enough DNA evidence to rule out other hypotheses?
2. What additional test takers do you need to achieve your research objective?
3. Are you using all the DNA types (atDNA, Y-DNA, X-DNA, mtDNA) that would help answer your research question?

Sometimes, there are not enough DNA matches in a testing company's database to help answer the question in your research objective. In this case, you will need to ask additional people to test their DNA. You need to develop a DNA testing plan to concentrate on testing people who will give you the most information about your research objective.

In genealogy research projects, we want to incorporate DNA test results from as many relatives as possible that descend from the subject of our research objective. Our goal is to obtain a representation of as much of an ancestor's DNA as we can via DNA matches because each match gives more substantiating evidence to confirm the ancestor's unique identity. The more descendants tested, the more likely it is that we will be able to utilize a higher percentage of DNA that the common ancestor passed on. The farther back the ancestor you are trying to prove, the more descendants you need to test because the likelihood of a descendant inheriting DNA that is shared with cousins diminishes with each generation.

Who are your targeted testing candidates? They are the untested descendants and collateral relatives of the person you are seeking in your research objective. Identify as many people as possible who descend from your research subject. Additionally, it is helpful to identify the descendants of the subject's siblings and the subject's cousins. You may also want to consider testing a person that can help you disprove a relationship. When we have a hypothesis, we are not only trying to confirm it; we are also trying to disprove all other hypotheses so that we know that the conclusion we reach is the most viable.

How do you identify descendants of your research subject? Trace the children and grandchildren of your research subject forward in time using records such as obituaries, FindaGrave.com, compiled family records, census records, newspapers, online family trees, searches in genealogy websites, people finding websites, etc. Add the descendants you have identified to your diagram.

Next, examine your diagram to pinpoint the living people who would be the most helpful to answer your research objective. The goal is to test people as close generationally to the research subject as possible. The most valuable test takers may be the people who are the oldest in the family; they are the most likely to have inherited larger amounts of DNA from the ancestor you seek because they are closer generationally to the ancestor. A research subject might have an 80-year old second great-grandchild and a 60-year-old great-grandchild, so explore the family tree fully for older living relatives and the youngest child of the younger children in a family seeking for a person who has fewer generations between them and the research subject. Other key individuals to target test are descendants from as many different children and siblings of the ancestor as possible.

Time, distance, and available finances are restrictions in targeted testing. Think through the best ways to make the most of your resources. Make a note of the limitations you have in a research project in your final research report. An economical way to access the results of more test takers is to identify descendants of your research subject who have already taken a DNA test and ask them to share their results with you. This can be done easily in AncestryDNA, for example.[41]

41. "Sharing AncestryDNA Results," *Ancestry Support* (https://support.ancestry.com/s/article/Sharing-AncestryDNA-Results).

As multiple descendants of your research subject are tested or share their results with you, you will develop a group of base test takers. These are the individuals who have taken a DNA test and given you access to their results. Analyzing the base test takers' relationships to each other is an important part of analyzing your sources. If all of your base test takers are documented descendants of your third great grandparents, and they all share DNA with each other as expected, you have a strong foundation. If, however, you notice that one of the base testers does not match any of the others as expected, you may want to investigate his line for a possible misattributed parentage event. See https://familylocket.com/rlpdna for an example table comparing the DNA shared among a group of base test takers.

Likelihood of Sharing DNA

As you target test relatives, remember that you will not share DNA with all of your distant relatives. However, you do share autosomal DNA with many of your close and distant cousins. DNA is inherited randomly, yet a generalized, predictable amount of DNA is typically shared between close family members. Many DNA testing companies report their theoretical probabilities of two cousins sharing DNA. A chart in the article "Cousin Statistics" on the *ISOGG Wiki* describes the probability that two cousins will share enough DNA for their relationship to be detected and is adapted in table 6.1.[42] The table includes data from 23andMe, AncestryDNA, and Family Tree DNA and has been updated with the latest 23andMe probabilities.

If you seek information about common ancestors with any of the cousin levels listed above, use the chart to assess the likelihood that you will be able to detect a common ancestor with a closely or distantly related cousin.

Second cousins nearly always share DNA. If you can identify second cousins to target test, you can almost certainly verify great-grandparents. Third cousins have a remarkably high likelihood of sharing DNA—around 90% or more. If you can locate third cousins to test, you are likely to confirm second great-grandparents. While the projected percentages decrease for more distant cousins, it is still possible to share DNA with them to support the relationships you are trying to prove through your research objective.

---

42. "Cousin Statistics," *International Society of Genetic Genealogy Wiki*, rev. 23:39, 8 November 2020, (https://isogg.org/wiki/Cousin_statistics); also, "The Probability of Detecting Different Types of Cousins," *23andMe* (https://customercare.23andme.com/hc/en-us/articles/212861317-The-Probability-of-Detecting-Different-Types-of-Cousins).

Table 6.1. Probability that two cousins will share enough DNA
for their relationship to be detected

Relationship	23andMe	Ancestry	FTDNA	Most Recent Common Ancestors
First cousins	~100%	100%	>99%	grandparents
Second cousins	>99%	100%	>99%	great-grandparents
Third cousins	~90%	98%	>90%	2nd great-grandparents
Fourth cousins	~45%	71%	>50%	3rd great-grandparents
Fifth cousins	~15%	32%	>10%	4th great-grandparents
Sixth cousins and beyond	<5%	11%	Remote (typically less than 2%)	5th great-grandparents
Seventh cousins	1.1%	3.20%		6th great-grandparents
Eighth cousins	0.24%	0.91%		7th great-grandparents
Ninth cousins	0.06%			8th great-grandparents
Tenth cousins	0.002%			9th great-grandparents

Testing More Than One Type of DNA

As you consider targeted testing strategies, be sure to consider testing more than one type of DNA. Y-DNA, X-DNA, and mtDNA results can offer powerful additional insight for interpretation of autosomal DNA evidence in the pursuit of your research objective. There are limitations on how DNA can be used in answering research objectives based on the nature of DNA inheritance. Autosomal DNA is most useful in identifying ancestors that are 6–8 generations back. Y-DNA is passed only from father to son to grandson, etc. Mitochondrial DNA is only passed matrilineally from mothers to their children and can address much older questions of relationship. X-DNA has a unique inheritance pattern and may be useful in identifying ancestors who fall within the inheritance pattern. See the inheritance charts in chapter one for more information. Examples of using more than one type of DNA are discussed below.

> **Y-DNA and atDNA:** While searching for the father of your third great-grandfather, you obtain access to Y-DNA results from a male who is directly patrilineally

descended from the third great-grandfather. Y-DNA matches give surname clues that may confirm or disprove an ancestor. You also have autosomal DNA results to help verify the generations between you and your hypothesized fourth great-grandfather.

mtDNA and atDNA: You are searching for the mother of your 2nd great-grandmother. You are matrilineally descended from her and have mtDNA results to compare with other DNA matches who claim to be matrilineally descended from women who are likely the mother or grandmother of the 2nd great-grandmother. Autosomal DNA results will help verify the generations between you and your third great-grandmother and hopefully help identify her.

X-DNA and atDNA: You are a female searching for your paternal great-grandparents. You inherited an X-Chromosome from your father. He inherited that X from his mother, which may have been a recombined X chromosome passed down from your father's maternal grandmother. Autosomal DNA shows that you and some other DNA matches are second cousins. Shared X-DNA may help guide you in identifying your shared great-grandparents.

Your Task

Revisit everything you have found about our ancestor. Look at documents you have already located and documents in the FamilySearch Family Tree, Ancestry public trees, MyHeritage trees, Wikitree, etc. Make a timeline for your ancestor, check the dates, and analyze the evidence. Try building a timeline in the RLP with DNA Airtable base. Chapter ten reviews Airtable research logs. Use the information in the automated timelines in FamilySearch and Ancestry to assist you. Write your questions, hypotheses, and ideas for future research in the notes section of the timeline page of your research log.

Continue building your DNA match diagram. See chapter three for more on diagramming tools. Consider including color-coding or using other designations for possible X-DNA carriers, mtDNA, and Y-DNA candidates. Analyze the information in your diagram using the questions discussed in this chapter. Analyze each of your matches to see what evidence they provide for your objective. Determine if you need to do targeted testing at this point.

CHAPTER 7

Locality Research and Ethnicity

Diana Elder

When you received your DNA test results, did you explore your ethnicity estimate to see what your genes revealed about your family origins? You may have been surprised by a small percentage of unknown ethnicity, or your results may have matched your family tree perfectly. Perhaps you wondered why ethnicity estimates updates keep changing and how much stock to give them.

A firm understanding of what ethnicity estimates can and cannot tell us provides an important framework for interpretation of genetic evidence. Additionally, knowledge of the research locality is key to our success as genealogists. Can DNA ethnicity estimates play a role in locality research? Because our DNA holds clues to where our ancestors came from and where they settled, we should not ignore this potential source of information. As with any genealogical source, we can analyze our ethnicity estimates—comparing and contrasting them across the various DNA testing companies. Used in conjunction with documentary research, ethnicity can help confirm or reject a hypothesis.

Most often, our goal in working with any DNA match is to identify the most recent common ancestor (MRCA). Looking at the locations suggested by ethnicity information can assist in reaching that goal. Additionally, reaching out to DNA matches might result in discovering experts in a locality who might share helpful research information about the records, repositories, and history of the area. The DNA match may also live in the locale and could assist with on-site research. Adding locality information to your DNA Research Log will keep this information organized.

In chapter six, you learned how to analyze your sources by creating a timeline for your ancestor's life events that included specific locations. You also evaluated your DNA matches and started viewing their trees. Did you notice any shared localities? To create your research plan, you will need to pinpoint a specific place to research. Then you will create a locality guide for the history, geography, records, and repositories that will inform the research.

Understanding Admixture/Ethnicity Estimates

You may have heard the terms "admixture" and "ethnicity estimates" used in the genetic genealogy community. Both refer to the genetic mix of various populations that make up your unique DNA. For example, my ancestry is broadly European from the British Isles, Western Europe, and Scandinavia. Those populations mixed widely with one another, so at this point, the DNA testing companies can only give me broad estimates. By contrast, an individual with ancestors from diverse populations or ethnicities, such as Northwestern European and Mexican ancestry, may have more success in distinguishing which portions of their ethnicity admixture originate from specific branches of their family tree. The following Ancestry DNA Ethnicity Estimate reflects this individual's known ancestry of Latin America, British Isles, and Scandinavian. The specific communities listed in Eastern Norway and Indigenous Americas–Mexico are useful clues for continuing the research in those locations.

- Norway   46%
  - Eastern Norway
  - Oppland
  - Etnedal, Nord Aurdal, and Nordre Land
- England, Wales & Northwestern Europe   11%
- Ireland   10%
- Scotland   7%
- Indigenous Americas—Mexico   7%
  - Michoacán & Southern Jalisco
    - Northern Michoacán
  - Central & Southern Mexico
- Sweden   6%
- Wales   5%
- Spain   4%
- Portugal   2%
- Indigenous Americas—Andean   1%
- Eastern Europe & Russia   1%

Each company defines geographic areas differently. One may include Denmark in a Scandinavian region while another company has it in a Northern European Region. Because of our ancestors' migration patterns, the ethnicity estimates are most accurate on the continental level. Some populations were more isolated such as the Finnish, Japanese, and Ashkenazi Jews. Those ethnicity estimates may prove more accurate as a result. As science evolves, it will be interesting to see how our DNA will be able to provide more information on our recent and ancient origins.

To determine your ethnicity estimate, each testing company uses a proprietary algorithm to compare your DNA to that of reference populations worldwide - a group of people with known origins in a specific location. Because each testing company uses a different reference population, your ethnicity estimate will vary among the websites. Additionally, the testing companies are continually adding to their reference populations and refining the science, so your ethnicity estimate will continue to change.

Let's take a brief look at each of the five main DNA testing companies and what they offer in the way of understanding our genetic origins. I will use my DNA estimates to illustrate the differences between companies in reporting ethnicity. My genealogical family tree shows the following breakdown:

- Maternal line: ¾ English, immigrated in the mid-1800s
- Maternal line: ¼ Danish, immigrated in the mid-1800s
- Paternal Line: British Isles, Germany, France, immigrated in the 1600s and 1700s

My great-grandmother was full Danish, so I would have received roughly 12.5 % of her DNA. Do the ethnicity estimates correspond? What can I learn from each company report?

23andMe—Ancestry Composition

23andMe creates an Ancestry Composition report using 45 populations with over 14,000 people of known ancestry.[1] Most of these are research participants reporting four grandparents, all born in the same area outside of the United States, Canada, or Australia. 23andMe also uses public reference data sets such as the Human Genome Diversity Project.

Your Ancestry Composition report in 23andMe breaks down the regions to specific areas and gives an estimate of when your ancestors lived in that region. My European heritage is reflected with 97.7% Northwestern European reported as the largest piece of my

---

1. "Ancestry Composition," *23andMe* (https://www.23andme.com/ancestry-composition-guide/).

genome.[2] That is broken down further to show specific European populations such as 7.9% Scandinavian. 23andMe detected two particular regions in Denmark that correspond well with the ancestral locations where documentary evidence suggests my ancestors lived.

Scrolling down the 23andme Ancestry Composition page will show additional information about your ethnicity: a timeline, a parental inheritance chart (if a parent has also tested), and a chromosome painting.

The Ancestry Timeline estimates my Scandinavian ancestors lived there in the mid-1800s, supporting what has been proposed in my documentary genealogical research efforts. Because my mother has also tested at 23andMe, I have additional information in the Parental Inheritance view.

- Northwestern European   97.7%
  - British & Irish   53.0%
  - French & German   18.7%
  - Scandinavian   7.9%
  - Broadly Northwestern European   18.1%
- Southern European   1.4%
  - Spanish & Portuguese   0.5%
  - Broadly Southern European   0.9%
  - Broadly European   0.5%
  - Trace Ancestry   0.3%
  - Unassigned   0.1%

Would you like to see your ethnicity mapped by chromosome? Continuing to scroll down the Summary page reveals the "Ancestry Composition Chromosome Painting." By selecting any of the listed regions, you can view which segments the company predicts originated from that specific ethnicity or region. The confidence level can be adjusted from 50% (speculative) to 90% (conservative. Combined with chromosome mapping tools on DNA Painter, the 23andMe Ancestry Composition Chromosome Painting tool could provide clues to an elusive ancestor. These segments can be downloaded as part of ethnicity raw data download and used for triangulation purposes in segment analysis. (Ancestry Composition > Scientific Details > Download Raw Data).

---

2. "Ancestry Composition for Diana Elder," database report, *23andMe* (https://you.23andme.com/reports/ ancestry_composition_hd/ : accessed February 2021), 97.7 % Northwestern Europe (British & Irish 53.0%, French & German 18.7%, Scandinavian 7.9%, Broadly Northwestern European 18.1%), Southern European 1.4%.

23andMe also identifies Maternal and Paternal Haplogroups if applicable. View these from the "Ancestry and Traits Overview" page. My mother and I share the Maternal Haplogroup U5b1c, and the company provides this description, "[U5b1] is broadly distributed both in western and eastern Europe today. It is relatively common in Scandinavia and Finland, especially in the isolated population of the Saami."[3] Given that our recent maternal line originates in Denmark, this designation makes sense. I did not receive the Y Chromosome from my father needed to determine a paternal haplogroup, so that page suggests I contact a father, brother, or another male relative to test. A male tester will see his paternal haplogroup in his results.

AncestryDNA—DNA Story and Ethnicity Estimate

Ancestry DNA utilizes a reference panel made up of recently tested people with known roots in a specific region. The reference panel started with a base of over 2,800 samples from two major genome projects.[4] Ancestry also added samples from a proprietary Ancestry DNA reference collection and Ancestry DNA samples from customers consenting to participate in research. Family trees were first consulted, and the sample was included if all lineages were traced back to the same geographic region.[5] The ethnicity white paper reveals Ancestry DNA uses quality control to remove outliers that might be introduced because of misattributions in the family trees. They also treat some populations differently if they are thoroughly admixed. Then they only include individuals on the reference panel if they are part of a clearly delineated group.[6]

How accurate are the percentages for each region listed on your DNA Story? As the name states, these are estimates, and as you click on each area, you'll see a range listed. The percentage reported is the most likely, but AncestryDNA explains that there are 1,000 reasonable estimates when compared to the reference panel.

For example, my AncestryDNA Ethnicity Estimate shows the following regions and percentages.[7]

---

3. "Migrations of your Maternal Line," *23andMe* (https://you.23andme.com/reports/maternal_haplogroup).

4. Catherine A. Ball, et al, "AncestryDNA Matching White Paper," updated 15 July 2020, *AncestryDNA* (https://www.ancestrycdn.com/support/us/2020/08/matchingwhitepaper.pdf), 20.

5. "AncestryDNA Reference Panel," *Ancestry* (https://support.ancestry.com/s/article/AncestryDNA-Reference-Panel?).

6. Ibid.

7. "Ethnicity Estimate for Diana Elder," database report, *AncestryDNA* (https://www.ancestry.com/dna/origins : accessed 18 February 2021), 63% England, Wales & Northwestern Europe, 12% Norway, 10% Scotland, 6% Ireland, 4% Sweden, 3% Germanic Europe, 2% Wales.

▣	England, Wales & Northwestern Europe	63%
▣	Norway	12%
▣	Scotland	10%
▣	Ireland	6%
▣	Sweden	4%
▣	Germanic Europe	3%
▣	Wales	2%

Exploring the 12% from Norway further showed that the range could be 0% -12% from this region. How does this compare to my genealogical family tree? Since my great-grandmother is full Danish, I would have inherited roughly 12.5% of her DNA, so this range makes sense. The Swedish ancestry of 4% could also factor into my Danish ancestry. The maps for both the Norway and Sweden regions include Denmark. Comparing my genealogical family tree to my ethnicity estimate provided additional confirmation of that family line.

The regions displayed in your Ancestry DNA Story are based on your DNA, indicated with a solid circle. Besides those, you may have Communities listed as part of your Ethnicity Estimate. These are shown with a circle surrounded by a dotted line and are based on shared ancestors and family trees. Communities will continue to evolve as the database grows. AncestryDNA explains that not everyone will have a Community for various reasons, but with more samples gathered and database growth, additional regions and Communities will be added.[8]

Comparing my Ancestry DNA Ethnicity Estimate with that of my mother revealed a difference in Communities.[9] My estimate showed none, whereas she had several listed (represented in the list below with an "o"). I was interested to see her English and Danish ancestry represented in specific Communities that could hold clues to unknown ancestors or verify known ancestral lines. Interestingly, her roughly 25% Danish ancestry appears to come from the Norway and Germanic Europe regions.

▣	England, Wales & Northwestern Europe	54%
○	The Midlands, England	
○	North West England & the Isle of Man	
○	South East England	

---

8. "AncestryDNA communities," *Ancestry* (https://support.ancestry.com/s/article/DNA-Genetic-Communities).

9. "Ethnicity Estimate for Anna Mae Shults," database report, *AncestryDNA* (https://www.ancestry.com/dna/origins : accessed 18 February 2021), 54% England, Wales & Northwestern Europe, 19% Germanic Europe, 13% Scotland, 9% Norway, 3% Wales, 2% Ireland.

▨ Germanic Europe	19%
▨ Scotland	13%
▨ Norway	9%
▨ Wales	3%
▨ Ireland	2%

Additional Communities

- ▨ Denmark
  - ◉ Jutland, Zealand, Funen, Lolland & Falster (from your regions England, Wales & Northwestern Europe; Germanic Europe)
- ▨ Mountain West Mormon Pioneers (from your regions England, Wales & Northwestern Europe)

How can exploring Communities help with your locality research? You may wonder why an immigrant ancestor left their homeland and the factors that influenced their decisions. If you have a Community identified as part of your DNA Story, you can map migration routes, read short synopses of the history, and understand more about the places your ancestors lived.

FamilyTree DNA—myOrigins

FamilyTree DNA defines 24 population clusters that include ancient origins as well as their unique population reference set. Several projects make up the reference set: the Human Genome Diversity Project, the International HapMap Project, the Estonian Biocentre, and 1000 Genome.[10] FamilyTree DNA validated these projects' data against individuals in the GeneByGene DNA database who had proven ancestors in a specific area.

Clicking on any of the 24 population clusters described in the Learning Center opens up a description of the area with the ancient origins described and the various populations that inhabited the area.[11] Examining the population clusters for your DNA can help

---

10. Razib Khan and Ruih, "myOrigins Methodology Whitepaper," updated 13 September 2017, *Family Tree DNA Learning Center* (https://learn.familytreedna.com/family-finder-autosomal-testing/myorigins-family-finder-autosomal-testing/myorigins-methodology/ : accessed 1 Nov 2020); web page archived at *Wayback Machine* (https://web.archive.org/web/20200312141425/https://learn.familytreedna.com/family-finder-autosomal-testing/myorigins-family-finder-autosomal-testing/myorigins-methodology/ : accessed 23 Feb 2021).

11. "Population Clusters in myOrigins," FamilyTree DNA Learning Center, *FamilyTree DNA* (https://learn.familytreedna.com/family-finder-autosomal-testing/myorigins-family-finder-autosomal-testing/myorigins-population-clusters/).

you learn about the diverse groups of people that inhabited a region and could be your forebears.

FamilyTree DNA reported my ethnicity as 100% European in myOrigins, with the following breakdown.

- Western Europe
  - Central Europe   55%
  - Ireland   40%
  - Scandinavia   5%
- Finnish
  - Finland   <1%

My reported Danish ancestry is only 5% of my ethnicity, with the remainder likely included in the Central Europe region—an excellent example of looking at these results on a continental level.

Are you interested in viewing the origins of your DNA matches? Clicking "Shared Origins" will reveal your closest relatives and show your shared ethnicities. If you have a specific ethnicity you're trying to match; this could prove useful. If your origins are broadly European, this will probably not be as helpful.

Are you curious about your ancient origins? FamilyTree DNA offers another opportunity to explore your DNA in "Ancient Origins." Learn more about the ancient groups that populated your regions—where they came from, where they settled, and connected haplogroups.

Living DNA—Ancestry

Living DNA provides a unique algorithm to show regional detail for your origins. This algorithm breaks Great Britain and Ireland into much smaller regions, and if you have ancestry in the British Isles, has potential for new discoveries.

The breakdown below illustrates my British Isles origins.[12] The 14.6% reporting of Southeast England corresponds with my great-grandfather's line out of Dover, in Kent County. My Danish ancestry appears as part of the Scandinavia region. If you have ancestors from the British Isles, Living DNA's specific regions could provide additional clues for research.

---

12. "Your Recent Ancestry Results for Diana Elder," *Living DNA* (https://my.livingdna.com/ancestry/recent : accessed 18 February 2021), 62.6% Europe (North and West), 37.4 % Great Britain and Ireland.

▦	Europe (North and West)	62.6%
◉	South Germanic	30.9%
◉	Scandinavia	17.1%
◉	Northwest Germanic	14.6%
▦	Great Britain and Ireland	37.4%
◉	Southeast England	14.6%
◉	South Central England	3.3%
◉	South Yorkshire	3.1%
◉	Northwest England	2.8%
◉	Northumbria	2.4%
◉	Central England	2.2%
◉	East Anglia	2.1%
◉	South Wales Border	1.9 %
◉	Ireland	1.9%
◉	Cumbria	1.6%
◉	North Wales	1.6%

Testing with Living DNA also provides both a maternal and a paternal haplogroup to help compare DNA with other individuals as part of DNA projects.

MyHeritage—Ethnicity Estimate

MyHeritage's Ethnicity Estimate includes Genetic Groups that identify ancestral origins among 2,114 geographic regions. The data set for Genetic Groups comes from the DNA data and associated family trees contributed by millions of worldwide users.[13]

Viewing my Ethnicity Estimate from MyHeritage, I saw that I again had mainly Northwest Europe and England percentages with two additional regions not reported by the other testing companies: East Europe and Iberian.[14] The North and West European regions likely include my Danish heritage. Viewed on the continental level, my origins continue to be broadly European, although reported differently here.

▦	North and West European	43.9%
▦	English	38.6%

---

13. "MyHeritage Launches Genetic Groups," blog post, 24 December 2020, *MyHeritage* (https://blog.myheritage.com/2020/12/myheritage-launches-genetic-groups).

14. "Ethnicity Estimate for Diana Elder," *MyHeritage* (https://www.myheritage.com/dna/ethnicity : accessed 18 February 2021), 43% North and West European, 38% English, 8% East European, 7% Iberia, 1 % Finnish.

▨ East European	8.1%
▨ Iberian	7.6%
▨ South Europe	7.6%
▨ Finnish	1.85

Drilling down into each region, you can view DNA matches who also share that ethnicity. My mother's DNA Ethnicity Estimate on MyHeritage shows a Genetic Group of Denmark and details specific regions within Denmark, common surnames, and common given names—drawn from the associated family trees. The ethnicity estimate corroborates her known ancestry of about 25% Danish admixture inherited from her full Danish grandmother.

GEDmatch Admixture Utilities

GEDmatch uses the term admixture and offers a variety of ways to look at your origins. Several third-party developers have created calculators to compare your DNA to a specific reference population, such as European, African, Eurasian, etc. Each calculator page provides information about the developers and links to their websites.

To experiment with the GEDmatch Admixture Applications, first select "Admixture (heritage) from the list of DNA Applications. Select a project from a dropdown menu and then how you want to process it. Next, you'll be prompted to enter the kit number to be analyzed and need to select the calculator model to use. The program will generate charts or graphs comparing your DNA to the reference population employed by the developer.

I used the Eurogenes K13 Model because of my European heritage. The program generated a list of percentages and a pie chart showing a large region labeled North Atlantic, reflecting my English and Danish ancestry. Interesting is the amount of DNA most commonly found in individuals residing in the Mediterranean region.[15]

▨ North Atlantic	55.40%
▨ Baltic	23.28%
▨ West Mediterranean	9.81%
▨ West Asian	5.77%
▨ East Mediterranean	2.62%
▨ Red Sea	1.10%

---

15. "Admixture Utilities for Diana Elder," *GEDMatch* (https://www.gedmatch.com/admixProp.php : accessed 18 February 2021), Kit # CH2465632, Eurogenes K13 Model, 55% North Atlantic, 23% Baltic, 9% West Mediterranean, 5% West Asian, 2% East Mediterranean, 1% Red Sea.

Limitations of Ethnicity Estimates

Although ethnicity estimates can be useful in locality research, there are limitations. As the science develops and the reference populations grow, realize that your estimate will likely change. Some origins are difficult to accurately identify using DNA because of the broad migration between countries. Looking at your ethnicity estimate on the continental level will be more reliable than pinpointing specific countries of origin.

Be wary of the potential for confirmation bias in viewing your ethnicity estimates. Seek to be objective in the evaluation of your results, not searching for the calculator that best fits your hoped-for ethnicity.

Locality Research

When combining DNA with documentary genealogical research, we look for two people living in the same location where conception could have occurred. How do you determine that location? After the initial analysis of the DNA and existing records has been completed, a specific research locality has likely emerged. You will need to search for new documentation that will aid in confirming or rejecting the hypothesis.

To create a viable research plan, first, it is necessary to explore the locality. Creating a guide for the county, state, or country will help you understand the history, laws, geography, and records that inform the research. Some of the items to include in the locality guide are gazetteers, migration routes, jurisdictions, and boundary changes. See the Locality Guide Template for additional ideas. Keep in mind that you should add those sources that pertain to the specific period for the research. A locality guide is fluid. You can add other records and resources as needed; for now, keep it simple and focused.

Case Studies

Let's look at three separate case studies where either ethnicity, location, or both were important in discovering genetic relationships. We'll study an adoptee case, an unknown grandparent born in the early 1900s, and a brick wall ancestor from the early 1800s.

Case Study #1: *Finding the Biological Father*

In some cases, ethnicity estimates can play a significant role in making discoveries. Mary (name changed) discovered she was adopted at age five and always wondered about her biological parents. She eventually located her birth certificate and found her mother's maiden name and a possible maternal family location. With documentary genealogy sleuthing, I helped her narrow the field of candidates, and she located her birth mother and several half-siblings. However, her birth mother refused to reveal information about her birth father, so Mary was at a loss until I suggested DNA testing.

Mary tested first at Ancestry.com, and we were interested to see a sizeable amount of Finnish in her ethnicity estimate indicating she was one-quarter Finnish, suggesting she had one grandparent of primarily Finnish ancestry. Looking at the ethnicity of a half-niece on Mary's maternal side, we saw that her niece had no Finnish ancestry. If Mary's Finnish grandparent had been from her maternal side, then her half niece should have had approximately 12% Finnish admixture. We concluded that Mary received her Finnish genes from her father, who was likely half-Finnish. By eliminating the DNA matches who also shared DNA with the maternal half-niece, we narrowed down Mary's paternal line ancestors. These separated into two distinct groups that shared DNA.

The first paternal group, those with Finnish surnames, had the shared locality of Gogebic County, Michigan, in their family trees. The challenge came with large families. One of the suspected ancestral couples had 16 children. Which of the 16 had a connection to Mary? Was the relationship back another generation? With so many descendants to trace, the most recent common ancestral couple was challenging to determine. What became apparent was that one of Mary's grandparents was full Finnish, descending from this group out of Gogebic County, Michigan.

The second paternal group had localities in Montana and ethnicity estimates mainly centering in the British Isles. Corresponding with these matches helped to build the family tree and revealed the most recent common ancestral couple for the Montana family. One of their descendants was Mary's grandparent. But which one?

The intersection of two people had resulted in Mary's unknown biological father. He was of half-Finnish ancestry from the Gogebic County, Michigan, family and half-British Isles ancestry from the Montana family. But it was unclear if we were looking for a Finnish grandmother or grandfather. Mary wrote messages to each of her closest DNA matches and eventually found a genealogist on the Finnish line who had traced the Gogebic County family's descendants. When I mentioned the possible Montana connection, he immediately remembered one of the family members who had moved to Montana. With more sleuthing in the records, I found Mary's grandparents' marriage—a grandfather of full-Finnish ancestry and a grandmother from Montana with roots in the British Isles. Their son was Mary's biological father. Analyzing Mary's ethnicity estimate and the common localities in her DNA match's trees were vital in solving this case.

Case Study #2: *Uncovering an Unknown Grandfather*

Jack Jr. never knew his biological grandfather. As a young boy, his father, Jack Sr., found his birth certificate and saw his surname written as "Green," not the surname of his adoptive father he had been using his entire life. His mother took the certificate away and never spoke of his birth father. Jack Sr. always wondered about his paternal biological line and the mysterious name of "Green."

After his grandmother and father's passing, Jack Jr. decided to try DNA testing to resolve this family mystery. He took both the Y-DNA test with FamilyTree DNA and an autosomal test with each of the DNA testing companies. Initial analysis of the Y-DNA test results revealed the surname of Robb for his paternal line, and this name also appeared in the trees of some of the autosomal DNA matches. Correlating the Y-DNA and some close autosomal DNA matches resulted in identifying a likely candidate for Jack Jr.'s grandfather. Still, Jack wanted to know more. What were the circumstances of his father's birth? Who was this man that could be his biological grandfather?

With DNA testing providing evidence of the relationship, research turned to the locality of Oklahoma City, Oklahoma, where Jack Sr. was born and raised. His mother had lived there her entire life. When did she come in contact with Mr. Robb? Were they in the same area at the same time to have conceived a child together? Creating a locality guide for this project focused on 1880–1950 in Oklahoma City and surrounding counties. Identified records included census enumerations, vital records, and city directories. The documentary research corroborated the DNA evidence and told the story of two people residing near each other in Oklahoma City in 1926. Read the complete research report at https://familylocket.com/rlpdna.

Case Study #3: *Connecting a Female Ancestor to Her Father*

Female ancestors born before 1850 are often the source of our research brick walls. Noted only as a tick mark on a census, subsequent records of their lives may or may not have reported names of parents. Documentary research can tease out the most likely candidate for a father using indirect evidence comparing shared localities and relationships, but can DNA add confirmation of a hypothesis?

In the case of Rachel Cox, Benjamin Cox emerged as the most likely candidate to be her father. Rachel was born about 1828 in Indiana and married in 1848 to Hickman Monroe Shults in Navarro County, Texas. The Texas marriage record revealed her maiden name as Cox, but no father was listed. Research eliminated all Cox men in Navarro County in the 1840s except Benjamin Cox, who was named with Rachel's husband in a list of road commissioners. He seemed a likely candidate, and researching him further uncovered this migration: Ohio > Indiana > Arkansas > Texas. Locality guides in the specific counties included links to maps, county histories, land records, and tax records. Research in these localities continued to point to a relationship between Rachel and Benjamin Cox.

Could DNA confirm this hypothesis that documentary research strongly supported? I added Benjamin Cox as a father for Rachel on my Ancestry tree, and ThruLines generated over seventy possible DNA matches for me as a direct descendant of Rachel Cox. Viewing the localities of the associated family trees again revealed Ohio, Indiana, Arkansas, and Texas, correlating with Rachel and Benjamin Cox's records. DNA evidence provided the final confirmation of what the records indirectly showed. Read the complete research report at https://familylocket.com/rlpdna.

 Your Task

Explore Ethnicity Estimates and Locations of Shared Matches

Consider what role ethnicity estimates could play in your research project. View the reports on each of the company websites to see if they match your genealogical family tree. Make notes about any conclusions in your Research Project Document.

Compare your DNA matches' ethnicity estimates to yours. Do they provide clues to the research question? What localities are named in your DNA match' trees or on the company websites? Add this information to your research log.

Create a Locality Guide

Now that you've created a research objective and analyzed the evidence, you can create a locality guide(s) to inform your research. Look at the DNA matches that might be related to you on the same side as the subject of your objective. Determine the time and place where their ancestors lived. Do they seem to match with what you know? If so, this will give you confidence in following this line of reasoning.

Next, review your timeline analysis. Which localities in the timeline seem reliable? Which may hold the answer to your research question? Choose a place and time to focus your locality guide. You may decide to create multiple smaller guides if your ancestor migrated often. You may also need to create a guide for the suspected most recent common ancestor. For example, the Benjamin Cox project included brief locality guides for researching both him and Rachel Cox in each county of their suspected residence. The guides had information that focused on the specific time of residence, such as tax lists, county histories, migration trails, and land records. Besides county information, state and federal records were also included.

In contrast, the Oklahoma City project needed only a guide for that locality. It included a map showing surrounding counties and records on the city, county, state, and federal levels that pertained to the time. Each research project is unique and will warrant a locality guide(s) to help you understand your ancestors' time and place. Your guide will inform your research planning, giving you new ideas of where and what to research. Additionally, it will be a working document that you can add to as you discover new resources.

CHAPTER 8

DNA Tools and Methodology

Robin Wirthlin

Just as you use diverse records and methodologies for your documentary research, many tools and strategies will streamline the process of working with your DNA and help you visualize the information needed to make connections.

The bell curve in figure 8.1 forms the basis for this chapter's organization. It illustrates a methodology for incorporating DNA into your family history research, moving from the simplest tools on the left to the most complex DNA research tools on the right. The bell curve's highest point suggests where you will likely spend the bulk of your time. The left half of the graphic shows tools not using segment data. The right half depicts those using segment data. Some projects may not require the more advanced tools, but others may benefit from their use.

Developers will continue to create new tools, and the following graphic can help you determine which tools to choose depending upon your research objective. Spending the time to learn to use these tools will increase your ability to work with your DNA results and progress toward your ultimate goals.

As the field of genetic genealogy is continually maturing, please refer to https://familylocket.com/rlpdna for the most up-to-date instructions and features of each of the individual DNA tools discussed in this chapter. Each section contains a bulleted list of tools with descriptions and examples following the list.

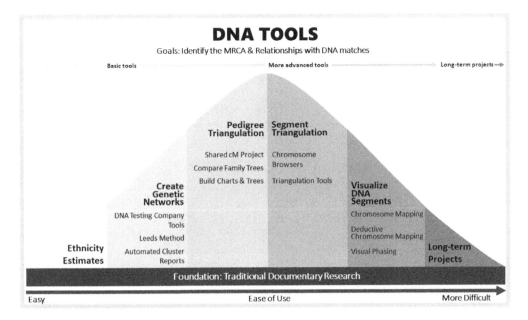

Figure 8.1. Bell Curve of DNA Tools. DNA research projects typically start from the left side and progress toward tools on the right as needed. Created by Robin Wirthlin.

See https://familylocket.com/rlpdna for a full-size image.

Ethnicity Estimates

DNA company reports of ethnicity estimates aren't specifically DNA tools but can be used as a tool in some instances to separate the DNA matches. Reviewing these at the beginning of a research project can provide important clues for the analysis. Every major DNA company offers a view of your admixture or ethnicity composition. See chapter seven for details and applications.

Finding Most Recent Common Ancestors (MRCA)

The purpose of using most DNA tools is finding common ancestors with your DNA matches. Both a DNA tester and a DNA match inherited at least one and perhaps more pieces of DNA from a common ancestor. A simple two-dimensional explanation of a shared ancestor, also known as a most recent common ancestor, is illustrated below.

Two ascending legs of a triangle represent the pedigree lines back to a shared ancestor. Depending on how close a DNA match is, there may be only one or two generations to

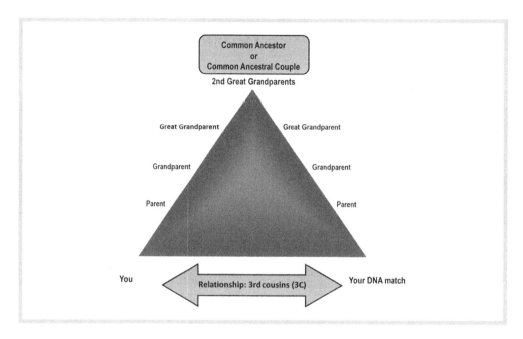

Figure 8.2. Diagram illustrating the relationship path to the shared common ancestor for third cousins (3C). Image created by Robin Wirthlin & Suzanne Chesney.

the shared ancestors, or there may be several generations between the matches and the MRCA. In figure 8.2, the ascending lines show the relationship between DNA testers (3rd Cousins) and their shared second great-grandparents.

The triangle in figure 8.3 illustrates the relationship path to a shared ancestor for second cousins once removed.

Create Genetic Networks

The concept of identifying the MRCA between two DNA matches is key in understanding the use of genetic network tools. You will notice in the DNA tools bell curve that we suggest using genetic network tools early in your process. Why use these tools first? Genetic network tools separate DNA matches into clustered groups based on their relationships to each other, making it easier to determine the MRCA for a group of shared matches. The cluster groups may include descendants of grandparents, great-grandparents, and so on. It may take some detective work to figure out the MRCA for each cluster.

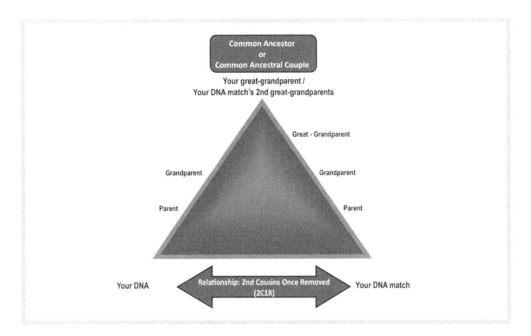

Figure 8.3. Diagram illustrating the relationship path to the shared common ancestor for Second Cousins Once Removed (2C1R).

Image created by Robin Wirthlin & Suzanne Chesney.

A cluster may be composed of matches who have different common ancestors with the tester along a single ancestral line. Some may descend from the tester's great-grandparents, while others may descend from the great-grandparents' parents or grandparents. In other cases, the MRCA may not be the same for all cluster members. Some members may be descended from a particular ancestral couple, and others may be descended from collateral relatives of that couple.

First, you will separate your DNA matches into groups related to your maternal vs. paternal sides. Next, DNA matches can be divided into four groups related to your maternal grandmother, maternal grandfather, paternal grandmother, and paternal grandfather. The DNA matches can be additionally divided into groups of people related to great-grandparents, 2nd great-grandparents, and so forth.

Manual Methods

Each atDNA testing company provides a shared matches tool or report. These reports identify DNA matches who share DNA with you and another match in your list. You can use these tools and reports to create genetic networks manually. To find these reports, look for the following pages at DNA testing company and third party websites. Chapter two provides additional information on these clustering tools.

- **23andMe** "Relatives in Common"
- **AncestryDNA** "Shared Matches"
- **Family Tree DNA** (FTDNA) "In Common With" (ICW)
- **MyHeritage** "Shared DNA Matches"
- **Living DNA** "Relatives"
- **GEDmatch**: People who match both kits, or 1 of 2 kits

Using the shared matches report from any company, you can create a color cluster chart that separates matches into four grandparent groups with The Leeds Method.[1]

Automated Methods

Two automated methods provide a visual grouping of DNA matches who share a common ancestry: AutoClusters and network graphs. These tools make use of techniques from a variety of disciplines to simplify and streamline genetic network analysis.

AutoCluster Programs

Automated AutoCluster programs display DNA connections in a matrix. This output is also called a "design structure matrix" and is a widely used technique for comparing engineering and project management information. Third-party tools, some of which were licensed by DNA companies, offer colorful matrix cluster reports at the click of a button.

- **Genetic Affairs** (23andMe, FTDNA)—http://www.geneticaffairs.com/features-autocluster.html
- **MyHeritage AutoClusters**—https://www.myheritage.com/dna/autoclusters
- **GEDmatch Tier 1** "Clusters, Single Kit input, Basic Version"—https://www.gedmatch.com
- **Collins-Leeds method** at dnagedcom.com—https://www.dnagedcom.com
- **DNA2Tree** for iPhone and iPad—https://apps.apple.com/us/app/dna2tree/id1458545344)
- **Shared Clustering** by Jonathan Brecher—https://github.com/jonathanbrecher/sharedclustering/wiki; https://github.com/jonathanbrecher/sharedclustering/wiki/Clustering-without-downloading-data

---

1. "The Leeds Method," *Dana Leeds* (https://www.danaleeds.com/the-leeds-method).

Evert-Jan Blom, the creator of Genetic Affairs, was one of the first to analyze DNA using Auto Clusters. The process involves using a computer algorithm that compares you to your DNA matches and then your matches to each other. You can use the AutoCluster analysis at Genetic Affairs for DNA test profiles from 23andMe and FTDNA.

MyHeritage and GEDmatch licensed the Genetic Affairs AutoCluster analysis for use directly from their websites. At MyHeritage, find the AutoCluster analysis in the DNA tools section. To access the AutoCluster analysis at GEDmatch, use Tier 1 "Clusters, Single Kit input, Basic Version." You can also incorporate DNA match data from other DNA company websites by exporting a CSV file from each company and uploading them to Genetic Affairs.

Building on the methods developed by Dana Leeds, the Collins-Leeds method is an automated cluster program accessed through the DNAGedcom website. Using the DNA Gedcom Client, gather match data from FTDNA, 23andMe, MyHeritage, and AncestryDNA, and the Collins-Leeds method will separate the DNA matches into clusters for you.

The DNA2Tree app, a subscription-based app for iPhone or iPad, can load your AncestryDNA matches into the program, find common ancestors, calculate DNA clusters, and even build a birth family tree at Ancestry.com.

Figure 8.3 is an example of a matrix cluster report created with Genetic Affairs. In a cluster report, DNA match names are listed both along the top and the left side of the chart. Generally, DNA matches are grouped with others that share a connection to a common ancestral line, and colors distinguish the clusters. The arrangement on the chart suggests how the clusters connect. To identify specific common ancestors, compare individual family trees of the people in the same cluster. Exceptions to the concept of sharing a connection to a common ancestral line occur in cases of endogamy, clusters composed of multiple allied families, pedigree collapse, or where there is more than one cluster for a single ancestral line.

DNA matches can only be in one cluster at a time because the computer algorithm that builds the AutoCluster reports doesn't support having a DNA match in more than one group. Gray squares outside of a cluster show a match with multiple connections. This can be accounted for in many ways - for instance, inclusion in another more distant generational cluster—representing second, third, and fourth great grandparents—or an allied family cluster (sometimes referred to as collateral lines - siblings, aunts, uncles, and cousins) or independent connections to genetic cousins. Furthermore, a match could be included in a more recent generational cluster but have common ancestors who are better represented in another cluster. This condition is true if they are a closer generational descendant of the more distant set of ancestors. They may match most, if not all, of the descendants of the cluster composed primarily of closer relatives, even though they descend from a more distant generation because there are more descendants to match in the closer cluster than there are in the more distant one.

EJ Blom explained how a DNA match is assigned to a cluster:

The number of links with a cluster is used as the deciding factor in cases where a relative could be a member of two clusters. [For example] if DNA Match A has 10 links to cluster 5 and 12 links to cluster 6, it will become a member of cluster 6. If there are new matches available that result in more links to cluster 5, it will switch cluster membership.[2]

In figure 8.4, the AutoCluster tool separated DNA matches from my family into groups related to my Christensen/Taylor great-grandparents, Taylor/Ollerton 2nd great-grandparents, Taylor/Spafford 3rd great-grandparents, and Spafford/Stiles 4th great-grandparents.[3] My second cousin, Tiffany Taylor, was placed in the same cluster as others who are related to our Christensen/Taylor great-grandparents. The clustering confirms what we already know from documentary evidence—that the Christensen/Taylor ancestral couple are our Most Recent Common Ancestors (MRCA). The tiny gray squares in the matrix for her shared DNA matches linked her to multiple clusters. Since I already knew Tiffany and how we were related, it was easier to determine which clusters were associated with several generations of our shared ancestors. The chart indicates that we also share more distant common ancestors extended along the Christensen/Taylor lines' ancestors.

Network Graphs

Another automated method of separating your DNA matches into clusters is to use network graphs. These graphs resemble 3-D pictures and show connected groups of related people in a beautiful display. Like the AutoClusters, a network graph also depicts clusters of matches and connections between them. Network graphs give you a powerful visual to analyze. If you'd like to create a network graph yourself, you have several options. Rootsfinder, NodeXL, and Gephi each provide a software program to input your DNA matches into to make your network graph. Before you start, you will need to use the DNA Gedcom Client (https://www.dnagedcom.com/) to download a spreadsheet of your matches and shared matches.

- RootsFinder (Rootsfinder.com)
- NodeXL (NodeXL.com)
- Gephi (gephi.org)

---

2. EJ Blom to Robin Wirthlin, "Note," 30 January 2021, personal correspondence, privately held by Robin Wirthlin, robin@familylocket.com, 2021.

3. Genetic Affairs, "AutoCluster Visualization for Ann Olsen," *Genetic Affairs* (https://www.geneticaffairs. com : accessed 3 October 2019), AncestryDNA data highlighting the connection with Tiffany Taylor (1C1R).

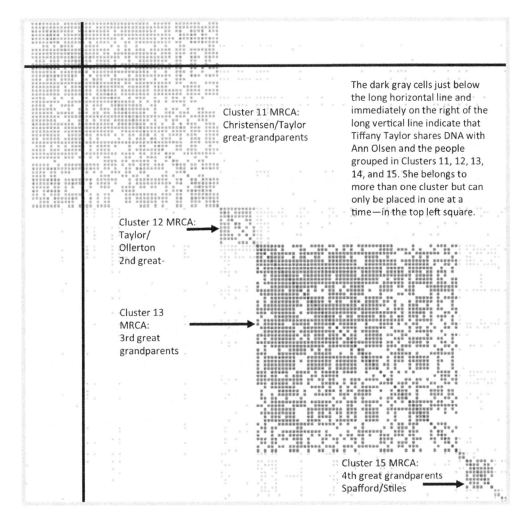

Figure 8.4. AutoCluster report from Genetic Affairs showing clusters from multiple generations

Rootsfinder is user-friendly and designed specifically for genealogy. It provides a comprehensive family tree, research, and DNA program that allows you to connect DNA results with people in your family tree. Additionally, you can import triangulation data from GEDmatch.com to visualize relationship clusters.

NodeXL and Gephi have a high learning curve and were not designed for genetic genealogists. However, if you invest the time to learn the program, you can manipulate the results in many ways. To learn how to make network graphs on your own, you will find

Shelley Crawford's blog posts at Twigs of Yore invaluable. She has laid out the process in a step-by-step way that is very accessible. Check out the posts at (https://twigsofyore. blogspot.com/2017/07/visualising-ancestry-dna-matchesindex.html).

Nodes in a network graph represent your DNA matches and the lines connecting them indicate a shared match to each other. When a group of matches has many connections to each other, they form a cluster. Each DNA match in a cluster of matches is likely related or connected along a shared ancestral line. An individual in the graph might connect to several clusters. This scenario could mean they are a closer relative than other DNA matches.

For example, your first cousin would connect to many clusters—those with descendants of your shared grandparents, great-grandparents, and 2nd-great-grandparents. DNA matches who are immediate family members are typically excluded from network graphs because they would connect to most of the clusters. Individuals who have pedigree collapse in their family may find that their network graphs don't have clearly defined clusters. Those with endogamy in their family may not be able to see any clear clusters emerge at all.

Let's look at an example of how network graphs can illustrate connections between known clusters and unknown clusters. Nicole used a network graph to point to a hypothesis for a brick wall question. She was looking for the parents of John Robert Dyer, born about 1813 in Tennessee. Documentary clues did not lead to parental candidates, but family tradition stated that his mother's name was Sarah Taylor.

The network graph in figure 8.5 shows DNA matches of a 2nd great-grandson of John Robert Dyer. In analyzing the network graph, Nicole saw a connection between cluster 12, John Robert Dyer's descendants, and cluster 3, descendants of Moses Taylor and Elizabeth Prevatte. Moses Taylor and Elizabeth Prevatte had a daughter and daughter-in-law named Sarah, who could have been the Sarah Taylor named in Dyer family tradition. The network graph showed a large cluster of DNA matches who all traced their trees back to the Moses Taylor family, providing a compelling hypothesis for future research.

Pedigree Triangulation

After grouping our DNA matches into genetic networks, we next seek pedigree triangulation, a methodology that most genetic genealogy projects will utilize. Pedigree triangulation identifies the common ancestor among a group of shared DNA matches by comparison of family trees.

The word triangulation brings to mind a triangle—a shape with three sides. In this case, it is actually a three-dimensional pyramid. The base corners represent you and at

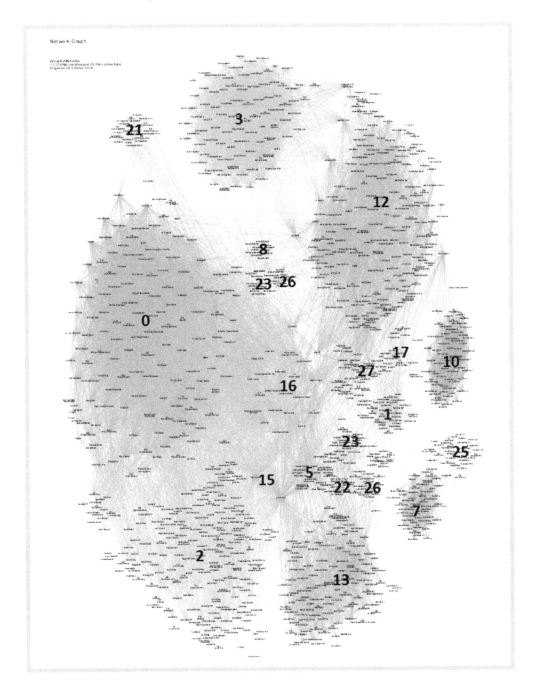

Figure 8.5. Network Graph for Dyer descendants.

Created by Shelley Crawford of ConnectedDNA, annotated.

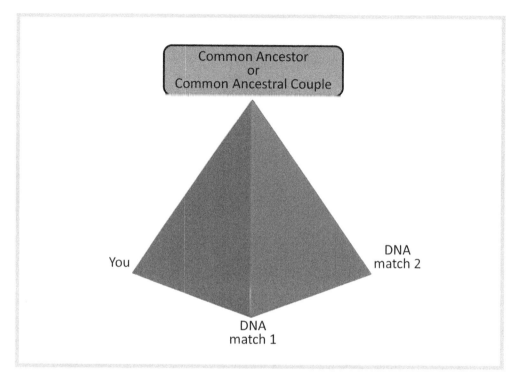

Figure 8.6. 3-D illustration of genetic genealogy triangulation

least two of your DNA matches. The top represents the shared ancestor from whom you each descend. See figure 8.6. Pedigree triangulation is a method of comparing your family tree to the family trees of two or more DNA matches to identify a shared ancestor or ancestral couple.

We try to identify the MRCA's that we share with DNA matches. We are looking for the common ancestors that are the closest generationally to us. The three or more DNA matches considered in confirming a common ancestor should descend from independent lines; in other words, the DNA matches should descend from different children of an ancestor.

To achieve pedigree triangulation, follow these three steps:

- Estimate relationships between you and your DNA matches (the more, the better).
- Compare two or more DNA matches' family trees (the more, the better).
- Build diagrams and trees; add DNA matches to your tree to illustrate the genetic connection to your ancestors.

Estimate the relationship between you and a DNA match

If you can estimate the relationship you share with a DNA match, you have a clue about how many generations back your shared ancestor is related. Each DNA company website provides the amount of shared DNA in either centimorgans or percentages. Use the Shared cM Project tool to identify possible relationships that can then be analyzed and verified. For more details on using the Shared cM Project, see chapter two.

Tools to Analyze the Amount of Shared DNA

- DNA match lists at DNA company websites:
  - 23andMe "DNA Relatives"
  - AncestryDNA "View All DNA Matches"
  - FTDNA "Matches"
  - LivingDNA "Family Networks"
  - MyHeritage DNA "DNA Matches"
  - GEDmatch (third-party tool) "One to Many DNA Comparison"
- Use the Shared cM tool to identify the possible relationships.
  - Shared cM Project at (www.DNAPainter.com)

Compare Family Trees

Because trees are integral to this step, this section will highlight some tools for building and comparing family trees. Remember, family trees as they are found online, and as most genealogists create them, show the family going back in time, perhaps with entire family groups. Rarely will they illustrate the path between you and your DNA match. Instead, they show parts of this path that must be completed through your own analysis of matches' family trees and the correlation of those trees with documentary evidence. If you can determine which ancestor you and your DNA matches share, you can verify that you are genetically related to that ancestor.

As you compare your family tree with those of your DNA matches, you can only really look at one family tree at a time, but you need to consider the family trees of multiple DNA matches. One way to do this is to open separate tabs on a computer screen, and another way is to print the horizontal pedigrees of DNA matches and look for shared or common ancestors. When multiple DNA matches share a common ancestor, there is robust support that an ancestor is biologically related.

Look for common surnames as you compare family trees that are attached to DNA matches' profiles. Explore the pedigrees and localities to find the MRCA shared by you and your DNA matches or shared between genetic cousins in the same genetic cluster. The list below includes tools to view and compare family trees with your DNA match.

Tools to Compare Family Trees

- DNA Testing Company Family Trees
  - Ancestry
  - Family Tree DNA
  - MyHeritage
- FamilySearch Family Tree (https://www.familysearch.org)
- WikiTree (https://www.wikitree.com)
- Geneanet (https://en.geneanet.org)
- Geni (https://www.geni.com/home)
- Filae (https://en.filae.com)
- Find My Past (https://www.findmypast.com)
- GEDmatch (https://www.gedmatch.com)
- DNAGedcom GWorks (https://www.dnagedcom.com)

Family trees at the various DNA companies are associated with a DNA match profile. Many of your DNA matches will not have a tree connected to their profile, and you will need to contact them for more information about their family.

Collaborative family trees provide another avenue for comparing family trees between you and your DNA matches. The FamilySearch Family Tree includes descendancy trees - a feature that shows descent from specific ancestors and can be useful in comparing trees. A free account is required to view the tree.

WikiTree, a shared family tree built by WikiTree members, provides information about its users' DNA tests. You can collaborate with other users as you compare shared ancestors and DNA test results. No account is required to view an individual's pedigree at WikiTree if they have shared a link with you.

Because it can be time-consuming browsing through multiple family trees, automated tools can aid in the analysis. DNA Gedcom tools search the online family trees attached to your DNA matches and help you identify your common ancestors. The specific tool to help with pedigree triangulation is called GWorks.[4] This tool compares GEDcom files consisting of family pedigrees for separate matches. In comparing the GEDcom files in GWorks, the program identifies common surnames that can help you search for your ancestors. To learn more about how to use DNA GEDcom and GWorks, see https://familylocket.com/rlpdna.

---

4. Mesa Foard and Karin Corbeil, "JWorks (v 0.512) and KWorks for FTDNA, 23andMe and GEDmatch Data: Automated Chromosome Browser Tools," *DNAGedcom* (https://www.dnagedcom.com/docs/GWorks_Howto_Updated.pdf).

Building Trees

Diagrams and family trees will help you visualize family connections and evaluate shared DNA to quickly see if there is missing information or conflicts regarding amounts of shared DNA and proposed relationships. It will also help you explain your research easily and quickly to others. See chapter three for detailed examples on building trees.

If there is no family tree associated with a critical DNA match, you may need to build a quick tree for them. Build the tree back approximately fifty years before the time when the ancestor you are attempting to identify lived. Use public record databases, obituaries, newspapers, social media, google searches, vital record indexes, etc., to look for clues about a DNA match's parents or grandparents to construct a family tree. The following tools may provide clues to help you build the tree. Each of these tools requires just a little bit of a tree (even if it is private or stumpy).

Tools to Build Trees

- 23andMe "Your Family Tree"
- ThruLines at AncestryDNA
- Theory of Family Relativity at MyHeritage
- Genetic Affairs AutoTree (http://www.geneticaffairs.com/features-autotree.html)
- Genetic Affairs AutoPedigree (http://www.geneticaffairs.com/features-autopedigree.html)
- WATO (What Are the Odds?) (https://dnapainter.com/tools/probability)

23andMe generates a tree based solely on the amount of DNA you share with your DNA matches and the amount that your DNA matches share with each other. Because it is based on DNA data with no reliance on documentary evidence, parts of the tree could be inaccurate, but it can also provide useful clues for where your DNA matches fit on the tree. You can edit the tree, but your matches cannot see your tree. It's just for you. Clues from the tree can help you separate your matches into meaningful clusters or groups.

ThruLines at AncestryDNA is a program that searches for people who appear in both the family tree that is connected to your DNA results and other Ancestry member trees. The feature creates a descendancy chart that shows suggested connections between you and your DNA matches. The potential relationships between you and your DNA matches are positioned in the descendancy chart, along with the amount of DNA you share. It's essential to verify the relationships in the suggested trees because some family trees in Ancestry have inaccurate family information.

The Theory of Family Relativity is a feature at MyHeritage that offers theories about how you and your DNA matches might be related. The tool lists one or more theories in an ascendency and descendency graphic that illustrates the generations from you to your common ancestor and back down to your DNA match. Shared Smart Matches, Shared Ancestral Surnames, or Shared Ancestral Places are elements that assist in identifying family connections between your family tree and others in the database. Family trees and historical records combined with the DNA theories simplify identifying the connection between you and your DNA match.

Genetic Affairs provides the AutoTree program, which reconstructs family trees for FTDNA profiles and identifies common ancestors among DNA matches. Genetic Affairs can directly gather the needed information from FTDNA and create an AutoTree for the DNA matches that have a family tree associated with their accounts.

Another tree-building interpretation tool at Genetic affairs is AutoPedigree. This tool uses AutoTree predictions to offer multiple hypotheses about how a person can fit into a created AutoTree, which can be vital in unknown parentage cases.

Tree-building tools provide a logical starting point or a shortcut to figuring out who your DNA matches are and how you connect to them. Before these features launched, it was necessary to look through each DNA match's trees, if they had a tree, look for common surnames and build a connection between your tree and their tree. It was more challenging to identify the relationships and figure out some of the DNA matches' identities.

After using pedigree triangulation and documentary research to identify common ancestors between you and your matches, or even just between your matches, the What Are the Odds? (WATO) advanced DNA tool found on DNAPainter.com can help you work out where a DNA tester may fit in a family tree. Often used for solving unknown parentage cases, WATO can help you discern how an unidentified DNA match is related to your family members. WATO is a good step after pedigree triangulation since it is most effective when there are more than two relationships. WATO uses the probabilities from the Shared cM tool at DNA Painter but considers them in tandem across multiple relationships to further narrow and pinpoint the most likely relationship scenarios.

Like any tool, WATO has strengths and limitations. A primary strength of WATO is the ability to enter DNA matches from the various DNA companies or GEDmatch. The tool can help narrow down the possibilities of biological parent candidates. WATO does not work well for families with endogamy, pedigree collapse, or multiple relationships. It also does not work well for matches less than 30–40 cM. WATO cannot definitively tell you that you have the correct biological parent or grandparent candidate. You will need to do additional documentary research and targeted testing to prove the relationship.

Pedigree Triangulation and the Benjamin Cox Case

Many tools can accelerate the process of pedigree triangulation, like Ancestry ThruLines, as seen with Diana's Benjamin Cox case. She found indirect evidence pointing to Benjamin

Cox as the father of her 4th great-grandmother, Rachel Cox. Assuming Benjamin Cox was the father of Rachel, his other children's descendants would likely be related in the range of fourth to eighth cousins. The possibilities would be third cousins three times removed, fourth cousins twice removed, fifth cousins once removed, sixth cousins, sixth cousins once removed, or sixth cousins twice removed.

Diana was overwhelmed by trying to find descendants of Benjamin Cox in her match list. She knew they would probably be sharing less DNA and would, therefore, be hidden in larger categories of relationships, including thousands of matches and mixed-in with distant relatives from many ancestral lines. She decided to add Benjamin Cox to the tree connected to her DNA test. Ancestry's technology searched user-created trees to find DNA matches that also had a connection to Benjamin Cox. ThruLines found sixty-six DNA matches that had Benjamin Cox in their family tree. Diana checked the trees' parent-child relationships for accuracy to see if they all genuinely intersected at Benjamin Cox as the MRCA.

Diana also used The Theory of Family Relativity to explore DNA matches on MyHeritage. Hoping to find a proposed line back to Benjamin Cox, Diana searched through the Theory of Family Relativity suggestions provided to her at MyHeritage by typing "Shults." This approach returned a theory of relativity suggestion for a DNA Match that descends from Hickman Monroe Shults and his wife, Rachel Cox. She could then check the documentation for the tree and use the DNA match as evidence.

After all of the research, Diana concluded that Benjamin was the father of Rachel Cox. There were matches that descended from all of Benjamin Cox's children that shared DNA with Diana or other family members who shared their DNA results with Diana for use in the research project.

Segment Triangulation

How can segment triangulation help you? This method can help you trace your family tree back even more generations—perhaps even beyond the ancestors you know about now. Triangulation relies on DNA segments shared by you and at least two of your matches on the same chromosome, which have to have come from a single shared ancestral source. If the common ancestor or ancestors shared between these three individuals (or more) can be determined using family trees and documentary evidence, then the triangulated DNA is compelling evidence supporting the proposed ancestral relationship.

Somewhere back in time, your ancestors passed DNA to their children, who passed it to their children, which eventually ended up with you. DNA segments are created through the process of recombination as the chunks of DNA originating from those ancestors gradually become broken down into smaller and smaller pieces of DNA. The goal of segment triangulation is to determine the ancestral origin of a single DNA segment shared between you and at least two other individuals.

Specifically, segment triangulation is a method of comparing segments of DNA from three or more people. If all three have inherited the same DNA segment on the same chromosome, they share a common ancestor—whether that ancestor is identifiable or not depends on available documentary evidence. The segments need to overlap on the same chromosome copy shared between at least three individuals. The exact stop and start positions do not need to be the same as long as there is a significant section of overlap.

For true triangulation, you must share the same segment on the same chromosome with at least two matches who descend from the common ancestor through independent lines; and the other two matches must also also share the same segment with each other. Only GEDmatch, MyHeritage, and 23andMe Advanced DNA Comparison have the ability to report segment triangulation. FTDNA does not provide triangulation information because it does not compare the other two individuals to see if they share that same segment of DNA with each other. AncestryDNA does not provide segment or triangulation information.

Several tools help you "see" the DNA pieces you and your DNA cousins inherited from specific common ancestors. Below are brief descriptions of the tools, and you can access the instructions and latest developments at https://familylocket.com/rlpdna.

Chromosome Browsers

Three testing companies and GEDmatch provide a chromosome browser. This tool helps you visualize the DNA that you inherited from common ancestors and compare segments of DNA that you share with your DNA matches. Detailed segment information includes chromosome number, start, and endpoints of segments.

Remember that you have two copies of each chromosome. You inherited one copy of each chromosome from your father and one copy from your mother. For the purposes of triangulation, overlapping segments must be on the same chromosome copy.

If you examine the DNA segments that you share with your DNA matches and know how you are related and which common ancestor(s) you share, you can assign the segments to that ancestor. After the segment has been "assigned" or identified as belonging to a specific ancestor(s), you can compare the segment data from other DNA matches. Just because the match shares the same segment on the same chromosome, it does not necessarily mean that they descend from the same set of common ancestors—it could mean that they descend from an ancestor of the most recent common ancestors.

Chromosome Browsers

- MyHeritage "Chromosome Browser—One-to-many"
- 23andMe "Advanced DNA Comparison"
- FTDNA "Chromosome Browser"
- GEDmatch "One to one Autosomal DNA Comparison," "One to One X-DNA Comparison," Tier 1 (Paid level) "2-D Chromosome Browser," "3-D Chromosome Browser," and "Compact Segment Mapper."

Segment Triangulation Tools

Several third-party tools can identify DNA segments shared by you and two of your matches on the same chromosome that originated from the same common ancestor. Imagine that you are one point of the triangle, and two of your DNA matches are the other points. Specific DNA segments that the three of you share at the same location on the same chromosome are triangulated. You can learn more about segment triangulation from Jim Bartlett's blog found at (https://segmentology.org).

Segment Triangulation Tools

- Genetic Affairs AutoSegment (http://www.geneticaffairs.com/features-autosegment.html)
- Genetic Affairs Hybrid AutoSegment (http://www.geneticaffairs.com/features-autosegment.html)
- DNAGedcom Jworks (https://www.dnagedcom.com/Auto/JWorks.aspx)
- DNAGedcom KWorks (https://www.dnagedcom.com/Auto/KWorks.aspx)
- GEDmatch Tier 1 Autosomal DNA Segment Analyzer (https://www.dnagedcom.com/adsa/Index.php)

The Genetic Affairs website states, "AutoSegment is a DNA segment-based clustering method that is available for segment data from MyHeritage, 23andMe, Family Tree DNA, and GEDmatch!"[5] The information in the AutoSegment report shows which DNA segments you share with other DNA matches. You can examine and work to identify the common ancestors who passed that DNA segment on to you and your DNA match. Suppose you can identify three or more DNA matches that share the same segment from the same ancestor;

---

5. EJ Blom, "AutoSegment," *Genetic Affairs* (http://www.geneticaffairs.com/features-autosegment.html).

this is triangulation. In that case, you can use that along with documentary record analysis to confirm your genetic relationship to the ancestor who passed that DNA segment on to you.

The Hybrid AutoSegment tool available at the Genetic Affairs website gathers DNA segment data from 23andMe, Family Tree DNA, My Heritage, and GEDmatch *together in one report*. Having the segment information in one place streamlines the process of examining, analyzing, and determining which of our DNA segments we inherited from specific ancestors. We don't have to compare segment data between computer files or manually import the data from different testing companies into one massive spreadsheet when we use this tool.

Another option for compiling DNA segment data is to use the DNA Gedcom Client to extract data from DNA testing companies, then use the data in JWorks and KWorks (tools from DNA Gedcom) or look at the data in a spreadsheet. Then you can see DNA segments that you share in common with your matches and identify triangulated groups that can lead to the identification of an MRCA.

The main steps for using DNA Gedcom are the following:

1. Register with DNAGedcom.com
2. Subscribe to the DNAGedcom Client (https://www.dnagedcom.com/docs/Welcome_to_the_New_DNAGedcom_Client.pdf)
3. Download files from FTDNA, 23andMe, MyHeritage, and GEDmatch through the DNAGedcom Client

Downloading the files requires some patience. It may take hours or overnight to extract the data. The good news is that you can still use your computer to do other things while file retrieval occurs. You can retrieve files from more than one DNA testing company at once. If you subscribe to Tier 1 in GEDmatch, you can download your DNA segment and "In Common With" information, which you can then use in JWorks and KWorks.

JWorks is a downloadable Excel macro program that sorts your DNA segment data, creates a spreadsheet of overlapping segments, and assigns ICW status if DNA segments overlap with others. Jay Pizarro created this program, which is accessible via the DNAGedcom.com website.

Kitty Munson Cooper created an online version of JWorks called KWorks that sorts your DNA data, creates a spreadsheet of overlapping segments, and assigns ICW to segments that overlap. KWorks is accessible through the DNAGedcom.com website.

If you subscribe to GEDmatch Tier 1, you can use the Autosomal DNA Segment Analyzer (ASDA) to see your DNA segments and those of your DNA matches that overlap.

The program also reports which people share DNA in common with (ICW) others. The image generated will help you identify likely triangulation groups.

As previously stated, using a tool to gather the segment information in one place streamlines the process of examining, analyzing, and figuring out which of your DNA segments you inherited from specific ancestors. For example, in researching my 5th great grandparents, I used the Hybrid AutoSegment tool to find DNA segments that my great-aunt (who I'll call Jane) shared with her DNA matches. Two of her DNA matches had posted their family trees in Family Tree DNA and one posted on MyHeritage, which helped me identify their shared common ancestors, John Killian and Lydia Ann Hopper. The Hybrid AutoSegment report highlighted other information that I could use as evidence and was much easier than comparing and analyzing each DNA segment.

The table included in the report listed the DNA matches and the overlapping DNA segments they share with Jane and possibly with each other. The caveat "possibly" is included because it is unknown if the DNA that Jane shares with the people on the list is located on her maternal or paternal copy of the specific chromosome. The DNA testers list showed a segment shared between Jane and Tester 3 on Chromosome 18 with a start point of 20,639,454 and an endpoint of 54,418,559. Twenty-three additional DNA cousins share the same or an overlapping segment of DNA in the same location.

One of the people on the list had an extensive family tree and shared our common ancestral couple, John Killian and Lydia Ann Hopper. The other people in the list sharing a portion of chromosome 18 either had small family trees or no family trees. Further research might include writing to them to learn more about their ancestors and building their family trees to verify our common ancestral connection.

Having the data gathered in one location simplifies visualizing DNA segments. It will also help identify the ancestors that DNA matches and myself or my great-aunt Jane have in common.

Visualize DNA Segments

Chromosome mapping aims to identify the ancestral origins of specific segments of DNA in your genome visually. Through this process, it is possible to see which segments you inherited from specific ancestors. It's important to remember that you can't visualize your own DNA. You can only see the DNA you share with your DNA matches. In a chromosome map, you are the base person against which the DNA match is compared. The chromosome map depicts the segments you share with a DNA match.

Chromosome mapping

Use your Autosomal DNA results to build a map of your chromosomes that shows segments you inherited from specific ancestors or ancestral couples. You can map your chromosomes on paper, in computer programs, or DNA Painter, a simple-to-use tool.

Tools for Chromosome Mapping

- **DNA Painter** (https://dnapainter.com)
- **Cluster Auto Painter** (https://dnapainter.com/tools/cap)
- **G-DAT** (https://www.getgmp.com)

DNA Painter uses only segment information, not raw DNA data, which ensures privacy because people cannot see the nucleotides at SNP locations in your raw DNA data. Once you identify the MRCA(s) between you and a genetic match, you can assign the DNA you share with a match to those ancestors and "paint" that shared DNA in DNAPainter.com. See figure 8.7. You can label it with the names of the ancestors that passed those DNA segments on to you. As you repeat the process, you create a chromosome map. Use information on the chromosome map to discover how other DNA matches are related to you.

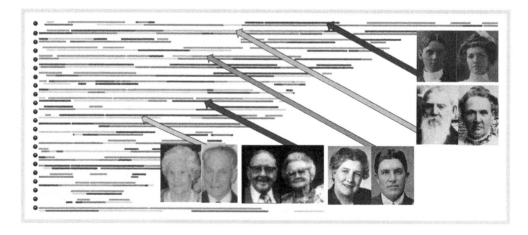

Figure 8.7. Chromosome Map screenshot created at DNAPainter.com. Annotated by Robin Wirthlin with photos of ancestors and arrows pointing to DNA segments inherited from them. Colored lines on the chromosome map indicate DNA segments shared with DNA matches that were inherited from the ancestral couples shown in the photos.

When you create a chromosome map in DNA Painter, you'll see two lines for each chromosome, the top line represents the paternal copy, and the bottom line represents the maternal copy. They are arranged from 1 to 22 with the X chromosome at the bottom of the map.

DNA Painter also features the "Cluster Auto Painter" tool, which generates a new chromosome map from the DNA segment data in cluster HTML files and AutoCluster reports from Genetic Affairs, MyHeritage, GEDmatch, and the Collins-Leeds method at DNAGedcom.

G-DAT (Genealogical DNA Analysis Tool) is an app for Windows, Mac, or Linux that helps you use your autosomal DNA test results for genealogy. This app replaces Genome Mate Pro (https://www.getgmp.com/). G-DAT can be used to analyze autosomal DNA data that is downloaded to your own computer. According to the website, its features include chromosome mapping, triangulation, and in common with (ICW) grouping, the ability to mark MRCAs, show ancestors on the X-DNA inheritance path, and analysis routines to aid in family tree research.

Visual Phasing

Visual phasing is a time-intensive way to map your chromosomes. This method provides a way to create a detailed map that identifies the DNA segments inherited from each of your four grandparents. Some of the starting requirements are a set of three siblings, determination, focus, and patience. The goal is to map crossover points in your chromosomes. These are points on the chromosome where DNA from your grandparents has switched places or recombined.

Tool for Visual Phasing

Steven Fox wrote a program in Excel that helps automate the process of Visual Phasing. The program can be found in the "Visual Phasing Working Group" on Facebook.[6] Blaine Bettinger wrote a 5-part series of instructions on how to do Visual Phasing on his blog.[7]

Challenges in Chromosome Mapping

A challenge you may encounter in mapping your chromosomes is that you may share multiple common ancestors with your DNA matches. If this is the case, you will share

---

6. Steven Fox, "Visual Phasing Spreadsheet," *Facebook* (https://www.facebook.com/groups/visualphasing/files).

7. Blaine Bettinger, PhD., "Visual Phasing: An Example (Part 1 of 5)," *The Genetic Genealogist* (https://thegeneticgenealogist.com/2016/11/21/visual-phasing-an-example-part-1-of-5/).

more DNA than expected with the DNA match, and it may be more challenging to identify which DNA segments came from a specific ancestor or ancestral couple. Some situations you may see in your family tree are the following:

- **Pedigree collapse** happens when related individuals have children. These children have fewer unique ancestors than expected because their parents have some ancestors in common.
- **Endogamy** occurs among some geographically isolated populations or populations who choose to marry primarily within the population for generations. As a result of this, the children inherit DNA from the founders of the population in multiple ways.
- **Lack of family tree completeness.** You may not know if you share multiple ancestors with a DNA match if you have some shorter ancestral lines because some ancestors haven't yet been identified. This is what genealogists refer to as dead ends or brick walls.

DNA Tools and Methodology for mtDNA, Y-DNA, and X-DNA

Up to this point, we've discussed tools and methodologies for using autosomal DNA. Now let's discuss tools for other types of DNA. See chapters one and six for additional information on these types of DNA.

mtDNA

Tools for mtDNA include the reports about haplogroups and the matching report at FTDNA. As a researcher, you take the information from the reports, analyze it, and correlate it with documentary research to draw conclusions. The following DNA companies give information about mitochondrial DNA:

- Family Tree DNA offers a full sequence mitochondrial test.
- 23andMe reports mtDNA haplogroups along with autosomal DNA results.
- Living DNA reports mtDNA haplogroups along with autosomal DNA results.
- MyHeritage and Ancestry include tested mtDNA markers in their raw data download files which can sometimes be used to estimate mtDNA haplogroup.
- Tools for estimating mtDNA haplogroup include James Lick's tools (https://dna.jameslick.com/mthap/).

Evaluating Your Family Tree

Go to DNA Painter > Ancestral Trees > upload or create a family tree > Choose Tree > DNA Filters > Show mtDNA path. DNA Painter can overlay an mtDNA inheritance path on an ancestral fan chart. The chart will help you visualize the ancestors from whom you inherited mtDNA.

Pedigree Triangulation

Contact your mtDNA matches to try to identify your common matrilineal ancestor. See the following websites for mtDNA haplogroups and mtDNA-related tools.

- **FTDNA:** mtDNA match list
- **23andMe:** mtDNA haplogroup as shown on the detailed DNA match page
  - There are separate mtDNA and Y-DNA haplogroup reports for 23andMe under all ancestral reports. Also, the 'browse raw data feature' or a 'raw data download' enables the evaluation of specific mtDNA markers and identifying those markers that were no calls. No-calls can have an important effect on your haplogroup designation.
  - You can also filter by haplogroup (may require an upgraded subscription).
- **Living DNA:** Ancestry > Maternal ancestry
- **Genetic Affairs:** AutoTree analysis of family trees of mtDNA or Y-DNA matches from FTDNA. If autosomal DNA matches and their family trees are available, AutoTree will add them to the analysis. This feature saves time finding a common maternal/paternal ancestor when you have tested your mtDNA or Y DNA.

Compare mtDNA, Y-DNA, Family Finder results

FTDNA "Advanced Matches" is the only tool today that uses all types of DNA available to help determine how closely related a match may be. You can compare matches from multiple types of tests you have taken at FTDNA. Choose which tests to compare, and then show only people that match in all selected tests.[8]

Other Resources for mtDNA Research

- The ISOGG Wiki has links to articles about mtDNA and tools: (https://isogg.org/wiki/MtDNA_tools)

---

8. "Advanced Matches," *FamilyTreeDNA Learning Center* (https://learn.familytreedna.com/user-guide/family-finder-myftdna/advanced-matching-page/).

- The Family Tree DNA mitochondrial haplogroup tree: (https://www.familytreedna.com/public/mt-dna-haplotree/L)
- mtDNA Haplogroup project (https://isogg.org/wiki/MtDNA_haplogroup_projects)
- mtDNA Maternal Lineage Projects (https://isogg.org/wiki/MtDNA_lineage_projects)
- mitoYDNA (https://www.mitoydna.org)
- Mitochondrial Geographical Projects (https://isogg.org/wiki/Geographical_DNA_projects)
- Phylotree (https://www.phylotree.org) Compare your results against the mitochondrial phylogeny.
- Some resources for interpretation include heat distribution maps at Eupedia (https://www.eupedia.com/europe/maps_mtdna_haplogroups.shtml)
- Descriptions of haplogroups (https://haplogroup.org/)

Y-DNA

The following tools can help you use your Y-DNA test results to find the Y-DNA inheritance path in your family tree, examine your Y-DNA matches, and identify your predicted Y-DNA haplogroup.

Overlay inheritance path for Y-DNA

Go to DNA Painter > Ancestral Trees > upload or create a family tree > Choose Tree > DNA Filters > Show Y-DNA path. This tool illustrates the ancestors from whom you inherited Y-DNA.

Examine your Y-DNA matches

The Y-DNA match list at FTDNA identifies other Y-DNA test takers who have the same or similar Y chromosome as you. The greater the genetic distance between you and others, the more distantly you are related.

Identify predicted Y-DNA haplogroup

Haplogroup predictions can guide you toward discerning between two historical men with the same name, surname research, or unknown parentage. Websites to find possible haplogroup matches are:

- FTDNA
- 23andMe

- Living DNA
- GEDmatch

Surname and Haplogroup Projects at Family Tree DNA

Surname and haplogroup projects can be used to identify which markers differ between your test results and those of a match. The differences can be used to identify shared and potentially significant mutations, which can help identify other individuals who do not match, whose results act as negative evidence.

TiP Calculator

The FTDNA TiP Calculator is located under the name of your DNA matches and estimates the generations between you, your Y-DNA match, and your common ancestor. Use the TiP report with caution to explore the probabilities that two men share a common ancestor within an estimated time period because it is known to underestimate the time to a common ancestor. TiP reports use mutation rates of markers and numbers of mismatches between two test-takers to calculate probabilities for generational distance to the common ancestors. These reports should be used with caution because they are only current up to the 37-marker level.[9] As FTDNA added more markers to the Y-DNA test, the reports were not updated.

Compare Y-DNA with others who have uploaded their Y-DNA test results

- Y- and mtDNA database (https://www.mitoydna.org/)
- Family Tree DNA Y-DNA haplogroup tree (https://www.familytreedna.com/public/y-dna-haplotree/A)
- YFull (https://www.yfull.com/)
- Y-DNA Warehouse (https://ydna-warehouse.org/)

X-DNA

Several tools can help you visualize X-DNA inheritance in your family tree. A summary is provided below. See https://familylocket.com/rlpdna for links to fillable charts and additional explanatory DNA charts.

---

9. James M. Owston, EdD, "Y-DNA Analysis for a Family Study," *Advanced Genetic Genealogy: Techniques and Case Studies,* Debbie Parker Wayne, editor, (Cushing, Texas: Wayne Research, 2019), 89.

Overlay inheritance paths for X-DNA

Go to DNA Painter > Ancestral Trees > upload or create a family tree and the DNA Filters tool will show you which ancestor potentially passed X-DNA to you. Focus on just these ancestors when you compare X-DNA matches to try to identify the common ancestors you share.

Create charts illustrating your X-DNA inheritance

Charts will help you visualize your ancestors that may have contributed to your X chromosome.

- Progeny Charting Software (https://progenygenealogy.com/products/family-tree-charts/)
- Debbie Parker Wayne's fillable X-DNA charts[10]
- Blaine Bettinger's X-DNA charts—handwrite your ancestors in the inheritance pattern[11]
- James C. Turner fillable X-DNA charts[12]

List of X ancestors

You can compare your list of ancestors who possibly passed on X-DNA with the ancestors of your DNA matches to see if you have the same common ancestors. The following tools can help you do this:

- Genealogical DNA Analysis Tool (https://www.getgmp.com)
- Wikitree (https://www.wikitree.com)

Biogeographical Information for the X-Chromosome

Biogeographical ancestry is the "estimation of one's biological, ethnic, and/or geographical origins based on DNA analysis."[13] Ethnicity estimates attempt to provide this

---

10. Debbie Parker Wayne, "Quick Reference Links" *Debbie Parker Wayne* (http://debbiewayne.com/pubs.php#quickref), Publications > Quick Reference Links by Debbie Parker Wayne> X-DNA.

11. Blaine Bettinger, "More X-Chromosome Charts," 12 January 2009, *The Genetic Genealogist* (https://thegeneticgenealogist.com/2009/01/12/more-x-chromosome-charts/).

12. James C. Turner, "X Chromosome Inheritance," *RootsWeb Freepages* (http://freepages.rootsweb.com/~hulseberg/genealogy/DNA/xinheritance.html).

13. "Biogeographical ancestry," rev. 19:00, 26 August 2015, *ISOGG Wiki* (https://isogg.org/wiki/Biogeographical_ancestry).

biogeographical information for DNA testers. You can learn more about the locations that your ancestors belonged at some point in the past through the 23andMe "Ancestry Composition." This report includes chromosomes and shows the continent or countries that ancestors who contributed to your X chromosome came from.

Your Task

Practice using DNA tools, take notes on how to use the tools in your research. Create a document with a list of tools you have tried and your answers to these questions:

- Why should I use this DNA tool?
- How can it help me?

Read and gain knowledge about the type of DNA you are using to help you understand it. For example, the Short Tandem Repeat DNA Internet DataBase (STRBase) from the National Institute of Standards and Technology, U.S. Department of Commerce brings together information about STRs, including scientific literature, technology, testing techniques, and more (https://strbase.nist.gov/). Other ideas:

- Look up a Y-DNA surname project for one of your surnames at FTDNA, join a surname project or haplogroup project or even start one.
- Read Roberta Estes' Million Mito blog post (https://dna-explained. com/2020/03/17/the-million-mito-project/).
- Join the Mitochondrial DNA Facebook Group.
- Fill in or color an X-DNA fan chart for yourself.

CHAPTER 9

Research Planning with DNA

Nicole Dyer

Now that you have reviewed your starting point information and have thought about DNA tools that might be applicable, you are ready to make a research plan. Have you ever included DNA sources in a research plan? Maybe you have created a research plan for documentary sources before but haven't added DNA sources. Each DNA project is unique, with different objectives, but all can follow the same guiding principles of an effective research plan. In this chapter, we will talk about the basic elements to be included as you create a plan that includes both documentary and DNA sources.

The purpose of a research plan is to determine which sources of information will help researchers uncover the answer to your research question. You will ask yourself which records, DNA test takers, analysis tools, and methods will answer your research question. As you grow in experience, your ability to select the most useful sources and tools will improve.

Research planning may seem like a burdensome extra step before getting started on the "real research." In reality, creating a research plan actually saves time. Your plan will help you stay organized and focused if your work is interrupted. If you leave a project for a few days, weeks, or even years, a well-written plan can help you pick up where you left off when you return to the project.

Differences between experts and novices underscore the importance of thorough problem analysis and planning. When an expert solves a problem, they come up with superior solutions that take minimal effort. How do they do that? Studies have found that experts spend a long time understanding the problem and recognizing significant patterns. They reconsider initial interpretations and develop new theories.[1] Novices, on the other hand, jump right in and begin working on the problem. They use trial and error to figure out what works. Novices tend to spend much longer solving the problem.

Research planning will help you become more like problem-solving experts. As you slow down, review known information, analyze carefully, and plan, you will realize the next best steps. Rushing to work on the case before careful planning can lead you down the wrong path. Figuring out the next logical steps through careful planning will save you time in the long run.

The goal of our research is to achieve genealogical proof. In order to get there, we need to plan carefully to access high quality sources and primary information. We should do reasonably exhaustive research and analyze the DNA of enough test takers branching from our ancestor through independent lines. If we neglect to consider these and other genealogy standards when planning, we may complete our research only to find we have a theory that can't be proven until we do further testing.[2] Planning for genealogical proof from the beginning of our DNA research projects helps us gather enough data to prove our conclusions.

Research in Phases

Are you going to reach genealogical proof with the first research plan you make for an objective? Probably not. Most DNA projects about ancestors in the past require research in multiple phases, each with its own research plan. Like client projects with limitations on time spent, projects for yourself sometimes have limitations. Perhaps you would like to finish the project before you go on a research trip. Maybe the upcoming family reunion is the deadline. Perhaps you are hoping to get the first phase done before a house remodeling project.

If you don't have natural deadlines or schedule breaks, it's helpful to give yourself a time limit and then assess what you have at that point. Researching on and on without writing your results and beginning another phase feels unproductive. Break your research

1. Wendy Hirsch, "How do you tell an expert from a novice? Look at how they plan," blog post, 21 September 2016, *Wendy Hirsch: The Art and Science of Change Implementation* (https://wendyhirsch.com/blog/planning-best-practice-partii).

2. Board for Certification of Genealogists (BCG), *Genealogy Standards*, 2nd ed. (Nashville: Ancestry.com, 2019).

into manageable chunks. You may also want to choose a budget for each phase to help spread out the cost of purchasing DNA tests.

One way to break your research into phases is to set a number of hours (i.e. 20 hours) or a length of time (i.e. two weeks). For example, you may give yourself one month to work on the initial research phase for a project. When that's complete, you may have a hypothesis to test and devote the next month to researching that hypothesis.

Principal Research Question and Sub-Objectives

The overarching objective for your project, or principal research question, is the question of identity or relationship that you seek to answer. For example:

> **Principal Research Question:** Who was the father of John Robert Dyer, who was born about 1810–1813 and died in 1879 in Hawkins County, Tennessee, and married Barsheba Tharp about 1830?

The sub-objectives are more specific questions for each phase of the research. They may be yes or no questions to help eliminate various hypotheses.[3] Each phase might include either documentary sources, DNA sources, or both. For example:

- **Sub-Objective 1:** When and where was John Robert Dyer born? (Documentary Sources)
- **Sub-Objective 2:** Is Robert, the documented 2nd great-grandson of John Robert Dyer, a biological descendant of John Robert Dyer? (atDNA and Documentary Sources)
- **Sub-Objective 3:** Which cluster of Robert's DNA Matches includes descendants of John Robert Dyer? Which cluster of DNA matches could include descendants of John Robert Dyer's father? Who is the MRCA for that cluster? (atDNA and Documentary Sources)
- **Sub-Objective 4:** Was Robert Daugherty, who married Sarah Taylor, the father of John Robert Dyer? Who were his children? (Documentary Sources)
- **Sub-Objective 5:** Was James Taylor, who married Sarah Daugherty, the father of John Robert Dyer? Who were his children? (Documentary Sources)

---

3. Catherine Desmarais, "Reconstructing the 18th Century Family - The Northamer Case," *Course 11: Meeting Standards Using DNA Evidence—Research Strategies*, 2020 Syllabus, Salt Lake Institute of Genealogy (Salt Lake: SLIG, 2020), 80.

Each of these sub-objectives is a phase of research I have completed in order to find the answer to my principal research question to discover the parents of John Robert Dyer. So far, the results have been inconclusive, so I will be continuing to another phase of research. Phase 6 will include analyzing atDNA cluster results of additional John Robert Dyer descendants. Robert's Y-DNA results have not revealed any close matches yet, but I hope to find a candidate as part of testing a specific hypothesis.

A traced relationship, as mentioned in sub-objective 2, refers to a relationship that has been found through documentary sources. *Genealogy Standards* reminds us to distinguish between genetic and other types of relationships. Standard 56 reminds us that we should only declare a relationship is genetic when evidence supports a genetic relationship.[4] If genetic sources haven't been consulted yet, a relationship we find through documentary sources is a "traced" relationship.

Sub-objectives 4 and 5 were phases focused on testing specific hypotheses for John Robert Dyer's parents and finding documentary records to help. Standard 50 says that after eliminating all other possible conclusions, the evidence should point to just one answer to the research question.[5] Are there DNA matches who are unaccounted for in the cluster? Is there a hypothesis that some evidence points to? Is there other evidence pointing to a competing hypothesis? Reasonably exhaustive research means that you may go through several additional phases of research, testing and eliminating competing hypotheses.

Using Documentary and DNA Sources Together

When choosing a research question with the intention of applying genetic evidence, it's best to start with a person you've already thoroughly researched in the documents. This provides a strong foundation for your DNA analysis. As you move through various research phases, you will go back and forth between documentary and genetic sources. Some phases will focus only on documentary sources. Other phases will focus more on DNA evidence. When you use DNA evidence, you will be using documentary sources as well.

Each professional genealogist has a unique approach to their research process. However, most agree that the process of research, analysis, correlating genetic evidence, correlating documentary evidence, and writing are overlapping processes.[6] If you don't

---

4. BCG, *Genealogy Standards*, 2nd ed., 32.

5. BCG, *Genealogy Standards*, 2nd ed., 29.

6. Desmarais, "Reconstructing the 18th Century Family - The Northamer Case," 89.

write as you go along, it's important to write a report at the end of each phase, including your intermediate conclusions and ideas for future research.

Knowing that you will do research in phases helps you focus on the current phase without being distracted by ideas for future research. You can put your ideas for hypotheses to test and methods to try in a list of future research suggestions that you will examine at the completion of the phase.

How to Create a Research Plan

Your overarching research plan for the principal research question is dynamic and flexible. New evidence may alter the intended sequence of planned research tasks. You don't need to plan out the exact order of the research phases. Typically, the next phase is not decided until you have finished the current phase. After the initial phase, another sub-objective may emerge if you discover a different hypothesis to test. Additionally, new DNA matches may lead to a fresh hypothesis.

It is best to create a research plan for the current phase you are in. Start with what you know and summarize the reliable facts. Use reasoning and deduction to come up with a rough hypothesis to guide your selection of sources. List several sources to search, then choose the best three or four sources to prioritize in an efficient sequence. Let's go over each of these steps in detail.

Summary of Known Facts

The first part of a research plan is a summary of known facts. What do you already know about the research question? Knowing your starting point is essential. It guides you to records and locations grounded in clues from your research subject's life. Reviewing this starting point information is an important step to prepare you for crafting a hypothesis. Your summary might be a list of information or a narrative that details the starting point.

In previous chapters, you have gathered information from documentary and DNA sources and organized them. You created a timeline with documentary evidence and a diagram showing known test takers and relevant DNA matches. You have added notes to DNA match profiles and viewed DNA test reports. Review this information and compile a list of reliable known facts. You should list known facts from documentary sources and from DNA sources.

Summary of Known Facts in Documentary Sources

Review your timeline. List the most reliable information from original records and primary informants where possible. If you have a clue from an authored source that you want to pursue, include that in your summary. Focus on the facts that relate to your objective and help identify your research subject. For more ideas on how to do this, refer to *Research Like a Pro: A Genealogist's Guide,* chapter four.

Summary of Known Facts in DNA Sources

Review your DNA matches diagram. Which matches are relevant to the objective? You may want to include an image of your diagram in this section of the research plan. In the beginning phases of a project incorporating DNA evidence, you may not have much starting point DNA information, but you can still discuss the test takers and databases you have selected. For example, in a project to discover Barsheba Tharp's parents:

> Barsheba Tharp's 2nd great grandson, Robert, has taken an autosomal DNA test at Ancestry and transferred it to MyHeritage and Family Tree DNA. Many of his matches who descend from Barsheba Tharp and John Robert Dyer have been identified.

You may want to discuss how the base test takers and known relevant matches descend from the research subject. You can also include a table showing how your base test takers share DNA with each other in expected amounts or how the base test takers share with other descendants of the research subject in expected amounts. For an example of this, see table 9.1.

For research phases building on past DNA research, you may have additional known information like a relevant shared match cluster or a DNA match whose tree contains an ancestor of interest. You might also include shared matches, ethnicity, the ethnicity of matches, clustering results, or segment information. For example:

> A network graph was created for Robert Dyer and his two brothers with their AncestryDNA matches by ConnectedDNA. The graph shows a pink cluster, #12, that includes known descendants of Barsheba Tharp and John Robert Dyer. The closely connected blue cluster, #3, is known to include matches to John Robert Dyer's probable mother, Sarah Taylor. Clusters 0 and 16 are closer Dyer matches. The MRCA for the other clusters connected to cluster 12 is unknown: clusters 10, 17, 27, 1, 8, 23, 26. Matches in these clusters could be relevant to the objective.

Table 9.1. DNA Matches of Robert who Descend from Barsheba Tharp

Match Name	Relationship to Robert	Shared DNA	Shared cM Project 4.0 relationship range and average[a]
Julia	3C	28 cM[b]	0–234 cM, average 73 cM
Sarah	3C1R	60 c[c]	0–192 cM, average 48 cM
Roy	Half 2C	268 cM[d]	10–325 cM, average 120 cM

a. Blaine T. Bettinger and Jonny Perl, "The Shared cM Project 4.0 tool v4," *DNA Painter* (https://dnapainter.com/tools/sharedcmv4.)

b. *AncestryDNA*, DNA match between Robert and Julia, sharing 28 cM (https://ancestry.com).

c. *AncestryDNA*, DNA match between Robert and Sarah, sharing 60 cM (https://ancestry.com).

d. *AncestryDNA*, DNA match between Robert and Roy, sharing 268 cM (https://ancestry.com).

The Barsheba Tharp case was an objective for finding the parents of the tester's 3rd great grandmother. Below are three additional examples of known facts for objectives common in autosomal DNA research.

Unknown Match Objective: How are DNA matches Carlene and Jonah related? Carlene and Jonah share 576 cM of DNA. The known facts include:

- Jonah and Carlene share 576 cM at AncestryDNA
- Carlene's ethnicity is 50% Swedish and 50% British Isles
- Carlene's four grandparents' surnames are Peterson, Johannsson, Campbell, and Cox.

Unknown Parent Objective: Maria was adopted and was able to locate her birth mother. She is now seeking her biological father through DNA research. The known facts include:

- Maria's maternal cousin Jose is a match at AncestryDNA and shares 1,052 cM.
- The shared matches between Maria and Jose can be eliminated from consideration because they are likely only related on Maria's maternal side.
- The closest non-maternal matches (likely paternal) include Harrison, 789 cM, and Josefa, 306 cM.

Unknown Ancestor Objective, initial phase: Who was one of the biological parents of Jamil's 2nd-great-grandfather Moses Roberts? Known facts include:

- Jamil, his sister, and his brother share the expected amount of DNA for full siblings. They are the base testers.
- Twelve DNA matches to the base testers descend from Moses Roberts and are shown in a diagram. A table shows that they shared the expected amounts of DNA for the traced relationship.

Unknown Ancestor Objective, later phase: Was Jemima Jones the mother of Moses Roberts? Known facts include:

- Jamil, his sister, and brother triangulate with other descendants of Moses Roberts on Chromosome 2, from 4.8m to 45.4m, a 59.8 cM segment.
- Fifteen DNA matches who descend from Jemima Jones share DNA on chromosome 2 on overlapping parts of the segment that was mapped to Moses Roberts.

Additional facts that might be known at the start of a new phase of research include confirmation of a genetic relationship to a grandparent, great-grandparent, second-great-grandparents, and so forth back to the research subject. This is recommended before embarking on a research project to identify ancestors that are more than four generations removed from the test taker since shared cM amounts at this level include many possible relationships. Also, the probability of being related in more than one way increases the further back in time you research. Beginning with genetic confirmation for each generation back to the research subject provides a strong foundation for the project. It also helps narrow the list of DNA matches being considered by focusing on shared matches of identified descendants of the research subject.

Mitochondrial DNA

When creating a research plan where mtDNA is being used, the known facts will be a little different than the known facts from autosomal DNA. They may include the man or woman's name who was tested, the type of sequencing, mutations, haplogroup, names of matches, the genetic distance of match, and a match's most distant matrilineal ancestor. For example:

Mitochondrial Full Sequencing was done for Barbara at Family Tree DNA. She has 228 matches. None of the matches are a genetic distance of 0, but 98 matches are a genetic distance of 1. Her haplogroup is H3b-G6129A. The H branch is found mainly in Western Europe.

Mitochondrial DNA is more effective when used to compare two descendants who could share a common matrilineal ancestor. The known facts for this type of project in a phase to find relevant test takers might say:

> Mitochondrial Full Sequencing was ordered at Family Tree DNA for Deanna, a matrilineal descendant of Barsheba Tharp. The results have not been returned yet. Barsheba Tharp's hypothesized mother is Judy Vernon. One matrilineal descendant of Judy Vernon has already refused DNA testing. Judy Vernon had several daughters who could have living matrilineal descendants.

Y-DNA

Known facts at the start of a project using Y-DNA may include the name of the man whose Y-DNA was tested, which Y-DNA test was taken, haplogroup, names of matches, genetic distance, most distant patrilineal ancestor of matches, tested individuals also descended from the most distant proposed ancestor, surname project groupings, and so forth. For example:

> Y-37 test results for Robert Dyer include no matches with the surname Dyer. The closest matches are a genetic distance of 2, and the surnames are Young, Kennedy, and Meenagh. The predicted haplogroup for Robert is R-M269. Robert Dyer is participating in the Dyer surname project at Family Tree DNA and his results are in the "ungrouped" section. There are 288 total members in the Dyer Surname Project and 18 Y-DNA Subgroups. Robert is also participating in the R L513 and Subclades project and is grouped with several Nicholsons who are all estimated to be in the R-M269 haplogroup.

Working Hypothesis

After creating a list of known facts, the next step is to propose a theory that will help you decide which sources to examine. What is the current hypothesis you want to test by gathering relevant data?

Research Phases and Hypothesis Development

Initial phases of documentary research may not have specific hypotheses with names of people to test, just a theoretical profile of a person—i.e., the mother of John was probably born 1762–1800 in North Carolina and married about 1812 to a Dyer in Tennessee.

In a later phase of research, you may have the names of a couple who you are testing whether they could be the parents. Your hypothesis would be more specific and include dates and places of migration, places where the child might have been born, and circumstances that could explain conflicting information or situations. i.e., If Sarah Taylor had a child after her husband died, there may be a guardianship record in the courts showing that her brother was appointed guardian.

Deduction

If you have no actual person named in your hypothesis, you can use deduction and logic to create a rough hypothesis. For example:

> Who were Jacob Huffmaster's parents? He was born in 1812 in North Carolina. Jacob stated in a pension application that he was born in Craven County. He gave several of his children the middle name of Miller, which isn't a surname from his wife's side of the family. Search for a Miller—Huffmaster marriage before 1812 in Craven County, North Carolina.

This rough hypothesis helps you know where to look. You don't need to know exactly what happened, but an educated guess can help you get to more concrete hypotheses.

To incorporate DNA into your hypothesis, you can utilize the same method of deduction and logic to create a working hypothesis. Start with one of your DNA known facts, then make an inference based on the clues and shared cM project data. For example, if you're searching for the parents of your 2nd-great-grandfather:

> DNA matches who descend from my known 2nd-great-grandfather are 3rd cousins and share between 0–234 cM. DNA matches who descend from his unknown parents will be 4th cousins and share between 0–139 cM. If the unknown parents had additional spouses, cousins descending from them could be half 4th cousins, sharing between 0–74 cM. Other matches who descend from the unknown parents but are one generation closer could be 3rd cousins once removed, sharing between 0–192 cM, or one generation further, 4th cousins once removed, sharing between 0–126 cM.[7]

Writing this hypothesis makes it clear that you need to look for matches in the range of 0–192 cM to find the unknown parents of your 2nd great grandfather.

---

7. Blaine T. Bettinger, "The Shared cM Project Version 4.0 (March 2020)," PDF, *The Genetic Genealogist* (https://thegeneticgenealogist.com/wp-content/uploads/2020/03/Shared-cM-Project-Version-4.pdf).

Methods

You can create DNA hypotheses based on a method. Examine what you could discover by doing certain tasks. Here are some ideas:

- **Clusters:** Who was the father of John Robert Dyer? The known facts section includes a network graph, and you have identified cluster #12 as the descendants of John Robert Dyer (figure 9.1). You can hypothesize that the closely connected cluster #3 is a group whose MRCA couple is John Robert Dyer's parents. This leads to a search of the pedigrees of everyone in cluster 3 to look for a couple where their pedigrees all intersect.
- **Segments:** Who was Barsheba Tharps' father? One of the known facts is that Barsheba's descendants inherited a specific segment of DNA on chromosome 5. The working hypothesis is that others who share this segment with you will also be able to trace their pedigree to Barsheba Tharp or one of her ancestors. This leads you to search for others sharing in the same region at 23andMe, MyHeritage, Family Tree DNA, and GEDmatch.
- **mtDN:** Who was the mother of Johanna Elizabeth Korsgard, my 5th great grandmother? One of your known facts is an mtDNA match named Payton who matches your full sequence mtDNA test at a genetic distance of 0. You hypothesize that Payton's most distant matrilineal ancestor, her 9th great-grandmother, was an ancestor of Johanna Elizabeth. This leads you to trace the matrilineal descendants of Payton's 9th great-grandmother.

Theory Generators

As discussed in chapters three and four, you may want to use a "theory generator" to help you find an objective or hypothesis to test. MyHeritage DNA has a tool called The Theory of Family Relativity. It suggests ways that you could be related to DNA matches.

AncestryDNA ThruLines creates a similar suggestion. You receive a group of DNA matches who may be descended from the same common ancestor. Some ancestors will have dotted lines around them, meaning they are a proposed ancestor who is not yet in your tree. These are hypotheses that you can use in your research plan. Your research will then focus on accepting or rejecting the hypothesis. Before choosing one of these computer-generated hypotheses, follow the suggestions in chapter three to evaluate the ThruLines hypothesis.

Confirmation Bias

If you have found the name of a hypothesized parent to test with records, beware of confirmation bias. Our brains naturally like to look for evidence that confirms our beliefs. For

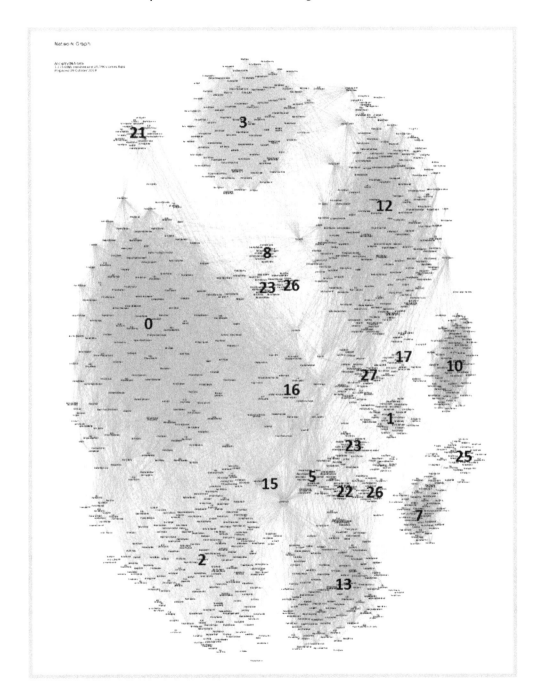

Figure 9.1. Network Graph for Dyer descendants.

Created by Shelley Crawford of ConnectedDNA, annotated.

example, you have a hypothesis that your fourth-great-grandparent, Emmanuel Powell, was the son of Hezekiah Powell. You search your DNA match list for the surname Powell and find a DNA match who descends from Hezekiah Powell. You decide that your hypothesis is right and add Hezekiah to your tree. Instead of analyzing the match with clustering, performing a pedigree analysis, reviewing documentary research, and comparing additional test takers to the matches, you have allowed one piece of evidence to confirm your bias.

It's difficult to stop our brain from looking only for evidence that supports our theory, but if we are aware of the possibility of confirmation bias, we will try harder to be unbiased. One way to avoid confirmation bias is to work as hard to disprove your hypothesis as you do to prove it.[8]

To combat confirmation bias in the example above, try to disprove the hypothesis that the common ancestor between you and the match is Hezekiah Powell by doing a pedigree analysis. The pedigree analysis might reveal that the match's tree is missing 50% of the possible ancestors at the 4th great grandparent level, due to missing maternal grandparents. You'll need to contact him for more information about his tree before you can use it as evidence. Shared matches and cluster analysis may also help. You may also find that the match is in a cluster which includes descendants from an ancestral couple on the opposite side of your pedigree, not descendants of Emmanuel Powell.

Identify Sources and Methods

Now that you have a hypothesis to test, what sources can provide data to confirm or reject it? What methods will you use to test the hypothesis? The next step of the research plan is to brainstorm a list of sources to search and methods to use. Later, you will prioritize your list and select the most useful options. Prioritizing which sources and methods to use works best if you have some experience trying various record groups, source types, methods, DNA tools, and strategies. You may need to try a new strategy that you don't have much experience with. If you have completed the suggestion to practice using DNA tools in chapter eight, hopefully, you will have several new tools to try. The locality guide, discussed in chapter seven, is also an integral step for identifying the most relevant documentary sources to examine.

---

8. Karen Stanbary, "Research Strategies and Decision Making," *Course 11: Meeting Standards Using DNA Evidence - Research Strategies*, 2020 Syllabus, Salt Lake Institute of Genealogy (Salt Lake: SLIG, 2020), 25.

Brainstorming a list of possible sources and methods helps get the juices flowing and takes the pressure off deciding what will be most efficient. You can decide that later—this step is all about listing the possibilities.

Documentary Sources and Methods

First, consider which documentary sources and methods could be applied. All phases of research in a DNA project will include documentary sources. The clues gained from DNA test results will lead us to people that need to be identified in their specific time and place. You can incorporate previously reviewed sources that you would like to examine again, new sources that you haven't consulted yet, and genealogical methods.

Review Previously Viewed Sources

We typically think of research plans as lists of new sources to consult. However, your plan might include sources you or others have already reviewed in order to gather more data. For example, you have an abstract of a deed, and you want to view the original. Perhaps a cousin wrote a family history, and it includes source citations that you want to verify. You might want to review the 1830 census and transcribe the names of the neighbors of your research subject two pages before and two pages after his entry.

Reviewing a set of records with a different focus is another way to revisit previously viewed records. Perhaps you initially looked for records dealing directly with your ancestor, and now you are looking for records where he is identified as a witness. For example, you could revisit parish registers, deeds, probate records, etc. Perhaps you previously searched the census for a specific family, and now you want to search it for individuals with the same surname, neighbors who were in the same area, and so forth.

Consult New Sources

New sources to consult include unexamined sources that have the potential to answer your research question. If you are searching for the children of Robert Daugherty, who was married in 1784 in Craven County, North Carolina, and died in 1844 in Warren County, Kentucky, you will list sources to search from both of those localities in the years 1784–1844. Your list should include specific record collections that might name his children and include the years that those sources cover. This helps you focus on just those sources that could actually answer the research question. The list for Warren County might look like this:

Marriage
- Bell, Annie W. B. *Record of Marriages in Warren County, Kentucky for the Period of Years 1796 to 1851 Inclusive.* Salt Lake City, Utah: Filmed by the Genealogical Society of Utah, 1971.

▧ Thomas, Helen Smith. *Warren County, Kentucky Marriages, 1797–1851: From the Original Marriage Bonds and Consents* Mrs. W. L. Rabold, 1970.

▧ Warren County, Kentucky. Marriage records, 1797–1897. *FamilySearch.* https://www.familysearch.org/search/catalog/294085.

Land

▧ Murray, Joyce Martin. *Deed Abstracts of Warren County, Kentucky, 1797–1812.* J.M. Murray, 1985.

▧ Andesite Press. *Warren County, Kentucky Deeds, Books A-C, 1797–1807.* Andesite Press, 2015.

Probate

▧ Bell, Annie Walker Burns. *Record of Abstracts of Wills in Warren County, Kentucky.* Seat Pleasant, Maryland: A.W.B. Bell, 1936. https://www.familysearch.org/library/ books/records/item/41383-record-of-abstracts-of-wills-in-warren-county-kentucky.

▧ King, June Estelle. *Early Kentucky Wills and Inventories, 1780–1842.* Southern Historical Press, Inc., 1933.

Genealogical Methods

Beyond sources to consult, your brainstorm can include methods or strategies to use. Some traditional methods used by genealogists include:

▧ Friends, family, associates, and neighbors analysis
▧ Census record analysis and correlation
▧ Tracing the ownership of land
▧ Tax records study
▧ Surname survey
▧ Military record and pension analysis and correlation

DNA Sources and Methods

Like documentary research, our brainstormed list of sources and methods can include sources of DNA information we have already reviewed, new sources of DNA information, and methods.

Review Matches from a Previous Test Taker

Most of the time you will be reviewing matches from a person who has already taken a DNA test. You may want to dive in deeper to find more matches that relate to your objective. Or you might be a match to a person whose results would help answer your research question. To review their data, you can ask them for permission to view their DNA test results. Often test takers at Ancestry will be willing to share their results with you as a viewer using the "share DNA results" feature.[9]

Another way to review the DNA test results of people who have already tested is to ask them to transfer to GEDmatch, where you can use their kit number to find their matches in the one-to-many utility and other comparison tools. Planning in advance to ask significant matches to transfer to GEDmatch can help you meet genealogy standard 54, which requires sufficient verifiable data.[10] This means that others who read our proof argument can go to GEDmatch and see for themselves that the data we are using is valid.

You may also want to ask DNA matches to transfer to a different website that offers more data or different matches. Many researchers have been successful in asking DNA matches to transfer to MyHeritage and Family Tree DNA, the two main companies who accept raw autosomal DNA uploads. While both companies offer chromosome browsers, only MyHeritage offers information on true triangulation.

Targeting New Test Takers

If the test takers who have already tested are not showing enough relevant matches to answer your research question, you may need to employ targeted testing. Your plan may include the task to find relevant descendants of the research subject and ask them to take a DNA test.

When creating a targeted testing plan, consider the test types and their limitations discussed in chapter one. You should also consider testing companies' strengths and weaknesses, database sizes, and types of users who typically test at a certain company (i.e., More Europeans test at MyHeritage DNA).

Standard 51 reminds us to target new test takers based on their DNA's potential to answer a genealogical research question.[11] Considerations for choosing individuals to test include:

- **Evidence independence:** consider selecting testers who descend from the hypothesized ancestor through unique lines.[12]

9. "Sharing AncestryDNA Results," *Ancestry Support* (https://support.ancestry.com/s/article/Sharing-AncestryDNA-Results).

10. BCG, *Genealogy Standards* 2nd ed., 31.

11. BCG, *Genealogy Standards* 2nd ed., 29–30.

12. BCG, *Genealogy Standards* 2nd ed., 27.

- **Types of DNA tests:** consider selecting testers who descend from the hypothesized ancestor through X-DNA, mtDNA, and Y-DNA inheritance paths.[13]
- *Ruling out irrelevant lines:* select testers for their ability to rule out unrelated lines and narrow down the matches.[14]
- **Adequate number of testers:** select enough testers to gather a body of evidence and rule out competing hypotheses.[15]

How do you know if you have an adequate number of testers? Determining the coverage of an ancestor's DNA in a particular database (like Ancestry or 23andMe) can help you determine when to stop testing additional relatives.[16] The more descendants who are tested from independent lines of descent from your research subject, especially those generationally closer to a research subject, the more coverage will be achieved. After you reach a certain number of testers, testing additional descendants of a research subject brings diminishing returns.[17] Paul Woodbury recommends testing additional relatives if the expected increase in coverage will be greater than 1–2%. His coverage formulas can be found online at the *Legacy Tree Genealogists* blog.[18]

If your DNA research project is on a line that has pedigree collapse or endogamy, your testing strategy should strive for maximum coverage of the research subject to help with filtering relevant matches and mapping segments to ancestors.[19] Finding potential testers who descend from a genetic pioneer, defined as a person who married outside the endogamous population, has been found to be an effective strategy for isolating which parent the shared DNA came from.[20]

I found this strategy to be effective when working on a branch of my family where two brothers from the Frazier family married two sisters from the Briscoe family. Many

---

13. BCG, *Genealogy Standards* 2nd ed., 29–30.

14. BCG, *Genealogy Standards* 2nd ed., 25.

15. BCG, *Genealogy Standards* 2nd ed., 31.

16. Paul Woodbury, "Covering Your Bases: Introduction to Autosomal DNA Coverage," blog post, *Legacy Tree Genealogists* (https://www.legacytree.com/blog/introduction-autosomal-dna-coverage).

17. Woodbury, "Covering Your Bases: Introduction to Autosomal DNA Coverage."

18. Woodbury, "Covering Your Bases: Introduction to Autosomal DNA Coverage."

19. Kimberly Powell, "The Challenge of Endogamy and Pedigree Collapse," Debbie Parker Wayne, ed., *Advanced Genetic Genealogy: Techniques and Case Studies* (Cushing, Texas: Wayne Research, 2019), 138.

20. Paul Woodbury, "Dealing with Endogamy," 14 October 2020, *Legacy Family Tree Webinars* (https://familytreewebinars.com/download.php?webinar_id=1292).

of Diana's DNA matches, who are descendants of Richard Frazier and Nancy Briscoe, her 2nd great grandparents, were double cousins. They had two common ancestral couples—Richard's parents and Nancy's parents. Diana's network graph showed a large cluster for all the Frazier and Briscoe matches, which did not separate into distinct clusters. This made it difficult to find matches who related to the unknown ancestor in my objective—Nancy's grandmother.

Eventually, I found a descendant of one of Nancy Briscoe's siblings in the AncestryDNA database whose descendants had not intermarried with the Fraziers. I messaged the match and asked him to share his match list, which he did. In addition to being descended from a genetic pioneer of sorts, he was one generation closer to the research subject. His network graph was not affected by the multiple relationships of the Briscoes and Fraziers, and I was able to find a distinct cluster of Briscoe matches to focus on.

Another discussion of targeted testing is found in chapter six, Analyze Your Sources. As you progress through additional phases of research and need to eliminate competing hypotheses, you may undertake multiple targeted testing plans.

Methods for DNA Analysis

After planning to review previous test takers' results or test new people, you can then decide what methods you will use to analyze the DNA test results. The tools discussed in chapter eight can give ideas for how to accomplish your analysis. Below is a list of methods commonly used for DNA analysis:

Autosomal DNA
- Ethnicity analysis
- Comparing multiple DNA kits with each other
- Collaboration
  - Asking matches for family tree information
  - Asking matches to transfer to additional databases
  - Acquiring permission to view others' test results
  - Inviting matches to take additional tests
- Create genetic networks
  - Shared matches and in common with lists
  - Leeds Method
  - Automated clustering
  - Network graphs
- Review statistics and probabilities
  - Diagramming relationships and comparing with Shared cM Project data
  - What are the Odds

- Compare segment data
  - Evaluation of segments
  - Segment triangulation
  - Chromosome mapping
  - Deductive chromosome mapping
  - X chromosome matches
  - Visual phasing
  - Coverage analysis and reconstruction of an ancestor's genome[21]

Y Chromosomal DNA

- Studying the haplogroup
- Evaluating genetic distance and earliest ancestors of matches
- Studying STR markers and mutation rates
- Building mutation history trees[22]
- SNP analysis
- Comparing the location of a match on the Y-DNA haplotree
- Analyzing surname project groupings
- Joining Y-DNA projects
- Family Tree DNA advanced matching—comparing Family Finder and Y-DNA results

Mitochondrial DNA

- Studying the haplogroup
- Evaluating genetic distance and earliest ancestors of matches
- Analyzing mutations and heteroplasmy
- Joining mtDNA projects
- Family Tree DNA advanced matching—comparing Family Finder and mtDNA results

---

21. Coverage and the reconstruction of ancestral genomes refers to Paul Woodbury's strategy of identifying unique segments shared between descendants of a research subject and key matches and comparing those genomes to matches to estimate the relationship. See Woodbury, "Covering Your Bases: Introduction to Autosomal DNA Coverage," para. 13.

22. For a discussion of how this is done, see Maurice Gleeson, "Building a Mutation History Tree with STR Data," blog post, 13 August 2015, *The Gleason/Gleeson DNA Project* (https://gleesondna.blogspot.com/2015/08/building-mutation-history-tree-with-str.html).

Methods that combine both DNA and traditional sources
- Building pedigrees for DNA matches
- Searching published trees to extend small trees of DNA matches
- Verifying pedigrees of DNA matches
- Pedigree triangulation among matches in the same cluster
- Identifying a time and place for a child's conception
- Descendancy research to locate candidates to target test
- Ancestral research to expand the hypothesized ancestor's pedigree
- Pedigree evaluation of DNA matches
- Surname searches in matches' trees
- Investigating Ancestry ThruLines or MyHeritage Theories of Relativity

Our research plans should include methods that help us meet standard 52 in *Genealogy Standards* about analyzing DNA test results.[23] This includes analyzing the tree completeness of DNA matches and keeping our minds open to the possibility of more than one MRCA couple between the tester and their matches. To meet this standard, we may want to add tree building and pedigree evaluation to our list of methods.

More in-depth discussion of tools that assist with DNA analysis methods can be found on our website at https://familylocket.com/rlpdna.

Prioritize Your Research Strategy

After creating a list of all the possible sources and methods you could use, the next step is to select just the most beneficial strategies and arrange them in a logical order. You may have a very long list of sources and methods. Which sources will be most efficient in answering your research objective? What is the next logical step after reviewing your starting point? Standard 15 recommends examining resources in an efficient sequence.[24]

In addition to considering what is most relevant and efficient, you can also take into account accessibility, cost, distance, and time. Some unindexed sources may take hours to search. If there is an indexed source that might also answer the question, it makes sense to search that first.

You need not jump straight to more time-consuming and expensive options unless you've already exhausted the avenues currently available to you. If you have not examined

---

23. BCG, *Genealogy Standards* 2nd ed., 30.

24. BCG, *Genealogy Standards* 2nd ed., 13.

the relevant genetic network and tried finding the pedigree intersection of that network, you probably don't need to work on chromosome mapping yet. The DNA bell curve in chapter eight helps decide which tools and strategies to use next. Start with the easier tools toward the left, then work with networks, and finally work with the advanced methods like segments, chromosome mapping, and visual phasing.

Although our list of possible sources and methods is long, the prioritized strategy should be short. Perhaps you will find a compelling clue in the first two sources you check, and that leads you down a different path. If you had planned ten sources to search, now that time spent was unnecessary.

You may want to separate your prioritized research strategy into two sections—documentary sources and your DNA sources and methods. Each project is different and will require different research plans. Don't overlook planning to research in the records! Often when an objective focuses on finding parents in the early 1800s, documentary records are paramount in uncovering the answer. At some point in your research, you will want to include sources that can provide historical, geographic, and legal context.

Below is an example of a prioritized research strategy for the objective of finding the parents of Barsheba Tharp, who was born in about 1813–1818 in Tennessee:

Traditional Genealogy Sources

1. Conejos County, Colorado death record for Barsheba (Tharp) Dyer: contact the county clerk to see if a death record was created when Barsheba died in 1889. This may contain the names of her parents and age at death and/or birthdate.
2. "Tennessee, Early Tax List Records, 1783-1895," *Ancestry*—search for Tharps; census records for Hawkins Co. aren't extant prior to 1830; state tax records can provide clues.
3. "Marriages (Hawkins County, Tennessee), 1820-1964," *FamilySearch*—Marriage records of Tharp children who could be siblings to Barsheba—not many prior to the 1860s extant.
4. 1850 Census for Lewis Tharp—find his children's names.
5. "Washington Co., Arkansas—Probate records, 1829-1931," *FamilySearch* - Wills and probate for Lewis Tharp; probably not extant—Washington County has record loss from a courthouse fire.

DNA Methods

- *Network graph analysis.* Use the ConnectedDNA network graph to identify common ancestors for the clusters surrounding cluster 12 to see if any of them are Tharp clusters

- *Pedigree triangulation.* Find the MRCA of matches in relevant clusters through research in published family trees to extend match's small trees; matches who share over 50 cM—build their tree in the Dyer Ancestry tree as a floating branch until the connection is found

What happens to the list of identified sources and methods if you are only prioritizing a few of them? If you do not find the answer in the resources you have prioritized, you can come back to your list of sources and choose the next steps. Research plans are flexible. What you find in the first search may dictate that you go in another direction than initially planned.

Learn About New Tools

In genetic genealogy, new tools and methods are being developed frequently. The more we try these tools and understand how they might apply to our research problems, the better we will be able to use them to our advantage. Our research plans will help us advance only when we can think of new methods beyond what we've always done in the past. Remember, tools are a means to an end. The goal is to use tools in order to solve family history problems rather than to use the tool for the sake of using the tool. Use the DNA tools that help you achieve your goals, and don't feel obligated to use a tool that doesn't fit with your case.

Your Task

It's time for you to make your own research plan. Use our Research Project Document template to set up your summary of known facts in documentary and DNA sources, working hypothesis, list of sources and methods, and prioritized strategy. Consider whether targeted testing should be considered. Choose sources and methods that will help answer your research question.

CHAPTER 10

Research Logs and Writing As You Go

Nicole Dyer

When working on a case involving DNA test results, it may feel like you look at hundreds of DNA match pages, reports, family trees, and shared match lists when you research. Maybe you record some of the sources you consult but can't remember where you saw that one piece of information or that one interesting DNA match. Do you want a better way to keep track of all the sources you consult in a DNA research project? It's time to take your research log to the next level and keep track of all the matches, trees, sources, and DNA tools you review.

What is a Research Log?

A traditional genealogy research log is used to track sources searched, results found, and include information to get to those sources again—call numbers, repositories, URLs, source citations, and document numbers.

Genealogists keep track of where they looked for information in their research log and whether they found anything. If you look in a source and don't find the information you were seeking, note the negative search in your log. This practice helps you avoid repeating searches. The entries in your research log are a reminder of where you left off and provide a convenient starting point for the next research session.

As you incorporate DNA sources into your research, you introduce a substantial amount of data. It is critical to the success of your research to keep track of all the DNA sources consulted in your research log. Logging the results of your searches helps you make connections between information items by putting them all in one place.

Many of the DNA matches researchers review do not yield a discovery of the most recent common ancestor immediately. Just like negative searches in a census database, we note the negative results of viewing a DNA match page when nothing is discovered. Eventually, we may need to return to this DNA match and dig deeper to determine the connection. Noting all clues from the DNA match, like surnames, shared matches, and common locations in the family tree, could prove useful in the future if captured in your log. Without a research log, you will probably forget the information you viewed, and it won't be available to you to correlate and form conclusions.

One of the distinctive and helpful elements of a research log is the URL for records and reports online. Recording the URL allows you to quickly return to the webpage where the record or negative search results were found. Even if you include a URL in a report's citation, it will usually be a shortened version of the URL. Having the full URL in the research log is beneficial for quickly returning to the record and person of interest on the record.

Tools for Creating Research Logs

There are many tech tools out there that can be used for keeping a research log. Tools that allow you to set up a table or spreadsheet are good. A tool with the ability to sort data and manage multiple tables is better. Tools that can link records between tables to minimize duplicate data entry are even better. This means you will, at minimum, want to use a spreadsheet, but a database tool is best.

Spreadsheet Programs

Spreadsheets like Excel and Google Sheets are go-to programs for research logs. You can enter your data in rows and columns, sort the data, add URLs to cells, and format them in many ways. Excel has more data-sorting and formatting options than Google Sheets, but Google Sheets is unparalleled in its collaboration features. If you are working closely with another researcher, you may want to consider Google Sheets.

Database Programs

To reduce duplicate data entry and keep track of multiple data points described in several ways, consider using a relational database tool. A relational database "is a type of database

Table 10.1. Customers and Orders

First Name	Last Name	Address	Phone	Date	Item	Amount
Joan	Carter	185 Center St.	596-2049	6/1/2019	Blue Skirt #12	$45
Lewis	Mann	300 5th Ave.	596-3014	6/2/2019	Red Shirt #2	$15
Joseph	Johnson	425 4th St.	596-3068	6/2/2019	Brown Belt	$20
Joan	Carter	186 Center St.	596-2049	6/15/2019	Yellow Shirt	$18
Joan	Carter	185 Center St.	596-2049	7/1/2019	Black Pants	$55

that stores and provides access to data points that are related to one another."[1] Data points are represented in tables. The rows in the tables can be linked to fields in other tables that describe the data point in a different way.

Imagine you are an online clothing retailer. You want to keep track of each order. You create a single table to track the information. See table 10.1.

The table helps keep track of each order but requires more time than necessary for data entry. It also takes up more space than is needed. Each time Joan makes a new order, you will have to re-enter her contact information. If you make a mistake entering her address, how will you know which one is correct? If her phone number changes, you will have to find each order and update them all.

The solution is to divide the information into multiple tables and not have duplicate locations for the same information. Instead of having one table, like the Customers and Orders table above, you can split the information into two tables—Customer Information and Order Information, as shown in table 10.2.

Keeping information in separate tables is called normalizing our data—"dividing the information into tables with the goal of having a place for everything, and everything in its place."[2]

---

1. "What is a Relational Database?" *Oracle* (https://www.oracle.com/database/what-is-a-relational-database/ : accessed 30 May 2020).

2. "Relational Database Concepts for Beginners," *Wofford College* (https://webs.wofford.edu/whisnantdm/courses/cs101/pdf/database/Relational_database_concepts.pdf : accessed 1 June 2020).

Table 10.2. Example of Normalized Data

Customer Information Table

Customer ID	First Name	Last Name	Address	Phone
504	Joan	Carter	185 Center St.	596-2049
505	Lewis	Mann	300 5th Ave.	596-3014
506	Joseph	Johnson	425 4th St.	596-3068

Order Information Table

Order ID	Customer ID	Date	Item	Amount
32	504	6/1/2019	Blue Skirt #12	$45
33	505	6/2/2019	Red Shirt #2	$15
34	506	6/2/2019	Brown Belt	$20
35	504	6/15/2019	Yellow Shirt	$18
36	504	7/1/2019	Black Pants	$55

Relational databases are useful for organizing data points in genetic genealogy as well: test takers, kit access, match information, correspondence, and research to find the common ancestor are all useful details to track in a DNA project database. You may also want to set up a table for segment information, surnames, and other data associated with the genetic cousins you are analyzing.

Airtable

Though many database options exist, Airtable is our favorite tool. It is user-friendly and easy to learn when compared with more advanced database tools that require knowledge of programming.

Airtable (https://airtable.com) is a web-based spreadsheet and database program that allows you to create links between tables, view your data in flexible ways, sort and group data, and create unique field types. In Airtable, a spreadsheet is called a base, and pages/sheets within the base are called tables. Within each table, rows are called records, and columns are called fields.

One of Airtable's most powerful tools for visualizing your research is the ability to group the rows in a table by a certain field. When I keep track of all the research I've done for each DNA match to build their tree and find the MRCA, my research log table can become lengthy. Grouping my research log table by the DNA match field allows me to see all the searches I've done on that person's family tree in a mini-research log within the main log.

Another useful feature of Airtable is the ability to create custom field types like long text, numbers, dates, multiple select, checkboxes, and attachments. I like using the checkbox feature to help me remember to follow the steps of my protocol for reviewing a significant DNA match. After I've figured out the MRCA, I add them to my Lucidchart diagram. I have a checkbox field in my DNA match table to remind me to do that. If I add a match from a company that provides segment data, I paint the DNA match with DNA Painter. To remind me to do that, I have a checkbox field in my segment data table labeled "DNA Painter."

The segment data table is formatted similarly to the spreadsheet you can download from DNA companies. It includes the name of the match, the chromosome number, start location, end location, shared cM, and SNPs. After copying and pasting segment information from various matches, the segment table can be grouped by chromosome, then sorted by start point. That way, the table becomes like a chromosome map. If you are comparing shared segments between multiple testers whose kits you manage, you can group the segments table by the tester. This shows you all the shared segments for one tester.

To view ideas for what tables and fields to include in an Airtable base, you can find my Airtable DNA templates online. Go to my page in the Airtable Universe (https://airtable.com/universe) by searching for Nicole Dyer. There you can copy my RLP with DNA bases to your own account and begin using them for your DNA research projects. Find more help with using Airtable for a DNA research log at https://familylocket.com/rlpdna.

Adding DNA Sources to a Research Log

There are many things you might want to track in your DNA research log: test takers, genetic cousins, match details, correspondence, segment data, locations, surnames, a log of tools used, and more. Tracking these in separate pages of a spreadsheet or database tool can help you stay organized. Figure 10.1 shows an Airtable base with several tables shown as tabs across the top.

People
People who test their DNA are key elements of a DNA research log. You will want to have a separate sheet in your log for keeping track of people, their trees, their contact info, and other pertinent data. You don't need to add all your matches, only the testers, and matches

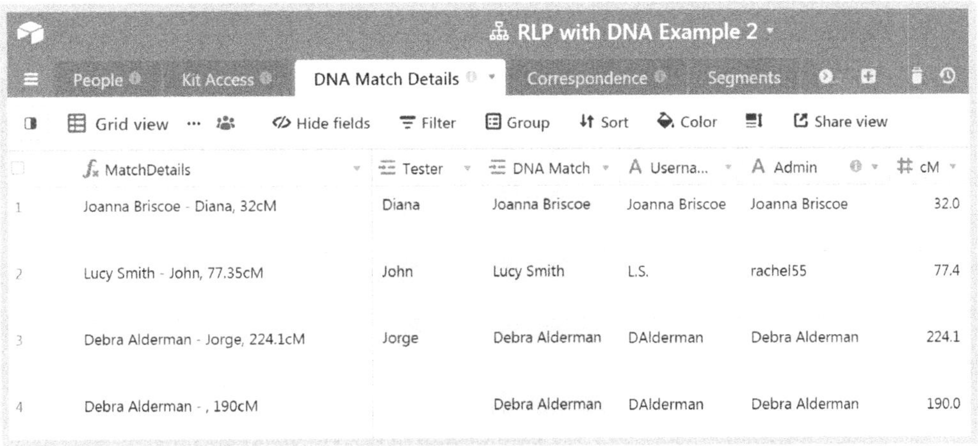

	MatchDetails	Tester	DNA Match	Userna...	Admin	cM
1	Joanna Briscoe - Diana, 32cM	Diana	Joanna Briscoe	Joanna Briscoe	Joanna Briscoe	32.0
2	Lucy Smith - John, 77.35cM	John	Lucy Smith	L.S.	rachel55	77.4
3	Debra Alderman - Jorge, 224.1cM	Jorge	Debra Alderman	DAlderman	Debra Alderman	224.1
4	Debra Alderman - , 190cM		Debra Alderman	DAlderman	Debra Alderman	190.0

Figure 10.1. Airtable base showing DNA match details table

relevant to your current project. Some genetic genealogists keep spreadsheets with all the matches for a particular tester. Instead, we recommend that you create a separate research log for each project or objective. Then, when adding matches to your log, you only need to include the matches that are relevant to the project at hand. To include all the matches in a match list would obscure the information you're trying to draw out.

When performing research for a client, I typically create a new research log for each project. If the client renews and wants to continue researching the same objective, I continue with the same log. Keeping the research log limited to a focused objective helps keep the size of the log manageable.

Here are possible column headers to use when logging people involved in a project:

- **Name:** name of the person who has tested their DNA or is relevant to the project in some other way
- **Role:** role the person plays in the project—typically either one of your base testers (who has shared their DNA results with you) or a DNA match to one of the base testers
- **Link to profile page:** link to the person's profile page at the testing company, if applicable
- **Link to family tree:** URL for the person's main family tree
- **GEDmatch kit number:** kit number for those who have uploaded to GEDmatch
- **Locations:** geographic places in an unknown match's tree that could help find the MRCA

- **Surnames:** surnames in an unknown match's tree that could help find the MRCA
- **Residence:** the person's place of residence
- **Age:** age of the person—could be useful in determining their generation
- **Email address:** email address for the person
- **Link to Facebook profile:** link to a person's Facebook profile page
- **Phone number:** the person's phone number
- **Address:** the person's address
- **Notes:** any notes about the person that could be helpful
- **Ethnicity information:** relevant information from the individual's ethnicity estimate
- **mtDNA haplogroup:** the mitochondrial DNA haplogroup, if they have taken a test at 23andMe, LivingDNA, or Family Tree DNA that reports mtDNA haplogroups
- **Y-DNA haplogroup:** the Y-DNA haplogroup, if they have taken a test at 23andMe, LivingDNA, and Family Tree DNA that reports on Y-DNA haplogroups
- **Tree/diagram Status:** checkbox to fill when you have added the person to your diagram or tree
- **Publication permission form status:** whether a person whose results you want to publish has returned a permission form[3]

Kit Access

Another item to track in your DNA research log is your test takers. You may have invited your siblings, aunts, uncles, and cousins to test. Additional relatives may share their results with you. A log of whose kits you have access to, tests they have taken, and how to access them can help you track multiple test takers. Here is a list of possible column headers to use:

- **Test taker name:** name of the individual who has taken a DNA test and given you access to view the results
- **Test taken:** the test that was taken—Ancestry, 23andMe, Family Tree DNA (FTDNA) Family Finder, Y-37, Big-Y 700, Mitochondrial full sequence, etc.
- **Admin:** the admin for the test, or if the person manages their own test, their own name

---

3. For examples of publication permission forms, see Nicole Dyer, "How to Prepare DNA Research Reports for Sharing," blog post, 6 November 2020, *Family Locket* (https://familylocket.com/how-to-prepare-dna-research-reports-for-sharing/).

- **Transfers:** companies or databases the test results were transferred to, like FTDNA, LivingDNA, MyHeritage, GEDmatch, Y-Full, etc.
- **Access details:** how to access the results, kit numbers, log in details (consider saving passwords in a more secure document not in the cloud)
- **Informed consent:** status of informed consent forms you have sent out and are waiting to be returned[4]

DNA Match Details

When a useful match is discovered between a test taker and a person in a DNA company database, you can track that in your log. If you don't create an entry in your log and record the ideas you had, it might be frustrating later to try to find the details.

Create one row in your table for a match relationship at a specific company. If you find that the same individuals match at another company, add another row. This allows you to track how much DNA is shared according to Ancestry and how much DNA is shared according to MyHeritage, since each company uses different thresholds and algorithms for calculating the amount of shared DNA. Add a separate row when another of your test takers matches that individual. This helps you track how much DNA is shared with a relevant match by various descendants of the research subject in your objective.

Column headers to use in the match details table include:

- **Test taker's name:** name of the person who has taken a DNA test and for whom you have access to their results
- **DNA match's name:** name of a person in the database who is a genetic cousin to your test taker
- **Admin:** the admin for the test, or if the person manages their own test, their own name
- **Username:** the username or display name if different than their full name
- **Shared cM:** amount of shared DNA between the test taker and the DNA match
- **Number of shared segments:** the number of segments; if provided by the testing company
- **Longest segment:** the length of the longest segment, if the testing company reports it

---

4. For an example of an informed consent form, see Blaine Bettinger, "Informed Consent Agreement and Beneficiary Agreement," blog post, 15 February 2018, *The Genetic Genealogist* (https://thegeneticgenealogist. com/2018/02/15/informed-consent-agreement-and-beneficiary-agreement/).

- **Genetic Distance:** genetic distance between the tester and their Y-DNA or mitochondrial DNA match
- **ICW/shared matches of interest:** shared matches that help you understand which branch of the family the DNA match is likely related through
- **Company/Test.** the testing company database where matching occurred
- **Link to match page:** URL for the match page at the testing company
- **Link to DNA match's tree**: URL for the DNA match's tree on the website where the match occurred
- **Cluster/Genetic Network:** number or color of the cluster a DNA match appears in from a cluster chart or network graph
- **Relationship:** traced relationship or estimated relationship of the test taker and the DNA match (i.e. 3C1R or 4–6th cousin)
- **MRCA:** most recent common ancestor(s) between the test taker and the DNA match
- **Expected cM range:** range of shared cM for the traced relationship from the Shared cM Project
- **Average cM:** average amount of shared cM for the traced relationship from the Shared cM Project
- **Within range:** whether the amount of shared DNA falls within the expected range for the traced relationship
- **Shared ethnicities:** ethnicities that the test taker and the DNA match share in common
- **Notes:** any information or comments you want to record about the match between these two people, i.e. they are double cousins, etc.
- **Attachments:** image showing a screenshot of the common ancestor hint

These column headings are ideas, not requirements. My Airtable bases include most of these suggestions, but I don't always fill in the entire row for each match. After reviewing a DNA match, I typically log the test taker, the DNA match, company/test, amount of shared DNA, number of segments, link to the match page, and link to the DNA match's tree. Anything else I can add is a bonus. If I don't know the relationship, I will typically add the company's estimate for the relationship column. If I don't know the common ancestral couple, I look at the shared matches and try to narrow down which side of the family it's on and put a guess there.

In the ICW column, I add shared matches of interest that help me see what line of the family the genetic cousin is probably related on. For example, if I see that Malcolm is a shared match with the client's first cousin on the Parker side, I might put "Parker Line?" in the MRCA field.

Table 10.3. Match Details Table

Tester	Match Name	Shared cM	Segments	Company	Link to Match Page	MRCA
Aaron	Don	196.0	8	Ancestry	https://ancestry.com...	John Watkins and Sue Parker
Aaron	Sue	112.0	7	Ancestry	https://ancestry.com...	John Watkins and Sue Parker
Leila	Malcolm	70.0	4	MyHeritage	https://myheritage ...	Parker line?
Leila	Delilah	68.0	2	FTDNA	No match page	?

An abbreviated example of a match details table is illustrated in table 10.3.

Correspondence

In chapter two, your task was to contact your matches and keep track of messages sent in a research log. Logging your correspondence with matches helps you get organized and have a place to put valuable information received from your matches. When I receive a message back from a DNA match, it's not usually at a time when I'm actively working on that project. It's nice to be able to open my research log, copy and paste their response, and come back to the project later. When I come back to it, I review any recent correspondence, review the stopping point of my last research session, and make a plan for the next steps. Often the next step is to use the information received from the match to build their tree to find the common ancestor.

Entries in a correspondence log include the name of the match, the date the message was sent, and the details of the message. Below are suggested column headings for your correspondence log:

- **Date:** date the message was sent
- **DNA match name:** name of the DNA match
- **Admin:** name of the person who is managing the DNA results, if any
- **From**: who is sending the message—this is helpful when working with another person's results
- **To:** who you are sending the message to—could be the genetic cousin or the person who manages their DNA kit
- **Type of message:** system used to send the message—i.e. the Ancestry message system, LivingDNA message system, email, Facebook message, phone, text, etc.

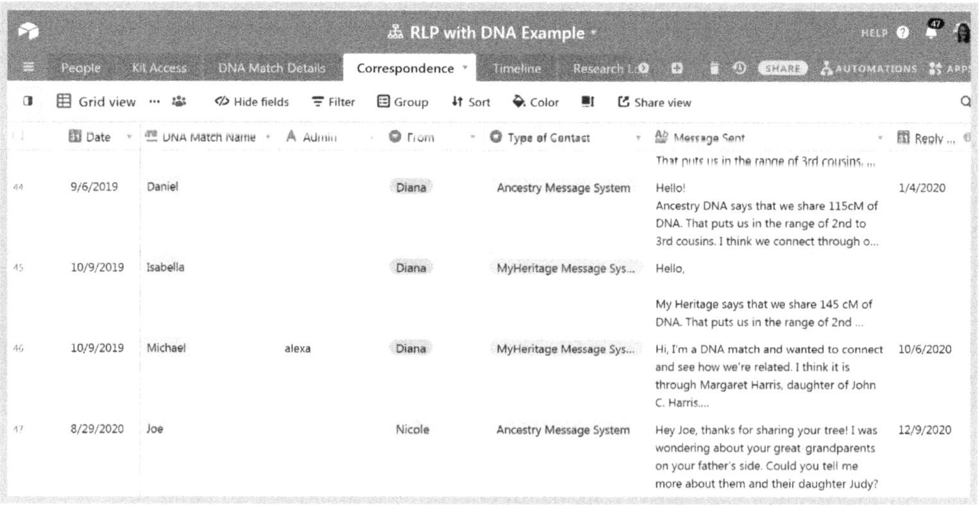

RLP with DNA Example

People | Kit Access | DNA Match Details | Correspondence | Timeline | Research L...

	Date	DNA Match Name	Admin	From	Type of Contact	Message Sent	Reply ...
						That puts us in the range of 3rd cousins. ...	
44	9/6/2019	Daniel		Diana	Ancestry Message System	Hello! Ancestry DNA says that we share 115cM of DNA. That puts us in the range of 2nd to 3rd cousins. I think we connect through o...	1/4/2020
45	10/9/2019	Isabella		Diana	MyHeritage Message Sys...	Hello, My Heritage says that we share 145 cM of DNA. That puts us in the range of 2nd ...	
46	10/9/2019	Michael	alexa	Diana	MyHeritage Message Sys...	Hi, I'm a DNA match and wanted to connect and see how we're related. I think it is through Margaret Harris, daughter of John C. Harris....	10/6/2020
47	8/29/2020	Joe		Nicole	Ancestry Message System	Hey Joe, thanks for sharing your tree! I was wondering about your great grandparents on your father's side. Could you tell me more about them and their daughter Judy?	12/9/2020

Figure 10.2. Example of a correspondence log table in Airtable

- **Text of message:** copy of the message sent or a summary of the message/phone call
- **Date reply received:** when a response was received to the message
- **Text of reply:** copy of the message received or a summary
- **Next action:** what needs to be done next based on the correspondence
- **Notes:** any additional comments about the correspondence

It's easiest to copy and paste the entire message into your correspondence table. This may seem like a lot of text for one cell, but you can typically hide the full contents in your table by adjusting the row height or using text wrapping. When you want to read the whole message, you can expand the cell. This is particularly easy in a database tool like Airtable. See figure 10.2 for an example.

Research Log

Within a DNA research spreadsheet or database, your research log table will track documentary sources searched and DNA tools you have used.

Entries Relating to a Specific DNA Match

Each DNA match may require several sources and searches to determine how they are related to the test taker. This means there may be several entries in a research log relating to one DNA match. Here are some possible research log entries for my AncestryDNA match John:

- searches in published family trees to find John's ancestors or extend his tree
- link to John's profile in my Ancestry tree showing the ancestors I found for him
- searches in other record groups to find John's ancestors
- white pages search to find John's contact info

Each of these items becomes one or more separate rows in the research log table. For each entry, note the details of what you found and your thoughts and ideas for the next steps. Often you will find multiple people with the same name, and you won't know at first which search matches the individual you are looking for. This is where a research log comes in handy. Simply add both search results as separate rows and continue to follow the clues. As you research, you will often be able to determine which result matches.

Many genetic genealogists utilize Ancestry.com or other tree-building services to build quick trees for DNA matches (which are marked private and unsearchable since they are not proven). If you do this, your quick tree may include records attached to individual's profiles which could replace some of the searches recorded in a research log. An entry in your log could be added to include a link to the quick tree and a summary of what you learned in the notes column, instead of all the searches you did to build the quick tree. See figure 10.3 for an example of the research log in an Airtable base. The example shows three searches performed to find more about the ancestors of Jaxon grouped into their own section.

Entries about Test Takers

When using the results of relatives whose pedigrees are unfamiliar to you, understanding the depth of their pedigree is important. You may decide to extend one of your tester's family trees to be sure you are finding all possibilities for common ancestors between them and their matches. You can include this research in your research log. Perhaps you will use a master family tree to build their tree and can just add one entry to your log with the link to their profile in the tree. Read more about creating a master tree in chapter three.

Entries about DNA Tools

To get the most out of DNA analysis tools, it's imperative to log your activities. You may be using several tools and reports to help you understand DNA information. Entries may

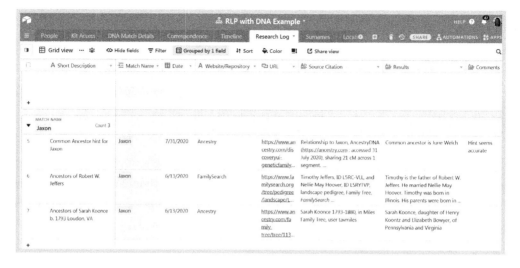

Figure 10.3. Example of a research log table showing searches for Jaxon's ancestors

include all kinds of reports from DNA companies and third-party tools, including:

- Leeds color clustering results
- cluster reports
- chromosome browsers
- chromosome mapping results
- segment triangulation data
- surname projects
- one-to-one DNA comparisons
- segment searches
- Ancestry ThruLines analysis
- MyHeritage Theories of Relativity analysis
- haplogroup reports
- diagrams created
- What Are the Odds? (WATO)

Keeping track of tools you have used and where you've gathered information about DNA relationships is crucial. Once I was assisting an adoptee with finding her birth parents. I made a diagram with Lucidchart showing her maternal and paternal matches. Then I switched over to WATO and added additional matches to find the most likely hypotheses. I forgot to keep track of this in my research log, so my research was spread out in different places. I came back to it a few months later and looked at the Lucidchart diagram. It didn't seem as complete as I remembered. I couldn't remember why I hadn't put everything I learned there. Then I went to WATO and found the rest of my information and conclusions. It would have been helpful to keep track of the work I did in WATO in my research log. I like to think of my research log as a central place to keep links for everything related to a particular project.

After you finish a session of research, check your research log to make sure it covers all the tools you used and what you did. You can think of it almost like a research diary—showing your activities for the research session. You can write notes about what you learned in the results or comments column.

For example, I was working on one of my ongoing projects to find the parents of John Robert Dyer. I found a match on GEDmatch named Georgia who seemed to be related to the case. Investigation into the match with Georgia created several entries in my research log. Georgia was already in my correspondence log, and I had saved her response that included her four grandparent's names. To determine how she was related to the test taker, I first compared segments with a one-to-one comparison on GEDmatch. Then I used DNA painter to overlay the shared segments on a chromosome map I had made at DNA Painter and found that the segments shared with Georgia overlapped other matches on the relevant family line.

Next, I researched Georgia's tree to extend it back a few more generations. I found that she descended from a man with the same surname as the research subject who lived in the same county. I was excited to find a hypothesis for the research subject's parent. I put each of these activities in my research log with my intermediate conclusions about the match. Keeping track of this in the research log helped me remember how the hypothesis developed and sparked ideas for further research.

DNA Informational Material

Your research log may also include links to DNA informational material. This information helps you or the client understand background information about DNA. You may want to cite the source of the explanatory information in your report. Contextual information about DNA inheritance and how DNA testing companies analyze the data and create reports give meaning to the data. If you read an article that helped you understand the DNA results, keep track of it in your log.

Reviewing DNA informational material is like searching for tax law information in a Tennessee book of statutes from the 1800s. The laws created at that time help you bring meaning to the information in an 1836 tax list. The same is true for understanding the information we see in a DNA company's report. An article about genetic distance and the TiP report at Family Tree DNA can help you bring meaning to the evidence in a Y-DNA match list. The "Ancestry DNA Matching White Paper" discusses how they phase your data and apply the TImber algorithm before amounts of shared DNA are calculated.[5] Books about genetic genealogy detail DNA inheritance and information for analyzing shared DNA as well. All of these could become entries in your log that you might use in the report.

The following entries about DNA informational material could be created in your log:

- informational articles at DNA testing company websites
- articles from the ISOGG Wiki
- books about genetic genealogy
- blogs or website articles by genetic genealogists
- Shared cM Project
- genetic studies

In a recent client project, I found an article at Family Tree DNA to explain why a close Y-DNA match was researched and saved it to my research log. The client had several relevant Y-67 matches, but only one of them was a genetic distance of 0. The article at Family Tree DNA shared the probability that a match of the same surname with a genetic distance of 0 would be related in 5 generations. It was 98%.[6] When it was time to write the report, I could quickly copy and paste the citation from my log to cite this article and show why studying the patrilineal line of this match was prioritized.

Below are possible headings for your research log table:

- **Date:** the complete date the database was searched or repository was visited
- **Website/Repository:** website, courthouse, library, archive, etc.
- **URL / Call #/ Microfilm #:** link to the record online to enable further quick reference to the record during the research process
- **Searching for:** type of record being searched, i.e. marriage, census, probate, etc.
- **Locality:** specific locality being searched; i.e. Otsego County, New York

---

5. Catherine A. Ball, et al, "AncestryDNA Matching White Paper," updated 15 July 2020, *AncestryDNA* (https://www.ancestrycdn.com/support/us/2020/08/matchingwhitepaper.pdf), 17–20.

6. "If two men share a surname, how should the genetic distance at 67 Y-chromosome STR markers be interpreted?" Learning center, *Family Tree DNA* (https://learn.familytreedna.com/y-dna-testing/y-str/two-men-share-surname-genetic-distance-67-y-chromosome-str-markers-interpreted/).

- ▪ **Date of Record:** date of the record or the dates searched when logging negative results
- ▪ **Source:** complete source citation where the detail was found
- ▪ **Results/Comments:** notes about how the collection was searched, what was found or not found; may be split into two columns to separate the details from the record and your comments about them
- ▪ **Document #:** number given to the document or attachment if used in the report (typically used for client reports)

How to Use Your Research Log

Now that we've covered what belongs in a DNA research log let's review the steps for using the log.

Set Up Your Log

Create a separate research log for each objective, with the objective clearly written at the top of the spreadsheet or in the description of the database. Remember that a focused research objective asks an answerable question about an identifiable research subject. For example, "Who was the father of John Robert Dyer, born about 1813 in Tennessee, died in 1879 in Hawkins, Tennessee, and married Barsheba Tharp about 1830?" Your research log should not include all the DNA matches of a test taker, only those pertinent to the objective. For the John Robert Dyer objective, I would include DNA matches to several of John Robert Dyer's descendants who have tested that descend from relevant Dyer ancestral couples, as well as more distant matches in the same genetic network who could trace back to a more distant Dyer ancestral couple.

Follow Your Research Plan

Follow your research plan and add entries to your log for each result from documentary sources and DNA sources consulted. Include DNA tools and other methods you try and what you learned from them. Some genealogists put their research plan directly into a research log spreadsheet so that it's easy to follow the research plan and log the results. Any longer abstracts, transcriptions, notes, and analysis can be added to the Research Project Document in the findings and analysis section.

Add the URL

Include full URLs for each research log entry. The links may be to a census record, a profile at an online family tree, a Y-DNA project, a list of search results, etc. For reports that you save to your computer, like auto-cluster reports, screenshots of match pages, network graphs, etc., you can include the link to them in your Google Drive or Dropbox account. I use Google Drive, and each file that I sync to the cloud is given its own URL. Alternatively, you could list the path to the file folder on your computer that contains the file.

The URL column is tremendously useful for quickly returning to online records. Some genealogists like using link shorteners, but I have found that it is much simpler to copy and paste the full URL into the cell of your spreadsheet log and format the cell, so the URL either wraps around or clips (hides behind the next cell) rather than overflowing over the next cell.

Create Source Citations

A good practice is to create source citations the first time you examine a source. Your log should have a column for the citation. (See chapter five to review how to make source citations). I create full source citations for documentary sources the moment I look at them. This practice helps me understand the record and makes writing the report go more quickly.

Your research log should also include entries where you found nothing. Write a citation for negative search results. Discussion of these findings should be included in the report and will need a citation. It's best to write the citation when you first do the search and not later when you write the report, so you can include all the pertinent information and avoid duplication of effort. The research log can also include details about the search terms used. See table 10.4 for an example of a research log with negative findings.

As you can see in the example citations above, I use a simplified version of the URL in my citation for the record or collection searched. I prefer this method because it enables the reader to click the link and easily see the record image. However, in my research log, I include the full URL. For example, the long URL below can be clipped after the question mark, and it will still take you to the image of the census. The question mark and what follows is the identifier of the indexed entry for the person of interest. When that is removed from the URL, it's not quite as useful because it doesn't highlight which person you are focusing on in the census. That's why I like to include the full URL in my research log.

Full URL: https://www.familysearch.org/ark:/61903/3:1:S3HT-6XQH-2J1?i=4&cc=1438024&personaUrl=%2Fark%3A%2F61903%2F1%3A1%3AMDD3-P5C

Simplified URL: https://www.familysearch.org/ark:/61903/3:1:S3HT-6XQH-2J1

When researching a genetic cousin's tree to find the common ancestor, I often search the Ancestry Public Member Tree database and the FamilySearch Family Tree. As I do this, I save the URL to my log but don't always create a full citation, since I'm using the tree

Table 10.4. Example Research Log Showing Negative Search Results

Date	Repository	Source Citation	Results
11/12/20	FamilySearch	Otsego County, New York, Wills and proceedings index, negative search for Clinton F. Anthony, 1792–1887; images, *FamilySearch* (https://www.familysearch.org/ark:/61903/3:1:33SQ-GYC5-4F5 : accessed 23 Nov 2020).	Searched for Clinton F. Anthony. Reviewed each name in the A surnames for books A–F.
11/12/20	Ancestry	"New York, U.S., Wills and Probate Records, 1659–1999," negative search for Clinton Anthony, *Ancestry* (https://www.ancestry.com/search/collections/8800 : accessed 24 Nov 2020).	0 results for "Clinton Anthony" 3 results for Surname: Anthony, Probate location: Otsego (exact)— Rhoda, David, and Peter Anthony
11/13/20	Ancestry	"Anthony Family Tree DNA Project—Y-DNA Classic Chart," Y-Chromosome DNA STR surname project results, negative search for Joseph Anthony, *Family Tree DNA* (https://www.familytreedna.com/public/anthony?iframe=yresults: accessed 13 Nov 2020).	No descendants with Joseph Anthony listed as their earliest paternal ancestor; a Joshua/Joseph Pace was listed in the unrelated grouping.

more as a finding aid. I do the same thing when I'm using digitized microfilm of a land index book—I don't write a full citation to the index book in my log, but I do save the link in my log and put a quick blurb in the citation column, like "Jefferson Co., NY Grantee index 1805–1885 A–E." Then, if I find a deed in the index, I identify the relevant deed book, turn to the correct page, and create a full citation to the actual deed. Remember, citations are to help another individual verify and review your work. You probably won't include index searches in a written report, but you will include citations for the original records.

For published trees, I create an abbreviated entry in the citation column with the following information:

Table 10.5. Example Research Log Showing Abbreviated Citations

Date	Repository	URL	Abbreviated Source Citation	Results
12/14/20	FamilySearch	https://www familysearch.org/ ark:/61903/3:1:3QSQ-G9W5-XKC3	Jefferson Co., NY Grantee index 1805–1885 A–E.	E:224 James Dole to Exrs of W. Constable
12/14/20	Ancestry	https://www.ancestry. com/family-tree/ person/tree/71135853/ person/36236292850/ facts	Richard Fain Dyer (1839–1921), Dyer Family Tree by Nicole Elder Dyer.	Richard had eight children, including Robert Luster
12/15/20	FamilySearch	https://www. familysearch.org/tree/ person/details/KW8H-Y9D	Robert Luster (1893–1982), ID KW8H-Y9D.	Robert was the son of Richard Fain Dyer

Ancestry Public Member Tree Database

- Name of the person of interest
- Date range of the person's life
- Name of the family tree
- Username of the Ancestry member who created it

FamilySearch Family Tree

- Name of the person of interest
- Date range of the person's life
- FamilySearch ID number of the person

You can create a formal citation from this information using citation templates when you write the report if you decide to cite the tree. Often the trees are just clues that lead to other information, so a full citation in your log isn't needed. Even if your citation is basic and quick, it's better than nothing. Table 10.5 is an example of a research log with abbreviated citations. Below are full citations created from the abbreviated citations in table 10.4.

- "Public Member Trees," Richard Fain Dyer (1839–1921), Dyer Family Tree created by Nicole Elder Dyer, database, *Ancestry* (https://www.ancestry.com/family-tree/person/tree/71135853/person/36236292850/facts : accessed 12/14/20).
- Robert Luster (1893–1982), ID KW8H-Y9D, "Family Tree," *FamilySearch* (https://www.familysearch.org/tree/person/details/KW8H-Y9D : accessed 12/15/20).
- You can decide which search results need to have a full source citation created in your log. Just remember it's best to create the full citation to anything you will use in your report.

Abstract or Summary of Results

Include what was found on the record or DNA tool in the results column. For documentary sources, this is usually an abstract of information in the record. If the document requires a full transcription, you can do that in a separate document. I use a Google Doc that I can link to in the results column. If you write as you go, you can simply transcribe the record directly into your report.

Summarize what was discovered from using DNA tools in the results column. For analysis of cluster charts, consider adding a separate row for what you learn about each cluster. See table 10.6 for an example.

Notes and Comments

Write notes about what you found in an optional notes column. You can include ideas about what to do next and possible connections between other entries. I like to keep this column separate from the results column and only put in the results column exactly what the record says. This is a good place to keep track of questions you have and conflicting information.

Download and Organize Images and Files

When should you download the document image and attach the citation? If you do it the first time you view the image, it will save you time down the road and help you stay within your time limit for client research. Leaving all the downloading of documents to the end of the project could mean that you go over time because you have to retrace your research and revisit every document. Insert the image of the record into the word processor you are using for the report and add a text box for the citation. Another way to accomplish this is to use an image editing program like Canva (https://canva.com) to add text to an image. Canva allows you to export several images as a PDF or export each image separately as a ZIP file.

Table 10.6. Research Log Entries for DNA Tools

Date	Tester	Source Citation	Results
3/12/19	Robert	Autoclusters for Robert, *MyHeritage* (https://myheritage. com : generated 12 March 2019), 104 matches from 40 cM to 350 cM with shared matches min threshold of 20 cM.	Cluster 6, blue, includes William Anderson, descendant of Joe Anderson.
3/12/19	Robert	Autoclusters for Robert, *MyHeritage* (https://myheritage. com : generated 12 March 2019), 104 matches from 40 cM to 350 cM with shared matches min threshold of 20 cM.	Cluter 8, orange, includes Maria Gomez, descendant of Jorge Martinez. This is probably the Martinez/ Thacker cluster.
8/19/20	Greg	Greg Family Tree, *23andMe* (https://you.23andme.com/ family/tree/ : generated 19 Aug 2020).	Larry is shown as a first cousin, helping separate the paternal side; Kim is an estimated 2nd cousin on the paternal side.

Give each document you are attaching to the report a number in the document number column of your research log. This is usually done at the very end of a client project when you know the order your attachments will appear in the report. You can then sort your research log by document number.

If you are researching for yourself, you may not want to use document numbers. Instead, this column could be a reminder to download the image, rename it, and save it to the appropriate folder on your computer. As discussed in *Research Like a Pro: A Genealogist's Guide,* decide on a file naming protocol. See table 10.7 for an example of a file naming protocol.

Do you have a filing system in place for the digital documents you download? If not, you may want to try a surname system. Diana and I use surname folders like Dyer, Elder, Harris, etc., which include folders for each ancestor we research within them. For example, our Dyer and Welch folders include the following files:

- DYER
  - Dyer, Augustus Washington
  - Dyer, John Robert
  - Dyer, Sarah Ann

Table 10.7. File Naming Protocol

Date	Description	Place
1949	Delayed Birth Cert Alice Frazier	Montague Co TX

1949 Delayed Birth Cert Alice Frazier Montague Co TX.jpg

- WELCH
  - Welch, George
  - Welch, Malissa

In our system, spouses of collateral ancestors don't get their own folder. Augustus Washington Dyer is a sibling to the mainline ancestor, so his wife's documents would be filed with his. Be sure to back up your local files to the cloud and to a separate location, like a hard drive that you give to a relative.

We create a separate folder within the genealogy folder for DNA data. Inside that is a folder for each test taker, which can include raw data files, DNA reports, cluster analyses, and spreadsheets of downloaded information. These files contain sensitive data, so it's a good idea to protect them with passwords or other security measures if possible.

Find, Sort, and Group within the Log

As you research and add entries to your log, you may come across patterns or clues. For example, the same surname or location may appear in several of your matches' trees. The great thing about having your research detailed in a log is the ability to search through your log to find associated information. I noticed that the surname "Douthit" kept popping up in one of my projects to find the parents of an ancestor. I searched the research log using the Ctrl + F keyboard shortcut to find the name Douthit in the log. I found that I had noted it three times for different matches in the surnames column. Being able to spot this pattern by using my research log was a huge benefit that sped up the research process.

Sorting your research log can also be helpful. Typically, a log is ordered by the date the searches were performed. However, if you have a column for the type of record you searched for, you can sort or group by this column to see all the census records, tax records, or land records grouped together. If your log includes a column for the date of the record, you could then sort your research log into a timeline of records you found. The entries with no date, like negative search results, would go to the bottom.

In a recent client project, I was searching in several counties in New York. I used the locality column in my Airtable log to group my searches by locality. This helped me see all the land and probate records I had found for a particular place and enabled me to quickly go back to the record I wanted when my log became somewhat long.

Write as You Go

Writing is a helpful practice because it helps you make connections. It raises questions and brings ideas for next steps. Abstracting information from the records in your research log is helpful but space in a table is limited. Detailed analysis, transcription, and ideas for what to do next can be included in narrative format in your Research Project Document or final report. When you write notes and intermediate conclusions in your report during your research, this is called "writing as you go."

Analyzing relevant evidence is an important part of the research process. You may already be doing it mentally and not writing it down. David Allen, a productivity expert, teaches that our minds should not be a place to hold ideas but a place to have ideas.[7] If we take the time to capture our thoughts on paper and record our analyses, we will follow a more efficient path of research and notice more connections between our findings.

The research project document, where you have added your objective and research plan, has a section for findings and analysis. This is a great place to add abstracts, transcriptions, analyses, and notes that don't fit in your research log. Then, when you write your final document, whether it's a report for a client, a report for yourself, a proof argument, etc., you will have notes and analysis already written to draw from. This makes the final report writing process less laborious.

When I come across a significant record that I know will be included in the report, like a census record, I create a census transcription table in the findings and analysis section of my research project document. Then, I transcribe the household data, so it's ready to put in the final report. If I find an important will or deed, I transcribe it so I can understand what the record says, understand the information in the document that could guide my next steps, and have the transcription ready for the report.

After following the first few steps of your research plan, you may come to an intermediate conclusion. This is a good time to take a break from searching in order to write. Some researchers like to spend a couple of hours researching, then an hour writing, then repeat the process. Each person and project are different. Try writing as you go, researching and writing in blocks, or another method that is most effective to you.

---

7. "What is GTD?" blog post, 1 February 2018, *Getting Things Done* (https://gettingthingsdone. com/2018/02/what-is-gtd-2/).

Instead of keeping notes and analysis in your research project document, you may want to go straight to writing the final report as you go along. If you know you are on the right track, and the ideas are flowing, this can be effortless and straightforward. However, if you have several possible answers to the research question to follow, you may not want to write any of the findings until a hypothesis emerges. If you are working for a client with time limitations, be careful that you don't research too long before writing the report. This could cause you to work beyond the allotted hours and become frustrated that you're spending too long on the project. Be sure to plan for plenty of time to write your report.

To write as you go, include the following in your report after adding an entry to your research log:

- reasoning behind doing a particular search or using a DNA tool
- transcript or abstract of the record
- source citation
- analysis of the source, information, and evidence
- meaning of the findings with regard to the objective
- description of the next logical steps

When you think about the next steps, take a moment to decide if you want to continue with your previously prepared research plan or if something in the current record or document leads another way. Often an important piece of information will be uncovered that will guide you down an unexpected path. If you decide that taking that path is best suited for a future research project, add the idea to the end of your report in the Future Research Suggestions section. Sometimes, you will want to pursue that path right away.

When should you conclude the research phase? When researching for a client, you may want to estimate the time it will take to write the final report and end the research phase that many hours before your time limit is up. Whatever you couldn't accomplish in this phase of research can be added to future research suggestions. If you are writing for yourself, conclude your research at the completion of a sub-objective, as discussed in chapter nine. If you won't be able to research or write for a few weeks or months, write your report now since your schedule has provided a natural stopping point.

Your Task

Follow your research plan and record your searches in a research log. Include the URL and source citation for each search result and DNA tool used. Summarize what you learn from DNA tools.

Write notes, analysis, and next steps in your research project document or final report. Templates for the research project document and the final report, as well as links to Airtable templates, are available at https://familylocket.com/rlpdna.

CHAPTER 11

Correlating Findings and Finishing the Research Report

Diana Elder

You have completed your research plan and reached some conclusions key to your objective. Now what? Writing a report will bring closure to the research and a starting point for the project's next phase. Using DNA in genealogy research requires the correlation of findings, both genetic and documentary. A research report offers the perfect medium to make these connections. It also provides something tangible to share with others and adds credibility to our research. When writing a report, we also have the opportunity to educate our readers about DNA inheritance and how it relates to genealogy.

Meeting Genealogy Standards

We generally undertake a DNA study to discover and prove biological relationships—especially those that can be unearthed no other way, such as an unknown parentage case or a brick wall ancestry question. The Genealogy Proof Standard provides five proof elements, with the final one referencing written conclusions.[1] We cannot achieve genealogical proof

---

1. Board for Certification of Genealogists (BCG), *Genealogy Standards,* 2nd ed. (Nashville: Ancestry.com, 2019), 3.

unless we present the evidence in writing. Our research report may include a combination of proof statements and proof summaries and could lead to a final proof argument.

The research report allows us to make a case by presenting our findings and correlating the evidence to draw conclusions. Often it is in the process of writing that we discover a fallacy that needs correction. We might notice a fact that needs shoring up or recognize the need for additional sources. *Genealogy Standards* provides a roadmap for what to include in our research reports and is an important reference.[2]

Meeting genealogy standards for writing about DNA raises several questions about organizing and illustrating the material.[3] How do we successfully integrate DNA test results with our documentary research findings? How do we analyze our findings for conflicts and agreement? What are effective methods to illustrate DNA information? How do we discuss DNA evidence? This chapter will address these questions.

Getting Started

Before beginning the report, consider your audience. Will this be a client report or a report for your own files? Are you interested in submitting a final proof argument to a genealogical journal? Each scenario might dictate a different tone and voice in the writing. Because of the complexity of correlating DNA and documentary evidence, a formal report will be the most useful in conveying the information. However, you may have helped a friend discover an unknown parent and want to give them a less formal report. Here are some examples of voice:

First / Second Person could be used for emailing a friend, family member, or fellow researcher describing the steps you took in discovering a genetic relationship.

> **EXAMPLE:** I found your unknown biological grandfather to be John Smith, born 2 December 1910 in Chicago, Illinois. You had two particularly good DNA matches that helped me narrow the pool of candidates.

Third Person is best used for a formal report for a client, yourself, or to share with other researchers. This report could also be uploaded to an online family tree or provide the basis for a journal article or family history book.

---

2. BCG, *Genealogy Standards,* 2nd ed., 40–41.

3. BCG, *Genealogy Standards,* 2nd ed., 32.

EXAMPLE: Using both documentary and genetic genealogy, the unknown biological grandfather of Emma Jones was discovered to be John Smith, born 2 December 1910 in Chicago, Illinois.

The biggest challenge you may face in writing a report is simply getting started. A basic structure can help you organize the findings and know what to write. Creating an outline forces you to think through the research and construct a logical flow as you present both the documentary research and the genetic evidence. Use the elements discussed below to construct an outline that will form the backbone of the research report.

Elements of a Research Report

- Research Objective
- Limitations
- Results Summary
- Background Information
- Body of the Report
- Conclusion
- Future Research Suggestions

If you started writing your findings as you followed your research plan and logged the research, you can copy and paste that text into the appropriate section, and then rewrite it as necessary.

Research Objective

Place the research objective at the beginning of the report to inform the reader of the definitive, answerable question that guided the research. Be sure to include the key identifiers such as complete names and vital information.

Be consistent with writing names in the report. You may have discovered multiple name variations for the ancestor. Decide on the spelling of the name to be used throughout the report whenever a reference is made to the ancestor. When quoting a record directly that uses another spelling, enclose the name with quotation marks. In the background information, you can list the name variations and explain the choice of one spelling for the name to avoid confusion.

Dates should be written using the genealogical format of day—month—year to avoid any confusion. Spell out place names instead of using abbreviations. States are separated from counties with a comma: Cassia County, Idaho. If the place name has changed, use the name at the time of the event. For example, an individual born in 1735 in the west part of Virginia would be listed as born in Virginia, although the area is currently the state of West Virginia. The background information or body of the report can address the change in jurisdiction.

> **EXAMPLE:** The objective of this research project was to prove the hypothesized relationship of Benjamin Cox as the biological father of Rachel Cox through DNA evidence and documentary genealogical research. Benjamin Cox was born about 1791 in Ohio, and died between 1870 and 1880 in Bell County, Texas. Rachel Cox was born about 1828 in Indiana, and died between 1870 and 1880 in Falls County, Texas. Rachel married Hickman Monroe Shults on 4 July 1848 in Navarro County, Texas.

Limitations

Next, address the limitations imposed upon the research. A client typically sets a specific number of hours for the project. For personal research, you may also want to determine how much time you will spend on a project. This can help you to come to a stopping point and write up the research findings to date.

Another limitation to note is the availability of records. The temporary closure of a repository might have affected the research. The need to travel to a repository for onsite research could also be discussed.

Limitations when working with DNA could include available matches at various testing websites, lack of DNA testers, or having DNA results on only one of the testing websites. Inform the reader of the data that was available for analysis.

> **EXAMPLE:**
> - The research was limited to ten hours.
> - Because of travel limitations, all original research had to be done online.
> - Ancestry DNA does not provide a chromosome browser, so most of the DNA comparison was made through pedigree triangulation.
> - Segment triangulation was limited by the unwillingness of Ancestry DNA matches to upload raw DNA data to FamilyTree DNA or GEDmatch for analysis.

Results Summary

A section at the beginning of the report that summarizes the research serves as a preview of the findings. Use action verbs such as "searched," "created," "studied," and "verified" to keep this section brief and informative.

Although the results summary comes before the body of the report, you will create it last. Once the report is complete, use a split screen or two monitors to have both the report and the project document open. Go through the report, summarizing the research that was conducted. Source citations are not needed because each fact will be supported in the body of the report with a citation.

EXAMPLE:

- Created a table showing the indirect evidence connecting Benjamin Cox and Rachel Cox.
- Correlated the records for each of the children of Benjamin Cox. Discovered common localities and migration paths among the six children and Benjamin Cox.
- Created a Lucidchart showing the DNA matches for descendants of Benjamin Cox.
- Built a descendancy tree for Benjamin Cox, including his proposed six children with DNA matches on Ancestry DNA ThruLines: Amy, Lavina, Sarah, Minerva, Rachel, and William Thomas Cox.

Background Information

The background information provides an opportunity to set the stage for the research findings. What are the known family relationships to DNA matches? Did pedigree charts, family group sheets, or oral history suggest an ancestral relationship that needed verification with DNA? Was past research summarized as the starting point for the project? Known ethnicity for the family could be discussed if important to the project. Location and migration could play a role in the research and could also be addressed.

This section can be added to throughout the writing of the report as needed or even created last once the body of the report is finished.

EXAMPLE: No record explicitly stating the names of the parents of Rachel Cox has been discovered. The first mention of Rachel in the records is her marriage to "Monroe Shoults," which took place in Navarro County, Texas, on 4 July 1848. Also present in Navarro County in August of 1848 was Benjamin Cox, named in a list of road commissioners. That list included an M. Shoults, almost certainly the Monroe Shoults of the marriage record. Both men appeared on a list dated November 1848 as commissioners for the road running from Corsicana to the Limestone County line. The two men would have known each other, and it is almost certain that Rachel Cox was connected in some way to Benjamin Cox. Was she a daughter, a niece, or another member of the extended Cox family? Research in the records and DNA evidence could provide evidence of a father-daughter relationship for Benjamin and Rachel Cox that the Navarro County, Texas, records hint at.

Spellings for Rachel's married name include Shoults, Shultz, Schultz, and Shults. The majority of the descendants of Rachel and Monroe settled on the spelling of Shults, which will be used throughout this report. When quoting a record, the spelling in the record will be used.

Body of Report

The body of the report holds our analysis of the DNA evidence, integrated with the documentary research. You can explain the DNA test results and the records searched, then correlate the genetic and documentary evidence. Correlation is the process of comparing the information found in the sources. You can discuss the strengths and weaknesses of each item. For example, you may want to show all the birth years of your research subject in a table to highlight the conflicts among them and show which is most accurate. You will need to resolve any conflicts discovered in the research. DNA is a new genealogical source, and you may also need to educate your reader on DNA inheritance patterns and methodology.

Organization

Organizing the order to present the research can be challenging. Because both the documentary research and the DNA evidence will be explained, one organizational method is to present the information and evidence from the records first, drawing some conclusions that support the DNA hypothesis. Presentation of the DNA test results can then follow, including analysis of the connections and evidence. Having introduced the ancestors through the records, the DNA discussion will make more sense to your reader.

In an unknown parentage case such as adoption, the DNA will likely be the starting point and could be discussed first, followed by a discussion of the records that back up the genetic evidence.

Create an outline before starting to organize your thoughts. Use headings and subheadings for both the DNA findings and documentary findings. For documentary research findings, you can organize chronologically, geographically, or by record type. For DNA research findings, you might consider writing about DNA inheritance patterns, setting a foundation of each DNA tester's path to the common ancestor, discussing the family trees of the DNA matches, and the analysis of the shared cM among the testers and DNA matches.

Presenting and Correlating the Documentary Research

As you present the documentary findings of your project, provide the context about each source to aid the reader. Why was each source searched? What information were you hoping to discover? If applicable, you could discuss the laws, history, geography, social settings, and economics of the area where the ancestor lived.[4]

One of the benefits of writing a research report is discovering a deficiency in our understanding of a record's context. For example, attempting to provide background information about the tax list we are citing may lead us to further research the laws and history of taxation in our locality. This can deepen our understanding of the record and even provide more insight into our research problem.

A discussion of the documentary research helps your reader understand the reasoning behind your conclusions. Whether your reader is a client, a fellow researcher, or your future self, providing an accurate picture of why the source was created can shed light on the information contained.

> **EXAMPLE:** The early settlers moved into the newly ceded lands for the purpose of obtaining a land patent from the United States federal government. To encourage western settlement, the federal government required settlers to apply for a land grant, and if certain conditions were met, the settler would receive a patent. The lure of new land was likely the reason Benjamin Cox moved west. A search of land patents awarded in Indiana revealed entries for a Benjamin Cox in the following counties and years: Wayne 1812, Randolph 1824, 1827, Dubois 1824, Jackson 1827, Rush 1826, Hendricks 1829, Boone 1834.

Any conflicts in the records should be discussed and resolved if possible. If not possible, further research could be suggested. Use indirect evidence to form preliminary conclusions that DNA findings could confirm.

Include negative searches to demonstrate thorough research. Negative searches may help you form a conclusion using that research as negative evidence. For example, a search

---

4. BCG, *Genealogy Standards,* 2nd ed., 36–7.

of all the tax lists in a county could show that a man died when he disappeared from the tax list one year, and the next year, his wife appeared to be taxed for the same land. An absence in the tax list could also point to a move. Negative evidence is a form of indirect evidence and is generally used with other evidence to form a conclusion.

> **EXAMPLE:** Research for this session commenced with examining the records of Delaware County, Indiana, the probable location of Benjamin Cox on the 1820 census. As noted in table 1, Benjamin Cox was present in the tax lists of Jefferson Township, Ross County, Ohio, until 1819. However, the 1820 tax list does not show a Benjamin Cox providing evidence that he had likely moved from the area by 1820.

Present information in a variety of ways to break up the narrative. Tables, bullet points, abstracts, transcriptions, maps, and snippets of images each serve to keep the reader's attention and illustrate the research findings. See the work samples for examples of these strategies.

Presenting and Correlating the DNA Research

Writing about the DNA analysis used in genealogy research presents several difficulties: protecting the privacy of living individuals, explaining the relatively new source of DNA, and clearly showing the analysis and correlation of DNA test results. Several strategies can help overcome these hurdles as you add DNA findings to a report.

Because most of our DNA matches are still living, their privacy must be respected when writing a report that has the potential to be shared publicly. If the report is only for your private files or the private files of a client, you would not need to anonymize DNA match names. However, if you or the client wanted to share the report online or with other family members, you could seek permission from DNA matches to include their full name or use pseudonyms to keep their identity private. See chapter twelve for more details on privacy issues in publications.

To thoroughly discuss a DNA match, list their name or pseudonym, amount of shared DNA, and identify the Most Recent Common Ancestor/Ancestral couple (MRCA). The source citation for the match can describe much of this information. If the DNA match has a family tree attached to their DNA results, that can be cited as well as any documentary research that verified family relationships.

Begin your discussion of DNA with a brief summary of how the type of DNA you used in the project is inherited. Quoting an expert from the ISOGG Wiki, a blog, or a book can add substantiation to the information. I used the following statement in a client project to explain Y-DNA inheritance.

EXAMPLE: Genealogy questions that have remained unsolved for years are being answered with the advent of DNA testing. Genetic genealogists Blaine Bettinger and Debbie Parker Wayne explain: "One of the oldest and most powerful genetic genealogy tools is the Y chromosome . . . Because each man's Y chromosome is nearly identical to the Y chromosome that his many-great-grandfather possessed, the Y-DNA line can be traced back very far." [5]

If you use ethnicity estimates, give a brief explanation of how those are derived and their limitations. If applicable, explain how the ethnicity reports provided clues to the research.

EXAMPLE: DNA testing can compare the DNA of an individual to contemporary people with known roots in a specific region. Jeremiah's paternal grandmother took the AncestryDNA test to determine if she had inherited Native American DNA from her grandmother Clara "Nelle" McCoy. Ancestry DNA uses a reference panel of 44,0000 samples and 70 overlapping regions and groups to determine its ethnicity estimate.[6]

Jeremiah's paternal line to his third great grandmother is the following: Jeremiah > Jeremiah Sr. > **Cassandra** > Fred Mills Sr. > **Clara McCoy**. Cassandra's ethnicity estimate on Ancestry shows only 1% Indigenous America—North. This is likely from her grandmother, Clara McCoy, who was thought to be half Native American. A person inherits 50% of their DNA from each parent, then roughly 25% from each grandparent, 12.5% from each great grandparent, 6.25% from each 2nd great grandparent, and 3% from each 3rd great grandparent. Because of the randomness of DNA inheritance, a person will not inherit these exact amounts. Ethnicity estimates are exactly that—estimates, but they can help to make connections with ancestors. Cassandra would have inherited about 25% of her DNA from her grandmother, Clara McCoy. If Clara McCoy were half Native American, she had a full Native American parent, and Cassandra would likely have inherited up to 12.5% from this great grandparent. With only 1% Native American report in the ethnicity estimate, it is possible that the full Native

---

5. Blaine T. Bettinger and Debbie Parker Wayne, *Genetic Genealogy in Practice* (Arlington, Virginia: National Genealogical Society), 23.

6. "What is a Reference Panel," *AncestryDNA* (https://www.ancestry.com/cs/dna-help/ethnicity/estimates). "Ethnicity Estimate 2020 White Paper," *AncestryDNA* (https://www.ancestrycdn.com/dna/static/pdf/whitepapers/Ethnicity2020_white%20paper.pdf).

American ancestor is a few generations removed. Figure 11.1 shows the portion of Cassandra's ethnicity estimate with the Native American portion labeled as "Indigenous Americas—North."

Figure 11.1. Cassandra's Ethnicity Estimate

Next, discuss the evidence from the DNA matches used in the project. Explain the possible relationships that are expected for the specific amounts of shared DNA and how those led to hypotheses that were tested against the documentary evidence. Including information about the Shared cM Project can help your reader understand how you formed the hypothesized relationships. Although you likely worked with many DNA matches, discuss those that were key in the research. You might reference the family trees of DNA matches that helped answer the research objective and discuss information about the most recent common ancestor.

EXAMPLE: The first phase of the research explored DNA matches for Diana Elder suggested by Ancestry ThruLines. For this phase of the research, additional DNA evidence was sought. The AncestryDNA matches of three additional descendants of Benjamin Cox through two independent lines were compared. Lucretia Becker Neill is a first cousin once removed (1C1R) and one generation closer to Benjamin Cox than Diana Elder. Lucretia's ThruLines revealed 138 DNA matches through Benjamin Cox, most of them in the range of 10–33 cM. A second cousin, Patricia Hoskins, showed 113 matches through Benjamin Cox, also most in the range of 10–33 cM. A third descendant of Benjamin Cox, John Jones, had 194 DNA ThruLines matches with a range of 6–41 cM.

Because Ancestry DNA does not provide a chromosome browser, the shared DNA matches of the four proposed descendants of Benjamin Cox were charted. Each descendant's path back to Benjamin Cox was outlined as well as the amount of shared DNA. Multiple matches were noted to the following proposed children of Benjamin Cox.

- Amy Cox 1813–1907, born in Ohio.
- Lavina Cox 1814–1895, born in Ohio.
- Sarah Cox 1816–1882, born in Ohio.
- Minerva Cox 1821–1902, born in Indiana.
- William Thomas Cox 1827–1912, born in Indiana.
- Rachel Cox 1828–1880, born in Indiana.

Reporting DNA connections can be challenging. Help the reader visualize relationships and DNA matches by inserting diagrams in conjunction with an explanation of the DNA findings. The following example shows a narrative introduction to a diagram.

EXAMPLE: Autosomal DNA testing examines matches across the 22 autosomes of an individual's genome and discovers connections with both paternal and maternal lines. Kenneth Jack Shaffer Jr. tested with Ancestry DNA which has a testing base of over fifteen million individuals.[7] Searching by the surname of Robb discovered a predicted 2nd cousin: Shandra, with shared DNA of 343 centimorgans across 12 segments.[8] This is a sizeable amount of shared DNA with a wide range of possible relationships. Those that are most likely are 1st cousin 1x removed or Half 1st cousin.

Viewing the pedigree for Shandra discovered the following Robb individuals: Alyce Elizabeth Bette Robb (1922–1998) > Richard David Robb (1897–1959) >

---

7. "Autosomal DNA Testing comparison Chart," rev. 18:10, 9 January 2021, *International Society of Genetic Genealogy (ISOGG) Wiki* (https://isogg.org/wiki/Autosomal_DNA_testing_comparison_chart).

8. "DNA matches for Jack Kenneth Shaffer Jr.," Shandra, sharing 343 cM, *Ancestry* (https://www.ancestry.com : accessed 5 April 2019).

Samuel David Robb (1862–1924)).[9] Figure 11.2 illustrates the hypothetical relationship of Half 1st cousin.

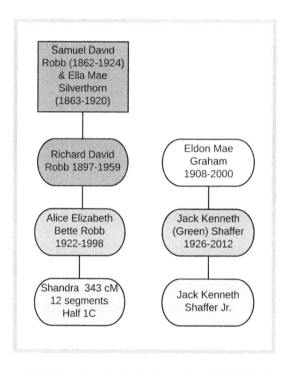

Figure 11.2. Hypothetical relationship of Half 1st Cousin

A variety of tables can detail the various DNA matches, amount of shared cM, segment data, etc. Table 11.1 shows several DNA matches for John Smith, which are important to confirming his biological relationship to his ancestor, Daniel Smith.

Source Citations

Citations for a DNA research report will give your work credibility and enable an independent genealogist to follow your research path and come to the same conclusions. If you have created a source citation in your research log for each documentary source consulted, adding the citation to the report will be simple. A lesson I learned the hard way

---

9. Shandra Family Tree," Public member tree, *Ancestry* (https://www.ancestry.com/family-tree/tree/ : accessed 5 April 2019).

Table 11.1. DNA Matches of John Smith to Confirm Biological
Relationship to Daniel Smith

DNA Match Name (MRCA)	Relationship to Bruce Arnold	Shared cM	Shared cM Prediction for Relationship[10]
Ben (Elbert Smith)	Uncle	1869 cM	1201-2282 cM (average 1741 cM)
Nancy (Elbert Smith)	1st cousin	939 cM	396-1397 cM (average 866 cM)
George (Elbert Smith)	1st cousin once removed	416	102-980 cM (average 433 cM)
Sally (George Smith)	1st cousin once removed	210	102-980 cM (average 433 cM)
Marvin (George Smith)	2nd cousin	73 cM	41-592 cM (average 229 cM)
Susan (George Smith)	2nd cousin	354 cM	41-592 cM (average 229 cM)
Dan (George Smith)	2nd cousin	308 cM	41-592 cM (average 229 cM)
Brad (Daniel Smith)	3rd cousin once removed	29 cM	0-192 (average 48 cM)
Doug (Daniel Smith)	3rd cousin	21 cM	0-234 (average 73 cM)

Source: "John Smith's DNA Matches," Ancestry (https://www.ancestry.com : accessed 23 Nov 2020),
comparing with Ben, Nancy, George, Sally, Marvin, Susan, Dan, Brad, and Doug.

is to create a citation the first time a record is viewed. Although you may need to revisit the records when writing the report, have a citation ready to insert saves time and makes the writing process smoother.

What details need a source citation? Use a citation to back up each fact that is not widely known. For example, stating the birth date of an ancestor requires a citation, but

10. Blaine T. Bettinger and Jonny Perl, "The Shared CM Project 4.0 tool v4," *DNA Painter* (https://dnapainter.com/tools/sharedcmv4), last updated 26 March 2020.

stating 1861 as the beginning of the Civil War does not. Besides citing the specific records used, cite references to information about the background, history, geography, laws, etc., that provide additional context for the research. Include a source citation for any DNA informational item used to educate the reader, such as charts or tables.

Records that were searched with negative results also need a citation. A simple way to create this type of citation is to cite the general information for the source then include "negative search for John Smith." If appropriate, the citation could also discuss search parameters and reasons that the search might have had no results.

Generally, citations for DNA sources are created as you write the report once you have selected the DNA information to include. If you have numerous matches, not all need to be referenced. Be judicious in choosing the best matches, then create citations for those, either gaining permission to include names or anonymizing them if the report will be published or distributed publicly.

A citation template for both documentary and DNA source citations can simplify the process. Create the template in a spreadsheet or document and add to it as new sources are used.

Use complete source citations throughout the report. When you are satisfied with the report's flow, subsequent citations can be shortened after their first use. If referencing documents included with the project as an appendix or document file, add document numbers to the citations.

Conclusion

The conclusion of a research report provides another opportunity to lead the reader through the research. Because the body of the report is completely sourced, no citations are needed in the conclusion. Present the main points of the research as clearly as possible using either narration or bullet points. Lead the reader through the findings and analysis. The conclusion should address whether the objective was met or not. If the objective was not met, future research needed to meet the objective can be referenced, then detailed in that section.

> **EXAMPLE:** This research project successfully identified more information about Benjamin Cox in early Indiana records providing a connecting point with his hypothesized biological daughter, Rachel Cox. Benjamin first appeared in Ross County, Ohio, tax records of 1810. He married Casiah Barbee in 1813 in Ross County and continued to be listed in the tax records there until 1819. By 1820 he had moved his household west to the Flat Rock Township in the Delaware Indiana Cession. Flat Rock became part of Bartholomew County in 1821 and Benjamin

received a land patent for neighboring Jackson County in 1827. By 1830, he was residing in Monroe County, Indiana.

Rachel Cox, born about 1828 in Indiana, would fit into the households of Benjamin Cox in 1830 and 1840 before her marriage in 1848 Navarro County, Texas. Tracing Rachel's proposed siblings discovered that Benjamin's oldest daughters, Amy and Lavina, married in 1834 in Bartholomew County, Indiana. Amy never left Indiana, but the remainder of Rachel's proposed siblings migrated to Arkansas then to Texas. By 1860, nearly all the siblings had married and resided in Belton, Bell County, Texas, near their father, Benjamin Cox. The exceptions are Amy who remained in Indiana and Rachel whose location in 1860 is unknown.

The DNA evidence revealed multiple shared matches between Rachel Cox descendants, Diana Elder, Lucretia Becker Neill, and Patricia Hoskins, and other Cox cousins descending through each of the proposed siblings of Rachel Cox. Combined with the documentary research which shows a similar migration from Indiana to Texas for Benjamin Cox and Rachel Cox, the DNA evidence also points to Benjamin as the biological father of Rachel Cox.

Future Research Suggestions

All research reports should conclude with ideas for the next phase of the research. Even if the objective is achieved, detailing a list of future research avenues can widen the horizons of what you might research next regarding an individual or family and record ideas for future research projects. Often with a DNA project, targeted testing should be performed to verify a hypothesis. Other avenues for further research could be finding additional documentary evidence or researching new lines discovered in the project. If you must leave the project for a period, when the research resumes, you will be able to quickly scan the suggestions and recall your thought process.

EXAMPLE:
- Order the original land application file from the National Archives for the Cox and Barbee land patents of Bartholomew and Jackson County, Indiana.
- Search tax, court, probate, and land records of Bartholomew and Jackson Counties for Daniel Barbee and Solomon and Benjamin Cox. Seek evidence for their connections to Benjamin Cox and Casiah Barbee.
- Verify trees of each DNA match shown on the Lucidchart of Benjamin Cox Descendants.

Documents

If you share the report with another individual, such as a client or a family member, including the documents referenced in the report will be useful. The records can be added at the end as an Appendix, organized in a digital folder, or combined into a single document in the order mentioned in the report. Be sure to attach the citation and document number to each record.

Formatting tips

Create a research report that is pleasing to the eye. The information your reader is trying to understand may be difficult, so using line spacing of 1.5 and a font that is easy to read like Arial, Times New Roman, or Calibri is helpful. Use a footer to track the page numbers and be sure the total number of pages is displayed on each page (1 of 28). Also include the name of the project and your name and date in the footer. If any of the pages become separated, each page will contain the identifying information as well as the total number of pages in the report.

   If using images, add a caption below for clarity. Add a title to each table and check to make sure the headings and information items are readable. Footnotes just for the table can be added using the superscript capabilities of the word processing program and the letters a, b, c, etc., after each entry. Add another row at the bottom, merging the cells horizontally. Use this row to add each citation that corresponds to the footnotes.

Tips for Excellent Writing

You do not have to be a skilled writer to produce an excellent research report. With effort and attention to detail, your report can be clear and readable. Several tips can help improve any report.

   Print out the report after writing the first draft. First, edit for understandability. Ask yourself several questions: Does the order in which the information is presented make sense? What sections might need an additional explanation? Did you explain the DNA findings clearly? Would a reader new to DNA understand your conclusions?

   Next edit for wording. Look for instances where you switched between first, second, or third person. Eliminate trite phrases and replace passive verbs such as "is," "was," and "were" with action verbs such as searched, determined, reasoned, etc. Keep a list of phrases that work well with explaining genealogy and DNA findings.

Use qualifying words such as perhaps, probably, likely, etc., when discussing preliminary conclusions. In our research, we may not be able to say for certain that an event occurred, and qualifiers will help us be more accurate in our reporting. We can still draw conclusions if the evidence seems sufficient. For example, if several indirect pieces of evidence are supported by the DNA evidence, we can conclude that our hypothesized relationship is likely. In genealogy, even with the best research practices, a new piece of information could overturn our conclusions. You can use a phrase such as "based on the evidence reviewed in this research session, it can be concluded. . .." Then if additional evidence comes to light in the future that requires a revision of your conclusion, you can still say that it was accurate based on the formerly available evidence. How can you know when you've achieved genealogical proof using DNA? See chapter twelve for a section on proof arguments and meeting standards.

Be consistent in writing DNA terms such as centimorgans or cM, percent or %, etc. Write the long form of the word and then the short form in parentheses: mitochondrial DNA (mtDNA).

Lastly, edit for spelling, grammar, and punctuation. Keep a good style guide handy such as the *Chicago Manual of Style* or use the online program *Grammarly* to check the report. Many word processing programs have grammar and spell checks that can greatly aid this process, but your own eye is the best proofreader.

Before sharing the report, ask a friend or relative to read it and give suggestions. What made perfect sense to you may not be understandable to someone else without your research background.

Your Task

W rite a report detailing both the documentary research and the DNA analysis. Whether or not you met the objective, you will have a record of the steps you followed and the reasoning behind your conclusions. This phase of the research will be well documented, and you will be able to start a new project using the suggestions for future research.

CHAPTER 12

What's Next? Publishing, Productivity, and Further Education

Nicole Dyer

N ow that you have written a research report, are you finished? Finishing a phase of research does not always mean that we have answered our research question. Your next step may be to use your future research suggestions as a research plan for the next phase of research.

If you have found the answer to your research question and have completed reasonably exhaustive research, you may be ready to turn your report or reports into a proof argument. Perhaps you are planning to share your research report or proof argument online or seek publication in a genealogy journal. This chapter reviews these next steps and gives tips for productivity and further DNA education.

Continue Your Research

Research projects involving DNA evidence can require several phases of research before the question is answered and genealogical proof is achieved. If you have ideas for future research, your next step can be to create a new research plan for the same overarching research question. Perhaps your next phase will focus on finding traditional records about a person or couple identified through DNA evidence. Maybe you will focus on finding the descendants of an ancestral couple so you can find candidates for Y-DNA or mt-DNA testing. You may want to focus on mapping DNA segments in DNA Painter. Perhaps your last project eliminated a candidate, and now you are moving on to another candidate for the parent of your ancestor.

Doing your research in phases can help you move forward and not feel overwhelmed. Give yourself 10–20 hours to research, and then write your next report. As you go along, be sure to write notes in your research project document. We sometimes want to spend longer than twenty hours, and that can work, but the longer you spend researching, the longer it will take to write your report when you're done. Don't fall into the trap of thinking you can only write a report when you've found your answer. Remember—it's in writing that we make the connections that lead us to actually find the answer!

Updating Family Tree Software

As discussed in chapter three, family tree software is important for staying organized, visualizing your family, and keeping track of your DNA matches and their descent from the common ancestor. It is also important to keep an updated family tree for preservation purposes. Hopefully, you will be able to pass on the research you have done to the next generation. Before you continue researching or move on to a new objective, the end of each phase of research is a good time to update your software program with the new information you have found.

You may also want to update the FamilySearch collaborative Family Tree if you use it. One benefit of using FamilySearch is finding cousins who you can recruit for DNA testing. It's also a way to get in touch with a relative of a DNA tester who has previously been unresponsive. I have found that FamilySearch users who have changed the profile of an unresponsive tester's grandparent are often a sibling or cousin to the tester. They can sometimes help you reach others considering the same research problem.

Adding new ancestors to your trees connected to your DNA results at AncestryDNA, Family Tree DNA, and MyHeritage will help you find more common ancestors with matches. Be sure to update those when you prove your relationship to another ancestor.

Sharing Research Reports

After concluding a phase of research, you may want to share your DNA report with interested relatives. You can do this even before you have fully reached a conclusion to encourage relatives to collaborate with you. When a relative sees your report, they will see that you are working according to genealogy standards and might decide to help you. It's helpful to have an ally to help recruit additional test takers from their side of the family. They may also give you permission to view their DNA results or use their information in a published case study. Perhaps you want to post your report online on your website or online tree.

Private vs. Public Sharing

What kind of sharing do you plan to do? **Private sharing** is emailing the report privately to a client, relative, reviewer, presenting to a small group, or sharing within a small closed group. **Public sharing** is posting the report on your website/blog, on the FamilySearch Family Tree, your Ancestry tree, or presenting a recorded presentation, and so forth. Anytime you post an article online for the public to see, that constitutes publication. Formal publication in a book or journal is similar to posting your report or article online. It's out there, available for the public to read.

Permission

If you plan to share privately, you may not need permission from the DNA test takers. In the case of a client report and sharing within a small closed group of reviewers, no permission is needed. The client already has access to their match list, and so you are not revealing information they don't already have. The small closed group of reviewers will agree not to share the living people's info they see before you share. If you are sharing with close family members who already have access to the match lists, the same applies— no permission is needed.

If you are emailing your report to multiple distant cousins, however, be cautious. You don't know what they might do with that report. They don't have access to the match lists you are using, and unless they agree not to share the document, who knows where it will end up. It would be ethical in this instance to make the names of DNA matches in the report private or get their permission.

To get permission from matches used in your report or written conclusion, it's a good idea to message them a succinct request that mentions how they are related to the ancestor in the report. They may not have each branch of their family tree memorized back to the ancestor you are interested in. When I messaged several of my matches all at once with a stock message asking for permission to use their name and match info in my Barsheba Tharp proof argument, some responded that they weren't sure who the Tharp ancestor was in their tree. They said, "Is this on the Harris line?" and "I looked in my tree and didn't see Lewis Tharp." As I messaged them back, I realized that I had extended their trees for them, and in my haste to message them (over 25 matches), I hadn't taken the time to explain their connection to the Tharps. What I learned from this is to establish communication with them before permission is needed. This will help them understand the DNA connection and set the stage for asking for their permission.

When I sent permission requests, several had follow-up questions about what data I would use and how it would be published. For matches at Ancestry, I stated that I wanted to use their name, their ancestry back to the common ancestor, and the amount of DNA they share with other descendants in the study. For matches where segment data is used, you can specify that you'd like to use chromosome information and possibly their GEDmatch kit number, if applicable.

About one-third of the matches I contacted responded to the first message. All who responded gave permission. Some wanted just their initials used. Another third responded after I sent them additional messages and reminders. I said, "I'm not sure if you got my first message, so I'm sending another to see if you had thought about my request."

Several responded that they had forgotten to message me back or that they hadn't got my first message because they don't log in to Ancestry very often. I got great response rates at 23andMe and MyHeritage. One very key match to the proof argument responded after four messages. He said he had been busy and then sick.

Some matches I contacted were dubious about my research, not understanding DNA methodology. I sent them a copy of my privatized report by email. After they saw the quality of my work, they were happy to provide permission. I recommend sending a privatized draft of your report to DNA matches. This allows them to see where their name and information will appear in the final product if they agree.

If a match has responded that they don't want to be included, we should respect their wishes and not use them, even in anonymized form. For those who are unresponsive to messages, we can still use them, but we need to anonymize their information.

You may want to provide a "permission to use" form for the participants of your DNA study to sign and return. This document typically outlines the ways you would like to use their DNA information. To see examples of permission forms, go to https://familylocket.com/rlpdna.

Anonymizing Living People

To share your reports with others, be sure to get permission from test takers and matches, as standards in the genealogy field require.[1] Otherwise, you should make the names of

---

1. The Genetic Genealogy Standards Committee, "Genetic Genealogy Standards," *Genetic Genealogy Standards* (https://www.geneticgenealogystandards.com/), Standard 8. See also Board for Certification of Genealogists (BCG), *Genealogy Standards* (Nashville: Ancestry.com, 2019), 32.

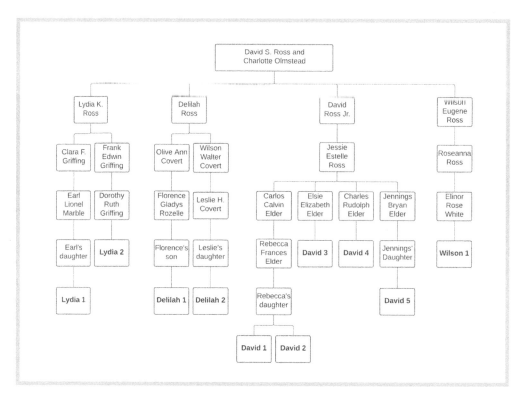

Figure 12.1. Anonymized DNA testers who descend from four children of David S. Ross and Charlotte Olmstead

DNA matches and other living people private in the report. To anonymize the names of DNA matches, consider using pseudonyms like "Descendant A," "Jane's Descendant #2," or "test taker 3," etc. In figure 12.1, the living test takers are anonymized and identified by the name of which child of David S. Ross and Charlotte Olmsted they descend from.

When anonymizing information about living DNA testers, you should try to remove any personally identifying information. Often the name of their parent is personally identifying, so you may want to remove that as well. In figure 12.1, many of the parents' names were changed to "Earl's daughter" or "Florence's son," so the gender was still shown. Gender could be important for showing possible matrilineal and patrilineal descendant lines, as well as X-DNA inheritance patterns.

To remove all personally identifying information for living people from your report, don't include initials, birth dates and places, names of parents, and so forth. Be sure to anonymize source citations as well as your diagrams. You can use the same pseudonym in the citation as you use in the diagram.

Safeguards Against Separation

Genealogy Standards suggests taking measures to be sure that your writing and the documentation that goes with it don't get separated as your work is shared.[2] One way to do this is to include your citations as footnotes on each page instead of endnotes. If an excerpt of your report or proof argument is shared, those reading it will still be able to see where the information in the report came from. Another safeguard is to include a footer with the page number and the total number of pages. This lets people know that there is a longer report that this excerpt they were given came from. You may also want to include a header that includes your name and email address so future readers of the report will know who to contact for the rest of the document.

You may also want to add a copyright notice to your report, along with contact information. This will enable readers to reach you about permission to use excerpts from your document.

Save as a PDF

To prepare your document for sharing, you may want to save it as a PDF. This makes it easy for anyone to read it. Almost everyone has the correct software to view a PDF file—on their mobile device, tablet, or computer. It is more difficult for others to read a Word document. Saving as a PDF also makes it harder for others to edit the document, which you hold the copyright to. Others should not be editing it without your permission. In Word, you can easily save a document as a PDF by clicking File > Save As > then changing the file type to PDF from the drop-down list. If you are using Google Docs to write your document, you can save that as a PDF in a similar way. Click File > Download > PDF Document.

If you have two separate files that you need to merge into one PDF, such as a report and a file including record attachments, you may want to use a PDF editor to help with that.

Publishing a Report Online

You have a PDF ready with your DNA report and want to share it publicly. How do you post it so others can review your conclusions? One simple option is adding it as a document in your public member tree at Ancestry.com. Another great option is FamilySearch Family Tree. This collaborative tree aims to have only one profile for each person in the tree. Find your relative and upload your PDF to their memories section. Doing this allows descendants of the research subject to see your written conclusion. If you have a blog or

---

2. BCG, *Genealogy Standards,* 2nd ed., p. 9, standard 8, "Separation safeguards," and 40–41, standard 74, "Reports," tenth bullet point.

a personal website, post your report there. Those who are searching the web for their ancestor's names will have a chance of finding it.

Proof Arguments

If you have reached a conclusion that you are ready to prove, it's time to write a proof argument. This is typically the kind of proof we need to write when including DNA evidence. Proof arguments are typically longer and include a lot of indirect evidence. DNA evidence is almost always indirect and must be correlated with documentary evidence. The three types of proofs are proof statements, proof summaries, and proof arguments.

Proof statements are simple phrases that state a genealogical fact. In order to prove something in just one statement, you should be able to provide a footnote with one or two citations as documentation for the statement. The information should not be conflicting. DNA evidence is sometimes used in a proof statement when a relationship is very obvious, like an autosomal DNA match between a parent and child.

Proof summaries are used when proving a genealogical fact requires more explanation than one statement. You may need a bulleted list of evidence, an explanation of conflicting evidence that is easily resolved, or two to three paragraphs of explanation. DNA evidence can be used in a proof summary. An example of this is when Y-DNA results are used and show a close genetic distance between two men whose relationship can also be proved with documentary research.

Proof arguments are longer than proof summaries. Genealogists write proof arguments for complex cases that include a large body of evidence. Proof arguments often include multiple pieces of conflicting information that are not easily resolved or where multiple hypotheses exist and must be disproved. Within proof arguments, you may also have proof statements and proof summaries that help build the case. DNA evidence in a proof argument may include many test takers and evaluation of several types of DNA.

To read more about types of proofs and writing proof arguments, see chapter seven *in Mastering Genealogical Proof* by Thomas W. Jones.[3]

Organization of a DNA Proof Argument

After several phases of research, all of which have produced notes, reports, and preliminary conclusions, you are now ready to assemble your results into a proof argument. You

---

3. Thomas W. Jones, *Mastering Genealogical Proof* (Arlington, Virginia: National Genealogical Society, 2013), 83–91.

may be able to reuse the writing and tables you have already created in research reports as you completed each phase of research. Outlining your evidence can be a helpful first step. As you list your evidence and arrange it logically, consider one of the following ways to organize the evidence.

Documentary Evidence then DNA Evidence

Proof arguments with DNA evidence about a question several generations back often begin with documentary evidence and end with DNA evidence. Following this model, start with an introduction that presents your research question. Then present each piece of documentary evidence in a logical order for the first half of the article. To meet the GPS element about reasonably exhaustive research, include all "reliable information potentially relevant to the research question."[4] Be sure you have tapped all relevant non-genetic sources.

After the documentary research has been presented, the second half of the article states that DNA was used to test the hypothesis reached with documentary research. The DNA section often begins with background information about DNA inheritance and methodology, then goes on to discuss the methodology used, presents the test-takers, their lines of descent, and DNA analysis. Following the body is a conclusion that sums up the evidence.

Weaving DNA and Documentary Evidence

Not all proof arguments start with documentary evidence and end with DNA evidence. Some choose to go back and forth between the two types of evidence. Karen Stanbary wrote "Rafael Arriaga, a Mexican Father in Michigan: Autosomal DNA Helps Identify Paternity."[5] Hers is the only case study in the NGSQ that deals with an unknown parent of a test taker. The test taker, Joanne, was adopted by her mother's sister, and no record named the father. After a short opening paragraph, Karen discussed which types of DNA were applicable to the research question. She then wove DNA findings with documentary evidence throughout the article. She used pedigree intersection of close matches to find several candidates, then eliminated all but one through targeted testing.

Jill Morelli's article, "DNA Helps Identify "Molly" (Frisch/Lancour) Morelli's Father," which was an unknown grandfather case, followed an organizational structure similar to Karen's. After five paragraphs of background information, the rest of the article included

---

4. BCG, *Genealogy Standards*, 2nd ed., 14.

5. Karen Stanbary, "Rafael Arriaga, a Mexican Father in Michigan: Autosomal DNA Helps Identify Paternity," *National Genealogical Society Quarterly* 104 (June 2016): 85–98.

DNA evidence interwoven with documentary evidence until the possible candidates were narrowed to one father for Molly.[6]

Patricia Lee Hobbs' NGSQ case, "DNA Identifies a Father for Rachel, Wife of James Lee of Huntingdon County, Pennsylvania," was the first in which DNA first identified a distant ancestor, as opposed to an indirect case confirmed with DNA.[7] She began with the fact that no traditional clues led to parents for Rachel, wife of James Lee, and shared the basics of Rachel's life after marriage. After this short intro, she jumped right into DNA clues that led to the Addleman family, Rachel's family of origin.

DNA Evidence then Documentary Evidence

Occasionally, genetic evidence is presented early in the article, followed by documentary evidence. This is the case in B. Darrell Jackson's article, "George Craig of Howard County, Missouri: Genetic and Documentary Evidence of His Ancestry."[8] The Y-DNA test results presented at the beginning suggest a common ancestor between the test-takers and a significant Y-match within a close number of generations. The match's earliest known ancestor, William Craig d. 1759, had a patrilineal descendant who possibly matched the George Craig of Howard County, whose origins were unknown. Darrell's exhaustive research on George Craig of Howard, Missouri, paired with genetic evidence, allowed him to bridge George's post-1806 timeline with the pre-1805 timeline of William Craig's grandson, George Craig of Virginia. The presentation of Y-DNA results upfront set the stage for the documentary research that followed.

Ultimately, the organizational structure of the proof argument is up to the author and should build the case logically, leading the reader through each evidentiary item. It is not a good idea to present research in the order it was found, as stated in standard 61 of Genealogy Standards.[9]

Figures

The DNA section of a proof argument typically contains a diagram showing the test takers' descent from the common ancestor. It's imperative that readers visualize the lines of

---

6. Jill Morelli, "DNA Helps Identify "Molly" (Frisch/Lancour) Morelli's Father," *National Genealogical Society Quarterly* 106 (December 2018): 293–306.

7. Patricia Lee Hobbs, "DNA Identifies a Father for Rachel, Wife of James Lee of Huntingdon County, Pennsylvania," *National Genealogical Society Quarterly* 105 (March 2017): 43–56.

8. B. Darrell Jackson, "George Craig of Howard County, Missouri: Genetic and Documentary Evidence of His Ancestry," *National Genealogical Society Quarterly* 99 (March 2011): 59–72.

9. BCG, *Genealogy Standards*, 2nd ed., 35.

descent. Providing a diagram is the simplest way to do this. You may need to use other types of diagrams to show lineages and pedigrees in a visual format.

The following figures are often used in DNA proof arguments:

- Lines of descent from a common ancestral couple
- Lineage of a single tester to the research subject
- Hypothesized relationships to the research subject
- Pedigree of a tester
- Pedigree of a DNA match
- Triangulated matches showing bars with overlapping segments

Tables

Incorporating DNA evidence requires that shared cM amounts, expected amounts of shared DNA, triangulation of segments, and other numerical data be presented. Often the best way to include this information is in a table or figure. Proof arguments with DNA evidence often include the following tables to present DNA data:

- Total shared cM that base testers share with each other
- Shared segments among testers
- Total shared cM and proposed relationships between testers
- Total cM shared among base testers and DNA matches
- Triangulated segments
- Tree completeness of testers
- Y-STR values of testers

Meeting Standards

Genealogy Standards includes many recommendations for how to meet the Genealogical Proof Standard when using DNA evidence, specifically standards 51–57.[10] Check your proof argument against the DNA standards to see if you have addressed all factors of DNA analysis that can affect the conclusion.

Standard 53 encourages genealogists to use a sufficient number of testers and matches. If we haven't tested enough people to rule out conflicting hypotheses, our conclusion may not meet the GPS. Targeted testing or asking cousin matches already identified in DNA databases to share their results with us can help. Chapters six and nine discuss targeted testing plans.

---

10. BCG, *Genealogy Standards,* 2nd ed., 32.

Standard 54 encourages researchers to include "sufficient verifiable data" in their written conclusions.[11] This allows readers to review the DNA match data for themselves. Often this means transferring DNA results to GEDmatch, although LaBrenda Garret Nelson's case study, "Parents for Isaac Garrett of Laurens County, South Carolina: DNA Corroborates Oral Tradition," in the *National Genealogical Society Quarterly* used three matches from the Family Tree DNA database that were not transferred to GEDmatch. Six test takers that were descended from the author's side of the family were transferred to GEDmatch, as were three who were descended from the hypothesized ancestor. The footnote stated that the three matches at Family Tree DNA had been reviewed by the editors.[12]

Be sure to meet the other standards in the manual as well. Standard 2, specificity, requires that each parent-child link be documented. This means that we should provide documentation for the parent-child links in our diagrams. This can be done as sources below the diagram. Recent case studies in the NGSQ have also used author-created Ancestry trees to document the parent-child links. This saves space in the printed journal; however, this doesn't mean the authors haven't reviewed the parent-child documentation thoroughly.

LaBrenda Garrett Nelson's article used both in-text citations for parent-child links and her Ancestry tree, which provides additional documentation for each link. She cited her Ancestry tree again, later in the case study, to document two of the test takers' pedigrees in a discussion about pedigree completeness.[13]

Publishing in a Journal

Submitting your work to a genealogical journal is a valuable way to publish your conclusions and become a better writer. *The National Genealogical Society Quarterly, The American Genealogist*, and *The New England Historical and Genealogical Register* are some examples of journals that accept case studies. Many local-level genealogical journals

---

11. BCG, *Genealogy Standards,* 2nd ed., 31.

12. LaBrenda Garrett-Nelson, "Parents for Isaac Garrett of Laurens County, South Carolina: DNA Corroborates Oral Tradition," *National Genealogical Society Quarterly* 108 (June 2020): 85–112, specifically 108.

13. Nelson, "Parents for Isaac Garrett of Laurens County, South Carolina," 100 and 105. Note 104 says "an author-created public Ancestry tree documents the lines of descent." The link to this tree was given again in notes 118 and 119 to document two test takers' pedigrees.

accept case studies as well. Be sure to read several issues of the journal and review their submission guidelines before submitting.

There are many benefits to publishing in a journal, including the satisfaction of proving your conclusion. Additional reasons to publish include receiving expert feedback and peer review, improving our writing skills, and validation. An additional benefit of having your case study published in a journal is sharing with others valuable methods and strategies that they can apply to their own cases.

Some of the challenges of submitting a DNA article to a peer-reviewed journal include contacting living test takers for permission, spending additional money on targeted testing to eliminate other hypotheses, and spending additional time. You may also disagree with some of the feedback you receive from the editor or peer reviewer, which can be challenging. Another challenge is fitting your case study into the page limit of the publication. Some journals aim for less than twenty pages, and that can be difficult when you are using 15-20 DNA testers. Documentation for the parent-child links alone could take up twenty pages! Fortunately, authors and editors have come up with creative space-saving ideas for including the documentation, like citing an attachment on their website or an author-created Ancestry family tree.

Productivity

It can be beneficial to review your productivity after a phase of research. Did you accomplish your objective in the amount of time you thought? Or did it take much longer? If you plan to develop your skills to the professional level, being able to estimate the time it will take for a research project is key. I use an online time tracker (https://toggl.com) to keep track of time spent researching and working on various projects.

Improving productivity is helpful for non-professionals as well. Evaluate the efficiency of your research plan and how you carried it out. Did you plan too much or too little? Did you spend too much time creating a tree for a small DNA match where you didn't find a common ancestor? What could you improve in the next phase of research? What did you learn from this project to help you become a better researcher?

Getting Things Done

One of our favorite systems for improving productivity is the Getting Things Done (GTD) method based on the book by David Allen.[14] He recommends that you keep track of all

---

14. David Allen, *Getting Things Done: The Art of Stress-Free Productivity,* revised ed., (New York: Penguin, 2015).

input (ideas, to-do items, inbox communications, etc.) in one trusted place that you review frequently. Capturing your ideas helps your brain relax and be able to focus better on the task at hand.

If you track to do items in a notebook that you never look at, this won't help. The weekly review is an important part of the GTD method. Go over your list of items to do and move them into categories: to do soon, to do later, someday maybe, etc. You can also organize your tasks by *where* you can accomplish them: at the computer, on the phone, reading, and the time it takes to accomplish them. When it's time to get work done, you can choose your next action from the list based on context, time available, and energy. To read more about applying GTD to family history projects, see Diana's series of articles at Family Locket.[15]

Education

After completing a phase of DNA research, you may feel that you need to spend time learning about DNA analysis and methods. If you need more instruction in DNA, make an education plan to help you reach your goal. Many books, courses, institutes, and other learning opportunities can help you reach your goals.

New DNA Tools

The genetic genealogy field is changing rapidly as more and more people test their DNA. New analysis tools are introduced frequently, and older tools are often updated. Is there a DNA analysis tool that you haven't tried yet? The best way to learn a new tool is to try it out. Often you can find a webinar or video that you can follow as you try it.

Many DNA analysis tools have user Facebook groups you can join to get help and learn from other users. Additional Facebook Groups, like Blaine Bettinger's Genetic Genealogy Tips and Techniques group, are available. Find a list of Facebook groups relating to genetic genealogy at https://familylocket.com/rlpdna.

Institute Courses

Genealogy institutes are distinct from conferences because they provide in-depth learning about a specific topic. Several genealogy institutes offer DNA courses. Popular courses at institutes sell out due to the small classroom size, so be sure to mark your calendar for the registration date.

---

15. The first article in the series is "Family History and Getting Things Done," 19 July 2019, *Family Locket* (https://familylocket.com/family-history-and-getting-things-done/).

Recommended institutes for learning about genetic genealogy include the Salt Lake Institute of Genealogy (SLIG), the Institute of Genealogy and Historical Research (IGHR), and the Genealogical Research Institute of Pittsburgh (GRIP). The Genealogical Institute on Federal Records (Gen-Fed) is also recommended but focuses on U.S. federal records. Institute courses are one of the best ways to learn the latest methods for using DNA evidence.

Books

Many authors have written about genetic genealogy. We have found the following books to be essential to our library:

- Bettinger, Blaine T. *The Family Tree Guide to DNA Testing and Genetic Genealogy, 2nd ed.* Cincinnati: Family Tree Books, 2019.
- Bettinger, Blaine T. and Wayne, Debbie Parker. *Genetic Genealogy in Practice.* Arlington, Virginia: National Genealogical Society, 2016.
- Board for Certification of Genealogists. *Genealogy Standards, 2nd ed.* Nashville: Ancestry.com, 2019.
- Holton, Graham S., editor. *Tracing Your Ancestors Using DNA: A Guide for Family Historians.* South Yorkshire, England: Pen & Sword Family History, 2019.
- Wayne, Debbie Parker, editor. *Advanced Genetic Genealogy: Techniques and Case Studies.* Cushing, Texas: Wayne Research, 2019.

Although books can sometimes become outdated as DNA testing companies change and new DNA tools and methods are developed, they are useful references for understanding DNA inheritance and genetic genealogy theory. If you are a professional genealogist, having relevant books is handy when you need to cite contextual information in research reports, proof arguments, published articles and other genealogical writing.

Articles

Reading case studies showcasing the use of DNA evidence is a great way to learn how to write your own proof arguments. Many journals include case studies with DNA evidence. Here is a short selection from the National Genealogical Society Quarterly:

- Henningfield , Melinda Daffin. "A Family for Mary (Jones) Hobbs Clark of Carroll County, Arkansas." *National Genealogical Society Quarterly* 107 (March 2019): 5–30.
- Hobbs, Patricia Lee. "DNA Identifies a Father for Rachel, Wife of James Lee of Huntingdon County, Pennsylvania." *National Genealogical Society Quarterly* 105 (March 2017): 43–56.

- Garrett-Nelson, LaBrenda. "Parents for Isaac Garrett of Laurens County, South Carolina: DNA Corroborates Oral Tradition." *National Genealogical Society Quarterly* 108 (June 2020): 85–112.
- Jones, Thomas W. "Too Few Sources to Solve a Family Mystery? Some Greenfields in Central and Western New York." *National Genealogical Society Quarterly* 103 (June 2015): 85–110.
- Mills, Elizabeth Shown. "Testing the FAN Principle Against DNA: Zilphy (Watts) Price Cooksey Cooksey of Georgia and Mississippi." *National Genealogical Society Quarterly* 102 (June 2014): 129–152.
- Morelli, Jill. "DNA Helps Identify "Molly" (Frisch/Lancour) Morelli's Father." *National Genealogical Society Quarterly* 106 (December 2018): 293–306.
- Posz, Darcie Hind. "Reexamining the Parentage of Anderson Boon of Lincoln, Marshall, and Obion Counties, Tennessee." *National Genealogical Society Quarterly* 107 (September 2019): 201–17.
- Stanbary, Karen. "Rafael Arriaga, a Mexican Father in Michigan: Autosomal DNA Helps Identify Paternity." *National Genealogical Society Quarterly* 104 (June 2016): 85–98.

View a complete list of NGSQ articles that include DNA at https://familylocket.com/rlpdna.

Webinars and YouTube

To keep up on changes in genetic genealogy, watch webinars that are broadcast by DNA companies and other DNA experts. Legacy Family Tree Webinars has a top-notch selection of previously recorded and upcoming family history webinars, many of which discuss the use of DNA evidence.

Some genealogy journalists share tips and how-to videos on their YouTube channel. Searching YouTube for a specific DNA tool or website can yield helpful videos.

Conferences

Genealogy conferences often include tracks dedicated to genetic genealogy. Many conferences publish video and/or audio recordings of past lectures for free or purchase after the conference. Some nationally recognized genealogy conferences include:

- National Genealogical Society Conference
- RootsTech
- Institute for Genetic Genealogy (I4GG)
- Southern California Genealogical Society Jamboree

Many more regional and local level genealogy conferences include lectures about genetic genealogy. Local genealogical societies often host well-known speakers. *Conference Keeper* (https://conferencekeeper.org/) is a helpful way to find upcoming conferences in your area and online.

DNA Testing Company Help Centers

To learn more about how to use a particular DNA testing company's website, we suggest using their help center. Each testing company has a learning center or help center, and several have blogs explaining how to use their features.

Online Courses

The National Genealogical Society (https://www.ngsgenealogy.org/) offers continuing genealogical study courses for genealogy, and two are specifically focused on DNA. One course is about autosomal DNA, and another about understanding and using DNA test results.

For a course specific to unknown parentage research, check out DNA Adoption (https://dnaadoption.org/). It is a website focused on helping adoptees find their biological parents and offers courses in genetic genealogy. Additional courses and study group opportunities can be found online.

Some academic institutions offer online courses. Excelsior College offers an Introduction to Genetic Genealogy. The University of Strathclyde offers an online postgraduate degree in Genealogical, Paleographic & Heraldic Studies that includes instruction in genetic genealogy.

Blogs and Podcasts

Reading blog posts is another way to keep up on DNA news and methods and see how others are using DNA evidence in their research. Find a list of genetic genealogy blogs to follow at Family Locket.[16] We enjoy listening to podcasts, and while there are not many that are focused solely on genetic genealogy, there are several high-quality genealogy podcasts that sometimes discuss DNA:

- The Genealogy Guys (http://www.genealogyguys.com/)
- Genealogy Gems (https://lisalouisecooke.com/podcasts/)

---

16. Nicole Dyer, "Resources for Learning About Genetic Genealogy," 16 July 2019, *Family Locket* (https://familylocket.com/resources-for-learning-about-genetic-genealogy/).

- Family Tree Magazine Podcast (https://www.familytreemagazine.com/genealogy-podcast/)
- Extreme Genes (https://extremegenes.com/)

If you are interested in learning more about unknown parentage and adoptee research, the CutOff Genes podcast (https://cutoffgenes.libsyn.com/) might be useful. And of course, our Research Like a Pro Genealogy Podcast (https://familylocket.com/category/research-tips/podcast/) includes many episodes detailing the RLP with DNA process and other facets of genetic genealogy.

Your Task

- Update your family tree software and continue with your research. Will you continue with another phase of research on this research question or choose a new one?
- Share your DNA report, whether privately or publicly. Be sure to get permission or privatize before publicly sharing.
- Write a proof argument. Consider submitting your work to a journal.
- Set goals for improving your productivity.
- Create a DNA education plan. How will you keep up with the changes in the field? How will you improve your skills and understanding?

As you focus on continuing education, practice, and productivity, you will be continually progressing and Researching Like a Pro with DNA.

APPENDIX A

Supplemental Material

To view a list of supplemental materials at *Family Locket*, go to https://familylocket.com/rlpdna.

Templates

We have included templates that you can use in your own DNA projects.

- **DNA Research Project Document**: Add your objective, research plan, research notes, and ideas for future research. Use these notes to write your final report.
- **DNA Airtable Base**: The Research Like a Pro with DNA (RLP with DNA) Airtable base is a DNA research log template you can use to track matches, correspondence, research, and more. Also included is a timeline table and citation template table, and additional tables to track DNA clues like surnames, locations, segments, etc. The base has been filled in with example data. After you copy the base to your account, you can duplicate it and toggle off the option to duplicate the records. This will give you a blank template to begin using.
- **Locality Guide Template**: This document is an outline showing possible sections for a locality guide. You can create a county, state, or country locality guide; or any other locality of interest to your research.
- **DNA Report Template**: This document is a simple outline that will help you format your final report.

Work Samples

The supplemental material at https://familylocket.com/rlpdna also includes several work samples.

- DNA citation templates
- Descendancy diagram examples made with Lucidchart
- Timeline made in Google Sheets
- Table showing DNA comparisons
- Locality guides
- Research plans
- Report examples
- Proof argument

Additional Material

We have written many blog posts about genetic genealogy. We have provided links to these articles on https://familylocket.com/rlpdna listed by chapter. We will continue to add blog posts with tutorials about using DNA tools and websites as time goes on. Also included in the list are podcast episodes where Diana, Nicole, and Robin talk about genetic genealogy topics.

APPENDIX B

Source List

DNA Testing Companies

- *23andMe Customer Support.* https://customercare.23andme.com.
- *Ancestry Support.* https://support.ancestry.com/s/.
- *Family Tree DNA Learning Center.* https://learn.familytreedna.com/.
- *Living DNA.* https://livingdna.com.
- *MyHeritage Blog.* https://blog.myheritage.com/

Websites and Blogs

- Bettinger, Blaine. *The Genetic Genealogist.* https://thegeneticgenealogist.com.
- DNAGedcom. https://www.dnagedcom.com/.
- Estes, Roberta. *DNA Explained—Genetic Genealogy.* https://dna-explained.com/.
- *GEDmatch.* https://www.gedmatch.com.
- *Genetic Affairs.* http://www.geneticaffairs.com/.
- *Genetic Genealogy Standards.* https://www.geneticgenealogystandards.com/.
- *International Society of Genetic Genealogy (ISOGG) Wiki.* https://isogg.org/.
- Larkin, Leah. *The DNA Geek.* https://thednageek.com/.
- Leeds, Dana. https://www.danaleeds.com/.
- Mount, Steve. http://ongenetics.blogspot.com/
- Perl, Jonny. *DNA Painter Blog.* https://dnapainter.com/blog/.
- Wayne, Debbie Parker. http://debsdelvings.blogspot.com.

Books and Print Publications

Allen, David. *Getting Things Done: The Art of Stress-Free Productivity*, revised ed. New York: Penguin, 2015.

Bettinger, Blaine T. and Debbie Parker Wayne. *Genetic Genealogy in Practice.* Arlington, Virginia: National Genealogical Society, 2016.

Bettinger, Blaine T. *The Family Tree Guide to DNA Testing and Genetic Genealogy,* 2nd ed. Cincinnati: Family Tree Books, 2019.

Board for Certification of Genealogists. *Genealogy Standards*, 2nd ed. Nashville: Ancestry.com, 2019.

The Chicago Manual of Style: The Essential Guide for Writers, Editors, and Publishers, 17th ed. Chicago: University of Chicago Press, 2017.

Course 11: Meeting Standards Using DNA Evidence—Research Strategies. 2020 Syllabus, Salt Lake Institute of Genealogy. Salt Lake City: SLIG, 2020.

Jones, Thomas W. *Mastering Genealogical Proof.* Arlington, Virginia: National Genealogical Society, 2013.

Mills, Elizabeth Shown. *Evidence Explained: Citing History Sources from Artifacts to Cyberspace*, 3rd ed. Baltimore: Genealogical Publishing Company, 2015.

Wayne, Debbie Parker, editor. *Advanced Genetic Genealogy: Techniques and Case Studies.* Cushing, Texas: Wayne Research, 2019.

Work Samples

Sample 1: Discovering the Father of Jack Green Shaffer

Prepared by Diana Elder AG®, 18 July 2020

Objective

- Identify the biological father of Jack Kenneth (Green) Shaffer. Jack was born 10 July 1926 in Oklahoma City, Oklahoma, Oklahoma, and died June 2012 in Norman, Cleveland, Oklahoma. Jack married Marjorie McCormick on 31 March 1945 in Fort Sill, Comanche, Oklahoma.

Results Summary

- Searched birth records of Oklahoma for the birth certificate of Jack Kenneth Shaffer. Discovered two certificates: one for Jack Kenneth Green and one for Jack Kenneth Shaffer, both with identical birth information. Both certificates could be ordered by a family member with proof of relationship and the death of Jack Kenneth Shaffer.

- Analyzed the 1930 census, the first mention of Jack Kenneth Shaffer in the census. Noticed the surname of "Green" both for Jack and his mother, "Elda Green."

Determined that Elda likely gave the information and had probably invented the surname Green.

■ Searched marriage and divorce indexes for Oklahoma with no results for Eldon Mae Graham. Concluded she never married and stated "divorced" as her status on the 1930 census as an explanation for having a child and no husband.

■ Created a table of the city directories for Oklahoma City from 1925–1931, showing the Graham household. Noticed Eldon's use of the Green surname in 1927 and 1928 following the birth of Jack Kenneth Shaffer.

■ Analyzed the marriage of Miss Eldon Mae Graham and R.T. Shaffer on 25 December 1931. Noticed the use of "Miss" and "Graham" indicating a first marriage for Eldon.

■ Viewed the 1940 census showing Eldon "Susie Shaffer" with Richard, Jack Kenneth Shaffer, and Abner Graham. Analyzed the income data to get a sense of the household's relative status in 1940 compared to the neighborhood.

■ Researched the marriages for Jack Kenneth Shaffer. Discovered marriage records for the 1945 marriage to Margie McCormick and the 1947 marriage to Haroldine Salmon.

■ Analyzed Y-DNA test results for Jack Kenneth Shaffer Jr. and determined that his paternal father's surname was almost certainly Robb.

■ Analyzed Autosomal DNA test results for Jack Kenneth Shaffer Jr. Created a chart showing several matches with the Robb surname in their family trees. Determined the biological father of Jack Kenneth Shaffer was Richard David Robb.

■ Researched Richard David Robb in the city directories of Oklahoma city for the 1920s. Discovered his presence in 1925, residing with an Edith, near the Graham household.

■ Found the marriage of Richard D. Robb and Myrtle Hurley on 6 September 1921 in Canadian County, Oklahoma, and their listing in the 1926 city directory of Guthrie, Oklahoma.

■ Viewed Social Security records for Alyce Elizabeth Robb stating her parents as Richard D. Robb and Myrtle Hurley. Found an obituary on Find A Grave giving her children, one of them named Shandra. Connected Shandra to the autosomal DNA match of Jack Kenneth Shaffer Jr.

■ Discovered the divorce record of Richard David Robb and Myrtle Hurley in 1926.

■ Examined the 1930 census and noted the service of Richard David Robb in World War I. Viewed his draft registration of 1918 and researched military records on Fold3 with no results.

■ Determined research in the newspapers and cemetery could give details on his military service.

- Found Edith living with Richard D. Robb from 1932 - 1950 in San Diego. Searched for a marriage record with no results. Viewed details for Edith Ranier George on FamilySearch Family Tree.
- Analyzed Richard David Robb's WWII draft registration. Noted agreement of birth date and place with previous records.
- Examined the California Death Index for Richard David Robb listing a death date of 26 August 1959 and giving his father's surname as Robb and his mother's maiden name as Silverthorn.
- Researched Samuel David Robb and Ella Mae Silverthorn, the parents of Richard David Robb.
- Located the family on the 1900 and 1910 censuses. Noticed a male child of the correct age for Richard David Robb named Samuel Robb. Concluded this was the same person, and Samuel changed his name to Richard David Robb in adulthood.
- Used autosomal DNA evidence to connect Richard David Robb to his parents Samuel David Robb and Ella Mae Silverthorn.

Background Information

The client's father, Jack Kenneth Shaffer, was adopted by his stepfather, Richard T. Shaffer, and the name of his biological father was never revealed to Jack. He related the personal story that he found a birth certificate listing a different surname as a young boy, and his mother, Eldon Mae (Susie), immediately snatched it away from him and never spoke of it again. The family also had in their possession a torn picture supposedly of Jack's father with the partial name of Curtis Green written on the back.

A birth certificate could show a father for Jack Kenneth Shaffer. The Oklahoma State Vital Records Index contains two relevant entries with the same birth information of 10 July 1926 for Jack Kenneth Shaffer and Jack Kenneth Green. [1] Because the state of Oklahoma considers a birth occurring less than 125 years ago as closed, a copy of each certificate can only be ordered by a family member with proof of relationship and death of Jack Kenneth Shaffer.

Both indexed birth records show identical information except for the surname. Without viewing the actual certificate, it is impossible to determine when each certificate was created. The certificate for Jack Kenneth Green likely was made at his birth. The

---

1. Oklahoma State Vital Records Index, search for Jack born 10 July 1926, *OK2Explore* (https://ok2explore.health.ok.gov/App/BirthResults : accessed 2 April 2019).

certificate for Jack Kenneth Shaffer would have been created after his adoption by Richard T. Shaffer. Fortunately, DNA testing can now provide additional evidence for a biological parent relationship. When combined with genealogical research, a clear picture of the parentage of Jack Kenneth (Green) Shaffer emerged.

The name "Eldon" was often spelled "Elden" in the records. For clarity, the report uses "Eldon" unless quoting a record.

Documentary Records

1930 Census

The client's Ancestry public member tree showed the earliest located record for Jack Kenneth (Green) Shaffer as the 1930 census listing "Jack K. Green," grandson of the head of household Abb Graham. [2] The census enumerator noted Jack's age as 3 and 9/12, with his birth in Oklahoma and both parents born in Oklahoma. Listed directly above Jack is his mother, "Elda Green," daughter of the head of household, Abb Graham. The census also reveals Elda as 21 years old, divorced, and 17 years old at her first marriage. The head of the household was to provide the information, but in his absence, a census taker would often take the required information from anyone present on the day of his visit. Table 1 details the information for the household, which included Eldon's brothers, a sister-in-law, and two other young children. Eldon was likely taking care of the children on the home front while everyone else worked outside the home.

The census enumerator visited the Graham / Green household on 9 April 1930, and Jack's age of 3 and 4/12 corresponds perfectly with his 10 July 1926 birth year. Because Eldon's stated occupation was housekeeper, she was most likely to be home during the day. She probably reported the census information for the household, stating Jack's age and the surname of Green.

The census shows "divorced" for Eldon's marital status, implying a previous marriage. Searching online marriage indexes revealed no marriage record for a Graham—Green marriage in Oklahoma.[3] Oklahoma County has compiled an index of divorce records, and a

---

2. 1930 U.S. Census, Oklahoma Co., Oklahoma, population schedule, Oklahoma City, enumeration district (ED) 105, sheet 8B (penned), dwelling 162, family 174, Abb Graham household; digital image, *Ancestry*, (http://www.ancestry.com: accessed 4 Apr 2019,); citing NARA microfilm publication T626.

3. "Oklahoma, County Marriage Records, 1890–1994," negative search for Graham–Green marriage, *Ancestry* (https://www.ancestry.com : accessed 4 Apr 2019). "Oklahoma, County Marriages, 1890–1995," negative search for Graham–Green marriage, *FamilySearch* (https://www.familysearch.org/search/collection/1709399 : accessed 4 Apr 2019).

Table 1. Abb Graham Household—1930 Census

Locality	1930, Oklahoma City, Oklahoma								
ED, Sheet, Line	Enumeration district 105, Sheet 8B, Line 79								
Enumeration Date	9 April 1930								

Location			Description				Birth Place		
House	Family	Name	Sex	Age	Relationship	Occupation	Self	Fath	Moth
162	174	Abb Graham	m	61	Head	Floorman – High School	Kan	US	US
		Glenn Graham	m	27	Son	Office work – Furniture Co.	Ok	Kan	Mich
		Flossie Graham	f	26	Daughter-in-law	Line lady – Biscuit Co.	Tex	Tex	Ala
		Kathryn Graham	f	4 5/12	Granddaughter		Ok	Ok	Tex
		Angus Graham	m	25	Son	Laborer – Truck Co.	Ok	Kan	Mich
		Elda Green	f	21	Daughter	Housekeeper	Ok	Kan	Mich
		Jack K Green	m	3 9/12	Grandson		Ok	Ok	Ok
		Earl Graham	m	4 11/12	Grandson		Ok	Ok	Ok

search from 1926–1930 revealed no divorce record for an Eldon Green.[4] In the absence of a marriage or divorce record, Eldon almost certainly was not married at the time of Jack's birth and the term "divorced" was used to combat the stigma of the time against unwed mothers.

Oklahoma City Directories

City Directories fill in the ten-year gap between census records and reveal addresses, occupations, and hint at relationships. Searching the directories discovered different combinations of the Graham family resided at various addresses through the 1920s. Eldon's brother Angus, "Gus," was often listed at the same address as Abner and Eldon. The 1925 and 1927 listings also included Evelyn, likely his wife. This would not be Pearl, who he married in 1931.[5] Further research could discover a marriage for Angus Graham and Evelyn.

---

4. Oklahoma District Court, Divorce index, v. 1 1925–1935, negative search for Eldon Green, *FamilySearch* (https://www.familysearch.org : accessed 4 Apr 2019); FHL microfilm 2169554, item 2, images 815–823.

5. Ancestry public member tree, Shaffer/Parke/Faletti Family Tree, Angus A Graham, 1906–1967, *Ancestry* (https://www.ancestry.com : accessed 11 Apr 2019).

In 1929, Eldon, her brother, Kenneth J. Graham, and her father, Abner, lived at the same Oklahoma City address. Another brother, Glenn, and his wife, Flossie, resided with Eldon and Abner in 1930 and 1931. Table 2 details the various entries in the directories from 1925 1930 and shows the family's fluid movement.[6]

Eldon's surname changed between Graham and Green during this time. The city directories list Eldon as a Graham in 1925 and 1926, then as "Mrs. Eldon Green" in 1927 and 1928, following the birth of Jack Kenneth Shaffer. From 1929–1931 her name reverts to Eldon Graham, except for the 1930 census that lists her as Eldon Green. In each instance, Eldon lived at the same address as her father, Abner, even when going by "Mrs. Eldon Green." They moved often, but not far, continuously residing on 7th or 9th street. Eldon almost certainly took the name of Green without a marriage and possibly fabricated a story about her marriage.

The 1925 city directory reveals Eldon working as a packer at the Iten Biscuit company. An article published in 2013 described the history of this business.[7] The 105 x 140-foot building had five stories and a basement with 126,000 square feet of storage. The production and distribution of crackers and cakes employed numerous men and women. The building was state of the art, with each floor having a breakroom and bathrooms. The Iten Biscuit Company employed the people of Oklahoma City for 30 years, then was acquired by Nabisco. The 1912 city directory for Oklahoma City stated:

> A new industry employing from 400–500 persons is an event in the life of any city of ordinary size. The completion and putting into operation of the Iten Biscuit Co.'s plant is perhaps the most important single acquisition of 1912 to Oklahoma's commercial life. [8]

1931 Marriage: R. T. Shaffer and Miss Elden Mae Graham

A year after the 1930 census listing, "Miss Elden Mae Graham" and "R.T. Shaffer" were married by Lucien E. Wilson, a Justice of the Peace at Norman, Oklahoma.[9] The marriage

---

6. "U.S. City Directories, 1822–1995," for Abner, Nellie, and Elden Graham, 1925–1931, *Ancestry* (https://www.ancestry.com : accessed 4 Apr 2019).

7. Mary Phillips, "Biscuit Building Still Stands," 17 January 2013, *The Oklahoman* (https://newsok.com/article/3849559/biscuit-building-still-stands : accessed 9 April 2019).

8. "U.S. City Directories, 1822–1995," Preface, 1912, Oklahoma City, Oklahoma, City Directory, *Ancestry* (https://www.ancestry.com : accessed 9 Apr 2019).

9. "Oklahoma, County Marriage Records, 1890–1995," Cleveland 1928 - 1940, Shaffer-Graham, 1931, *Ancestry* (https://www.ancestry.com : accessed 4 Apr 2019).

Table 2. Oklahoma City Directories, 1925–1931

Date	Individual, Occupation, and Address
1925	Abner Graham (Nellie), Ever Pure Laundry **Elden M Graham, pkr at Iten Biscuit Co** Gus (Evelyn) 326 W 9th
1926	Abb Graham, helper Central HS **Elden Graham** Gus (Evelyn) driver Union Dairy 326 W 9th
1927	Abb Graham, floorman **Mrs Elden Green** 806a W 7th Glen (Flossie) Graham Flossie Graham floor lady 808a 7th
1928	Abb Graham, floorman **Mrs. Elden Green** Gus Graham 806a W 7th
1929	Abb Graham, janitor Central Sr High Sch **Elden Graham** Gus Graham dairyman Kenneth J Graham employee Union Dairy 808a W 7th Glenn A (Flossie) collr [sic] Jordan Furniture Co 1109 W 7th
1930	Abb Graham **Elden Graham** Glenn A (Flossie) collr [sic] Jordan Furniture co 1500 W 7th
1931	Abb Graham **Elden Graham** Gus A Graham janitor Glenna A (Flossie) employee Steffens Blue Ribbon Dairy Products 1500 W 7th

took place on 25 December 1931 and was likely a quiet affair witnessed by Mrs. Pearl Graham and Mabel Wilson. Pearl was Eldon's sister-in-law, married to Eldon's brother, Abner Graham. Angus and Pearl had married earlier that year, and Pearl was probably a good friend to Eldon as well as a sister-in-law. The name "Miss Eldon Mae Graham" used in the marriage license and certificate also points to Eldon being a single mother, despite her reporting of Green as a married name.

1940 Census

The 1940 census reveals the new family grouping of Richard and Eldon "Susie" Shaffer with Jack and Susie's father, Abner Graham.[10] The 1940 census is the only census that marks the informant with the ⊗, which was Eldon. She had started going by "Susie" and gave "Susie Shaffer" as her name. She stated that she was 31 years old, Oklahoma-born, and had attended school through the second year of high school.

Eldon reported her husband, Richard, was 34 years old, Ohio-born, and had attended high school through the fourth year. His employment as a "time keeper" at a tank manufacturing company had earned him $1800 in 1939, equivalent to about $33,000 in 2019. His income placed him in the middle of the neighborhood, according to the 1940 census. The Shaffer household also had the added income from Abner Graham's job as the custodian at the public school. His pay of $1260 in 1939 is equivalent to about $23,000 in 2019. Combined, the household income in 1939 would have been about $3,060, equal to about $55,600. The family rented their home for $35 per month or about $650 in 2019.

Marriages of Jack Kenneth Shaffer

On 31 March 1945, Jack Kenneth Shaffer applied for a marriage license in Comanche County, Oklahoma. He gave his age as 21 years and his residence as Fort Sill, Oklahoma. The bride-to-be was Miss Margie McCormick, age 18, of 134 E Park, Oklahoma City, Oklahoma.[11] The couple was issued the license on 31 March 1945 and married that day by Oren C. Reid, an Ordained Minister of the First Baptist Church of Lawton. Mrs. E.E. Townley and Harry I. Howard witnessed the wedding. On 30 December 1945, Jack Richard Shaffer was born to the couple. The couple divorced soon after this marriage and each

---

10. 1940 U.S. Census, Oklahoma Co., Oklahoma, population schedule, Oklahoma City, ward 3, enumeration district (ED) 78–87, sheet 10B (penned), dwelling 1954, family 286, Richard Shaffer household; digital image, *Ancestry* (http://www.ancestry.com: accessed 4 Apr 2019,); citing NARA microfilm publication T627.

11. "Oklahoma, County Marriage Records, 1890–1995," for Shaffer–McCormick, 1945, *Ancestry* (https://www.ancestry.com : accessed 11 Apr 2019).

remarried.[12] Oklahoma divorce records were searched with no results for this divorce.[13]

Jack remarried soon after the end of his first marriage. He and Haroldine Salmon applied for a marriage license on 28 March 1947 in Oklahoma City, Oklahoma.[14] No marriage certificate was noted in the marriage book, so the couple likely did not return with the finalized certificate. With Haroldine, Jack had four additional sons.

DNA Test Results

Research in traditional genealogical records revealed no clear information on the biological father of Jack Kenneth Shaffer, so DNA test results for Jack's son, Jack Kenneth Shaffer Jr., were analyzed. DNA testing has become a proven method for discovering biological relationships, and in a close relationship such as grandfather, can positively establish that relationship. Several types of DNA tests exist and can be used in tandem. This research project used Y-DNA and autosomal DNA tests to prove a father for Jack Kenneth (Green) Shaffer.

Y-DNA Testing

Genealogy questions that have remained unsolved for years are being answered with the advent of DNA testing. Genetic genealogists Blaine Bettinger and Debbie Parker Wayne explain: "One of the oldest and most powerful genetic genealogy tools is the Y chromosome . . . Because each man's Y chromosome is nearly identical to the Y chromosome that his many-great-grandfather possessed, the Y-DNA line can be traced back very far."[15]

Jack Kenneth Shaffer Jr. took the 67 marker Y-DNA STR (Short Tandem Repeat) test at FamilyTree DNA, and matches revealed various surnames: Robb, Thompson, Roach, Roche, Fitzgerald, and Kelley.[16] The closest match was J. R. Robb, with a genetic distance of 3. The other testers matched at a genetic distance between 4 and 7.

---

12. Ancestry public member tree, Shaffer/Parke/Faletti Family Tree, Marjorie Ellen McCormick, 1926–1978, *Ancestry* (https://www.ancestry.com : accessed 11 Apr 2019).

13. Oklahoma Historical Society Research Center, negative search for divorce of Shaffer, 1945–47, https://www.okhistory.org : accessed 9 April 2019).

14. "Oklahoma, County Marriage Records, 1890–1995," Shaffer–Salmon, 1947, *Ancestry* (https://www.ancestry.com : accessed 11 Apr 2019).

15. Blaine T. Bettinger and Debbie Parker Wayne, *Genetic Genealogy in Practice,* p. 23.

16. "Y-DNA—Matches," for Jack Kenneth Shaffer, Jr. Kit #MK32181, *FamilyTree DNA* (https://www.family-treedna.com : accessed 4 April 2019).

When analyzing a Y-DNA STR test, each difference or mutation between two men is added up, and the total is termed genetic distance. The greater the genetic distance, the further removed the common ancestor will be. A father and son would likely have 0 as a genetic distance. More distant cousins would have a larger number for the genetic distance.

The closest match for Jack Kenneth Shaffer Jr. was J.R. Robb, with a genetic distance of 3. FamilyTree DNA estimates the common ancestor to be between 4–8 generations. Viewing the pedigree chart attached to J. R. Robb's results, the paternal line is J. R. Robb > James Robb (1916–2012) > James Robb (1889–1976) > James Robb (1859–1949) > William Robb (1830–1914). With the common ancestor 4–8 generations back, the connection would likely come with William Robb or further back. Although an excellent clue for a possible surname, the Y-DNA match to J. R. Robb was not close enough to determine a father for Jack Kenneth Shaffer.

Autosomal DNA Testing

Autosomal DNA testing examines matches across the 22 autosomal chromosomes of an individual's genome and discovers connections with both paternal and maternal lines. Kenneth Jack Shaffer Jr. tested with Ancestry DNA which has a testing base of over fifteen million individuals.[17] Searching by the surname of Robb discovered a genetic relationship: Shandra with shared DNA of 343 centimorgans across 12 segments.[18] This is a sizeable amount of shared DNA with a wide range of possible relationships. The Shared cM Project gives the following possibilities the highest probability.[19]

- 1st cousin 1x removed
- Half 1st cousin
- 2nd cousin
- Half 1st cousin 1x removed

The match, Shandra, has attached an Ancestry public member tree to her DNA results and viewing the pedigree discovered the following Robb pedigree: Alyce Elizabeth Bette

---

17. "Autosomal DBNA Testing Comparison Chart," *International Society of Genetic Genealogy Wiki* (https://isogg.org/wiki/Autosomal_DNA_testing_comparison_chart : accessed 9 Apr 2019).

18. "AncestryDNA Results for Jack Kenneth Shaffer Jr.," database report, *Ancestry* (https://www.ancestry.com : accessed 5 April 2019), predicting 2nd cousin genetic match with user Shandra, sharing 343 cM. The name has been changed for privacy.

19. Blaine T. Bettinger, "The Shared cM Project 4.0 tool v4," *DNA Painter* (https://dnapainter.com/tools/sharedcmv4/110 : accessed 16 July 2020), relationships for 343 cM.

Robb (1922–1998) > Richard David Robb (1897–1959) > Samuel David Robb (1862–1924) > William Taylor Robb (1820–1889) > William Robb (1771–1870) > John Robb (1763–1861) > James Robb (1745–1825).[20] Neither William Robb corresponded precisely with the William Robb listed as a possible ancestor of the Y-DNA match. Further research could verify the Robb line and discover the common ancestor.

Another testing company that specializes in autosomal DNA is 23andMe. Jack Kenneth Shaffer Jr. also tested with this company, and a close match, Derek, shares 2.65% DNA. The testing company indicates that Jack and Derek may share a set of great-grandparents.[21] Correspondence with Derek revealed the following:

> My paternal grandmother (Bette or "Granny Jones") was Alyce Elizabeth Robb born in Guthrie on June 9, 1922. Her parents were Richard David Robb and Myrtle Robb (nee Hurley). Bette passed away in 1998, but I'm guessing Richard is your suspect. I wasn't very close to my father's family, especially after I left the South in late 1998, so that's really all I know. I hope it helps.[22]

The match listed as Derek on 23andMe also appeared on the FamilyTree DNA match list and showed he and Jack Kenneth Shaffer Jr. shared 214 centimorgans.[23] Charting both of the close matches, Shandra and Derek, Richard David Robb emerged as the likely candidate for the father of Jack Kenneth Shaffer.[24] Jack Kenneth Shaffer was the hypothesized half-brother of Alice Elizabeth Bette Robb, illustrated in Figure 1.

Richard David Robb

With DNA evidence pointing to Richard David Robb as the probable father for Jack Kenneth Shaffer, research moved to discovering his life events and whereabouts in 1925. Was he residing in Oklahoma City, Oklahoma, where he would have met Eldon Mae Graham?

---

20. Public Member Trees," database, *Ancestry* (https://www.ancestry.com/family-tree/tree/4238986/family : accessed 5 April 2019),"Jones Family Tree," family tree by Carlasue1_1.

21. "DNA Relatives for Jack Kenneth Shaffer Jr.," *23andMe* (https://you.23andme.com : accessed 5 April 2019).

22. 23andMe messaging, 4 January 2019, from Derek; client information shared with researcher, 5 March 2019. The name of the match has been changed for privacy.

23. "Family Finder—Matches for Jack Shaffer," database report, *FamilyTree DNA* (https://www.family-treedna.com/my/familyfinder : accessed 18 July 2020), match B.J., 214 cM, linked family tree showing B J > Private > Alice Elizabeth Bette Jones nee Robb > Richard David Robb and Myrtle Robb nee Hurley.

24. "DNA Matches for Jack Kenneth Shaffer Jr.," Lucidchart, created 18 July 2020.

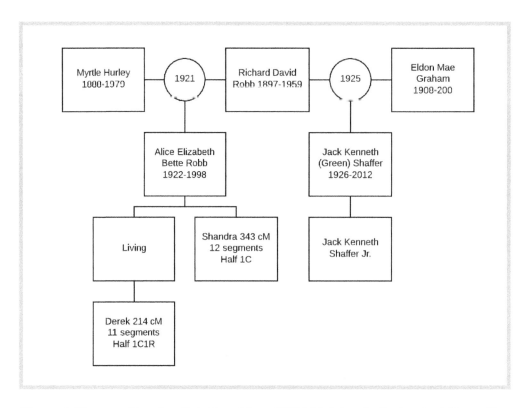

Figure 1. Diagram Showing Relationships of DNA Matches to Tester Jack Kenneth Shaffer, Jr.

City directories reveal Richard David Robb's presence in Oklahoma City in 1925.[25] Also listed with Richard is an Edith in parentheses, indicating she was his wife. Richard and Edith roomed at 118 W 8th. In 1925, Eldon Mae Graham and her father, Abner, lived at 326 W 9th. The proximity of the addresses makes it probable that this Richard Robb was the Richard David Robb of the DNA evidence. Jack Kenneth Shaffer was born on 10 July 1926 and would have been conceived in September of 1925. Although many individuals with the Robb surname appear in the Oklahoma City Directory for 1925, there is only one Richard Robb.

Although Richard and Edith may have been living together in 1925, they were probably not married. Richard D. Robb, age 24 and a resident of Guthrie, Logan, Oklahoma, had

25. "U.S. City Directories, 1822–1995," for Richard Robb, 1925, Oklahoma City, Oklahoma, City Directory, *Ancestry* (https://www.ancestry.com : accessed 9 Apr 2019).

married Myrtle Hurley, age 32, also of Guthrie, on 6 September 1921.[26] Albert Noah Smith, a minister of the Methodist Episcopal Church, performed the ceremony, witnessed by Mrs. H J Davis and Mrs. Idella Smith. The couple seemed to have made their home in Guthrie, as they are listed in the 1926 city directory of Guthrie, Oklahoma.[27] Unlike the Oklahoma City directory listing of 1925, which contains multiple Robbs, the 1926 directory has only Richard and Myrtle Robb.

The couple had only one child together, Alyce Elizabeth Robb. When she applied for a social security number in 1943, she listed her name as Betty Robb Stadler.[28] She named her parents Richard D. Robb and Myrtle Hurley. That indexed record also shows alternate names: Bette Robb Jones (1960) and Bette R Jones (1998). The 1960 record was created after her marriage to Carl C. Jones when she changed her name on her social security card. The 1998 record was created upon her death. Alyce's obituary, published in Logan County, Oklahoma, in the *Guthrie News Leader* on 5 July 1998, gives further evidence for her parentage.[29] One of the children named in the obituary likely wrote it.

JONES

> Graveside services for Alyce Elizabeth "Bette" ROBB JONES, 76, of Corpus Christi, Texas, will be July 5, at Seaside Memorial Park, Corpus Christi.
>
> Bette was born June 9, 1922, in Guthrie to Richard David and Myrtle HURLEY ROBB. She died June 27, in Corpus Christi. Bette married Carl C. JONES in Guthrie in 1950. He preceded her in death on June 7, 1974.
>
> Survivors are two daughters, Shandra and [private]; one son, [private].

This obituary notes a daughter, Shandra, the autosomal DNA match to Jack Kenneth Shaffer Jr. discussed previously. Richard David Robb was the father of both Bette Robb

---

26. "Oklahoma, County Marriage Records, 1890–1995," Canadian, 1920–1922, Robb-Hurley, 1921, *Ancestry* (https://www.ancestry.com : accessed 9 Apr 2019).

27. "U.S. City Directories, 1822–1995," for Richard D. Robb, 1926, Guthrie City, Oklahoma, City Directory, *Ancestry* (https://www.ancestry.com : accessed 9 Apr 2019).

28. "U.S. Social Security Applications and Claims Index, 1936–2007," Betty Robb Stadler, 1943, *Ancestry* (https://ancestry.com : accessed 9 April 2019).

29. *Find A Grave,* database and images (https://www.findagrave.com : accessed 9 April 2019), memorial page for Alyce Bette Robb Jones (9 Jun 1922–27 Jun 1998), Find A Grave Memorial no. 40332094, citing Seaside Memorial Park, Corpus Christi, Nueces County, Texas, USA ; Maintained by Dacanta (contributor 47158985). Names of the living have been changed or made private.

and Jack Kenneth Shaffer Sr., making them half-siblings. Bette was born in 1922 to Myrtle Hurley Robb, and Jack was born in 1926 to Eldon Mae Graham. Bette and Jack's children, Shandra and Jack Kenneth Shaffer Jr., share the appropriate amount of DNA for half-first cousins.

The marriage between Richard David Robb and Myrtle Hurley did not last, and the couple divorced on 5 November 1926 in Oklahoma.[30] The divorce record is an index only, and the website states "no further information available." Perhaps Richard's infidelity was the cause of the marriage failure, or maybe the infidelity was the result of an unhappy marriage.

Following his divorce in 1926, Richard David Robb moved back to Oklahoma City. The city directory of 1928 in Oklahoma City lists him again with Edith and notes his occupation as a cook.[31] By 1930, Richard had moved west to San Diego, California, where the 1930 census also lists him working as a cook in a restaurant.[32] He lived in a boarding house with several other men, all listed as lodgers. Although the informant for the census information is unknown, each man in the household probably provided his details. Richard's listing includes his age of 32 and his marital status as married with his age at the time of his first marriage as 23. This is close to his reported age of 24 on his marriage record to Myrtle Hurley. The 1930 listing also revealed his birthplace as Missouri and his parents' birthplaces as Virginia—good clues to discovering his origins.

Also noted on the 1930 census is Richard David Robb's service in the World War, which in 1930 referred to World War I. He registered for the draft on 24 August 1918 in Oklahoma City, Oklahoma.[33] The card lists several important details. His birthplace of Metz, Missouri, agrees with the 1930 census listing, but his father's birthplace is unknown. Perhaps Richard didn't know an exact place in Virginia, or perhaps as a young man, he really didn't know his father's birthplace and later learned of it. The details follow.

- ▪ Name: Richard Robb
- ▪ Age: 21 years

---

30. Oklahoma Historical Society Research Center, Divorce of Richard D. Robb and Myrtle Robb, 1926, https://www.okhistory.org : accessed 9 April 2019).

31. "U.S. City Directories, 1822–1995," for Richard D. Robb, 1928, Oklahoma City, Oklahoma, City Directory, *Ancestry* (https:/www.ancestry.com : accessed 9 Apr 2019).

32. 1930 U.S. Census, San Diego, California, population schedule, San Diego, enumeration district (ED) 83, sheet 10B (penned), dwelling 325A, family 373A, Richard D Robb lodger in Floyd E. Gordan household; digital image, *Ancestry*, (http://www.ancestry.com: accessed 10 Apr 2019); citing NARA microfilm publication T627.

33. "U.S., World War I Draft Registration Cards, 1917–1918," for Richard Robb, Oklahoma, Oklahoma City, Draft Board 2, Draft Card R, *Ancestry* (https://www.ancestry.com : accessed 10 Apr 2019).

- Date of birth: 29 June 1897
- Where born: Metz, Missouri
- Citizen of the United States
- Fathers birthplace: unknown
- Employer: Edwards Café in Oklahoma City
- Name of nearest relative: Mrs. Ophile Robb
- Address of nearest relative: Rt D2 Box 87, Garfield Arkansas
- Brown eyes, black hair, no physical disqualification

In August of 1918, American soldiers had just started arriving on the Western Front in Europe. The influx of new soldiers finally brought the war to an end with the signing of the armistice on 11 November 1918. Richard David Robb may have been among these soldiers. Unfortunately, 80% of the U.S. Army records from 1912–1906 were destroyed in the July 1973 fire at the National Personnel Records Center in St. Louis, Missouri. It is possible that a record for Richard David Robb did survive, and a search at the repository holding the remaining records could be conducted. The website Fold 3 specializes in military records, and a search for Richard David Robb found no results aside from the original draft registration card. [34] Newspapers of Oklahoma City could list soldiers, and his gravestone could give details of his service.

Edith joined Richard David Robb in California by 1932, where the San Diego city directory lists both individuals.[35] Richard is incorrectly noted as "Robt D," but the addition of Edith G to his entry provides evidence that this was the same person. Edith was also mentioned in her own right as the head nurse at the county hospital.

By 1940, Richard had become a salesman, working in the wholesale meat industry, and Edith was still working as a nurse in a hospital. [36] The census reveals that both Richard and Edith were in the "same place" in 1935, which correlates with the 1932 city directory listing. It also states that Richard was born in Missouri and Edith in Washington. He had completed an 8th-grade education, and she had completed two years of college. No children were listed on the census, although the couple had likely been together since

34. World War I, search for Richard David Robb, *Fold3* (https://www.fold3.com : accessed 10 Apr 2019).

35. "U.S. City Directories, 1822–1995," for Richard D. Robb, 1932, San Diego, California, City Directory, *Ancestry* (https://www.ancestry.com : accessed 9 Apr 2019).

36. 1940 U.S. Census, San Diego, California, population schedule, San Diego, enumeration district (ED) 62–29, sheet 6B (penned), house number 4231, family 86, Richard D Robb household; digital image, *Ancestry*, (http://www.ancestry.com: accessed 1(0 Apr 2019); citing NARA microfilm publication T627 roll 448.

1925 when they lived in Oklahoma City at 118 W 8th.[37]

Richard David Robb settled in San Diego with Edith. No marriage record has been located for the couple. Either they were never married, or it is possible that they married in an unusual location, and the record will surface in time. The FamilySearch Family Tree gives additional details for Edith. She was born 11 July 1891 in Washington and died 21 January 1973 in Fort Worth, Tarrant, Texas.[38] Her full name was Edith Ranier George.

When the United States entered World War II in 1941, Richard was required to register for the draft. His draft card reveals the following information.[39]

- Name: Richard David Robb
- Residence 4233 Front Street San Diego, California
- Age: 44 years
- Birth: 29 June 1897, Metz, Missouri
- Name and address of contact: Mrs. R.D. Robb 4233 Front St San Diego, California
- Employer: C. M. Kuhlken 1811—"C"
- Description: 5'9 ¼" 150 pounds, brown eyes, brown hair, dark complexion

No military records were discovered for Richard aside from his draft registration.[40] Because of his age, he probably never served in this war. The 1950 census has not yet been released, which would reveal more information about Richard. Still, the 1950 city directory of San Diego shows him and Edith residing on 4233 Front Street, the same address listed in the draft registration.[41] Richard worked as a salesman, and Edith supervised nurses at the county hospital.

Richard David Robb died on 26 August 1959, as reported in the California Death Index.[42] A death certificate could be ordered from the state of California that would include

---

37. "U.S. City Directories, 1822–1995," for Richard Robb, 1925, Oklahoma City, Oklahoma, City Directory, *Ancestry* (https://www.ancestry.com : accessed 9 Apr 2019).

38. *FamilySearch* Family Tree, details for Edith Ranier George LRGJ-4S4, (https://www.familysearch.org/tree/person/details/LRGJ-4S4 : accessed 11 Apr 2019).

39. "WWII Draft /Registration Cards for California, 1940–1947," Richard David Robb, order number 11,316, digital image, *Fold3* (https://www.fold3.com : accessed 19 Apr 2019).

40. "World War II," negative search for Richard David Robb, *Fold3* (https://www.fold3.com : accessed 10 Apr 2019).

41. "U.S. City Directories, 1822–1995," for Richard D. Robb, 1950, San Diego, California, City Directory, *Ancestry* (https://www.ancestry.com : accessed 9 Apr 2019).

42. "California Death Index," Richard David Robb, 26 August 1959, San Diego, *Ancestry* (https://ancestry.com : accessed 10 Apr 2019).

Table 3. Samuel D. Robb Household, 1900, Jasper County, Missouri

Locality	1900, Webb City, Joplin township, Jasper County, Missouri						
ED, Sheet, Line	Enumeration District 50, Sheets 30A & B, Line 48						
Enumeration Date	22 June 1900						
Location						Birth Place	
House	Family	Name	Birth Date	Relationship	Occupation	Self	Fath	Moth
595	627	Samuel D. Robb	Dec 1861	Head	Teamster	WV	WV	Penn
		Ella M. Robb	June 1862	Wife		WV	WV	WV
		Harry H. Robb	July 1885	Son	At school	WV	WV	WV
		William Robb	Nov 1888	Son	At school	Penn	WV	WV
		Mary Robb	Feb 1891	Daughter	At school	Pen	WV	WV
		Ella Robb	Jan 1893	Daughter	At school	Penn	WV	WV
		Margaret Robb	Jan 1895	Daughter		Penn	WV	WV
		Samuel Robb	Jun 1896	Son		MO	WV	WV

additional details. The indexed record does provide his father's surname as Robb and his mother's maiden name as Silverthorn, an excellent clue to prove his parentage.

Samuel David Robb and Ella Mae Silverthorn

Records created during the life of Richard David Robb serve to connect him to his parents, Samuel David Robb and Ella Mae Silverthorn. As mentioned previously, the California Death Index reports his mother's maiden name as Silverthorn and his father's surname as Robb. Richard repeatedly gave his full birth date as 29 June 1897 and his place of birth as Metz, Missouri.

A birth certificate could list parents, but Missouri did not begin keeping registration for births until 1910.[43] The first census listing Richard as a child is the 1900 census. Conflicting information found in the census record is the listing of "Samuel" instead of "Richard" for the son born in 1896. The month of June is correct, as is the birthplace of Missouri. Information for Ella indicated that she had borne seven children, and seven were living. Is the child listed as "Samuel," Richard David Robb?

The 1900 census household of Samuel and Ella Robb shows only six children, but

---

43. "Missouri Birth & Death Records Database, Pre-1910," negative search for Robb birth, *Missouri Digital Heritage* (https://s1.sos.mo.gov : accessed 10 Apr 2019).

Table 4. Samuel D. Robb Household, 1910, Jasper County, Missouri

Locality		1910, Carterville Ward 2, Joplin township, Jasper County, Missouri						
ED, Sheet, Line		Enumeration District 59, Sheet 2B, Line 69						
Enumeration Date		15 April 1010						
Location						Birth Place		
House	Family	Name	Age	Relationship	Occupation	Self	Fath	Moth
105	39	Samuel D. Robb	47	Head	Ground boss	WV	Unknown	Unknown
		Ella M. Robb	46	Wife		WV	WV	WV
		Harry Robb	23	Son	Machine man	WV	WV	WV
		William Robb	21	Son	Machine man	Penn	WV	WV
		Mary Robb	19	Daughter		Pen	WV	WV
		Ella Robb	17	Daughter		Penn	WV	WV
		Margaret Robb	15	Daughter		Penn	WV	WV
		Samuel Robb	12	Son		MO	WV	WV
		Lelia Robb	8	Daughter		Ark	WV	WV

the 1880 census sheds light on the question of Ella's children.[44] That census lists Ella as the youngest daughter in Eliza Silverthorn's household and reveals another child for Ella, Clifford Ashley Lodge. The census shows this child's relationship to Ella's mother as "grandson of youngest daughter, bastard."

The 1910 census lists the Samuel and Ella Robb family still residing in Jasper County, Missouri.[45] The census reports that Samuel and Ella had been married 28 years, were in their first marriage, and Ella was the mother of eight children with eight living. Added to the family since the 1910 census was a daughter, Lelia. Richard David Robb was still known as Samuel Robb. His age of 12 in April of 1910 correlates with a birth of June 1897, and his birthplace of Missouri also correlates with his reporting in his draft registration

44. 1880 U.S. Census, Hancock County, Missouri, population schedule, Poe District, enumeration district (ED) 221, page 5, dwelling 46, family 47, Eliza J. Silverthorn household; digital image, *Ancestry*, (http://www.ancestry.com: accessed 10 Apr 2019); citing NARA microfilm publication T9.

45. 1910 U.S. Census, Jasper County, Missouri, population schedule, Joplin Township, Carterville City, enumeration district (ED) 59, sheet 2B, house 105, dwelling 38, family 39, Samuel D. Robb household; digital image, *Ancestry*, (http://www.ancestry.com: accessed 10 Apr 2019,); citing NARA microfilm publication T623.

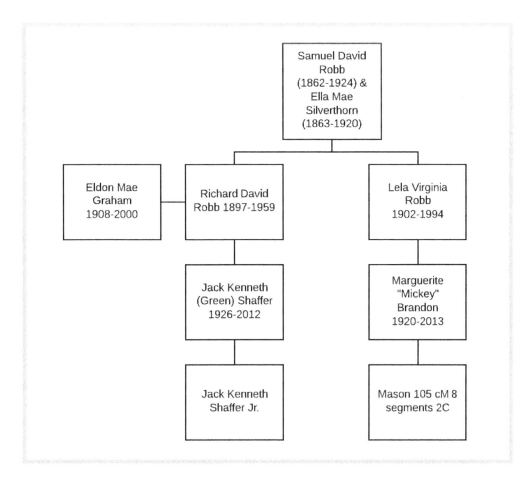

Figure 2. Diagram Showing Relationships of DNA Match to Tester Jack Kenneth Shaffer Jr.

information. It appears that sometime between the 1910 census and the 1918 draft registration, "Samuel" became "Richard David."

In 1910, Samuel D. Robb worked as the ground boss for the Lead & Zinc mine in Jasper County, Missouri, with his two oldest sons. The birthplaces of the children from the 1910 census listing give clues as to the approximate migration of the family: West Virginia > 1888 Pennsylvania > 1896 Missouri > 1902 Arkansas > by 1910 Missouri.

With the conflicting evidence of "Samuel" versus "Richard David" Robb, autosomal DNA evidence again provided further proof of the relationship of Richard David Robb to parents Samuel David Robb and Ella Mae Silverthorn. Ancestry DNA showed a match for Jack Kenneth Shaffer Jr, grandson of Richard David Robb, with Mason, grandson of Lela

Virginia Robb.[46] The amount of DNA shared was 105 centimorgans across eight segments, within the range for 2nd cousins.[47]

The family tree attached to the DNA match, Mason, provided proof of Lela Virginia Robb's parents, her marriage to Jack Edgar Brandon, and her daughter, Marguerite "Mickey" Brandon.[48] Analyzing the relationships showed that Jack and Mason share great grandparents, Samuel David Robb and Ella Mae Silverthorn, as shown in the following chart.[49]

Conclusion

At this point in the research session, time had expired. Much had been accomplished through DNA and documentary research. The evidence shows the father of Jack Kenneth Shaffer to be Richard David Robb. Richard had married Myrtle Hurley in 1921 but lived with Edith George in Oklahoma City in the mid-1920s. The 1925 Oklahoma City directory lists Richard Robb and Eldon Graham in the same neighborhood. Their relationship is unknown, but the result was the child born in 1926 and named Jack Kenneth Green by his mother, Eldon. Eldon also used the surname Green in the 1930 census and some city directory listings.

Richard David Robb divorced Myrtle Hurley and moved to San Diego, where he lived the rest of his life with Edith George. No marriage record has been discovered for them. Eldon Graham married R. T. Shaffer on 25 December 1931, who adopted Jack Kenneth Shaffer.

Researching the previous generation of Robb's discovered the family of Samuel David Robb and Ella Mae Silverthorn, the parents of Richard David Robb. In 1900 and 1910, the household of Samuel David Robb included a son named Samuel, who was born about the same time as Richard David Robb. Samuel likely changed his name to Richard David

---

46. "AncestryDNA Results for Jack Kenneth Shaffer Jr," database report, *AncestryDNA* (https://ancestry. com/dna : accessed 18 July 2020), predicting 2nd cousin genetic match with user "J.M." "J.M." identifies his great grandparents as Samuel David Robb (1862–1924) and Ella Mae Silverthorn (1863–1920).

47. Blaine T. Bettinger, "The Shared cM Project 4.0 tool v4," *DNA Painter* (https://dnapainter.com/tools/ sharedcmv4/110 : accessed 16 July 2020), relationships for 343 cM.

48. "Public Member Trees," database, *Ancestry* (http://www.ancestry.com : accessed 18 July 2020), "Jay Miller Family Tree : family tree by Jay Miller, profile for Lela Virginia Robb (1901–1894, married to Jack Edgar Brandon), documented data.

49. "DNA Matches for Jack Kenneth Shaffer Jr.," Lucid Chart, created 9 April 2019.

Robb in adulthood. DNA evidence provided additional confirmation of the connection of Richard David Robb to his parents.

Suggestions for Future Research

- Order the birth certificates for Jack Kenneth Green from the state of Oklahoma. Will need to provide proof of relationship and death of Jack Kenneth Shaffer
  - Jack Kenneth Shaffer
  - Jack Kenneth Green
- Search newspapers of 1918–1920 of Oklahoma City, Oklahoma, for lists of soldiers serving in WWI for Richard David Robb.
- Search for the cemetery/headstone for Richard David Robb. Military details could be given in those records created at death and burial.
- Order the death certificate of Richard David Robb from the state of California. Richard died on 26 August 1959.
- Search California marriage records for the marriage of Richard David Robb and Edith George about 1930.
- Continue researching the Robb lines seeking additional DNA evidence.

Thanks for allowing me to research your family! I look forward to continuing as desired.

Diana Elder AG®

Sample 2: Who was the Father of Barsheba (Tharp) Dyer?

Prepared by Nicole Elder Dyer, 1 March 2021

Finding a woman's parents in the early 1800s is challenging. No original record names the father of Barsheba (Tharp) Dyer. One son's death certificate provides her maiden name.[1] Two county courthouse fires in Tennessee and Arkansas complicate the search for parental connections. Family records, proximity, and naming patterns provide clues to Barsheba Tharp's family of origin. DNA matches provide evidence of kinship between Barsheba and the Tharp family who migrated from Fauquier County, Virginia, to Hawkins County, Tennessee.

John Robert and Barsheba Dyer

Descendants of Barsheba Tharp and John Robert Dyer believe Barsheba was born 8 September 1813 in Hawkins County, Tennessee, a daughter of a John Lewis Tharp or John Robert Tharp.[2] Family lore says Barsheba and Robert were both orphans who "met when both were working."[3] Barsheba and Robert probably married about 1830, but no marriage

---

1. "Tennessee Deaths, 1914–1966," database with images, *FamilySearch* (https://familysearch.org/ ark:/61903/1:1:NS8L-22N : 22 Aug 2020), Hawkins County, Richard F. Dyer, 3 Feb 1921, file no. 18; citing Tennessee State Library and Archives, Nashville. Informant Bob Luster reported Richard's mother's maiden name as "Marsha Thorp," and birthplace, Tennessee.

2. Nancy Mildred Beals DeWitt, "Dyer-Tharp Family History," unpublished family history, p. 1; image online, contributed by FamilySearch user "dale howard," attached to Barsheba Tharp, ID LZKK-MM7, 10 October 2019, *FamilySearch Family Tree* (https://www.familysearch.org : accessed 22 Aug 2020). See also Nancy Mildred Beals DeWitt, "John Robert Dyer and Barsheba Tharpe: Valley of The Terrapins, Slow and Steady Wins the Race," article online, contributed by LindaCroy1, attached to John Robert Dyer (LZKV-1TV), 10 April 2016, *FamilySearch* (https://www.familysearch.org : accessed 22 Aug 2020). This is an expanded draft of Nancy's Dyer-Tharp history. The date of the writing of this article is unknown, but must have occurred before Nancy Mildred Beals DeWitt died in 2009.

3. DeWitt, "Dyer-Tharp Family History," p. 1.

records are extant for the couple.[4] Hawkins County experienced significant record loss in an 1863 courthouse fire, perhaps explaining the missing record.[5]

Barsheba and her family resided in Hawkins County, Tennessee, in December 1879 when her husband, Robert Dyer, passed away.[6] Six months after Robert's death, Barsheba was enumerated on the 1880 census in Hawkins County as a sixty-four-year-old widow, born about 1816 in Tennessee, with Tennessee-born parents.[7] Barsheba remained in Hawkins until March 1889 when she migrated with her children by train to Sanford, Colorado and died there on 12 May 1889.[8] No civil death record or headstone has been located for Barsheba Dyer.[9]

Barsheba's Birth and Marriage

Barsheba Tharp's birth year conflicts in the records. Robert Dyer's 1830 household

---

4. Hawkins County Archival Project, Marriage License and Bonds Index 1789–1844, p. 3, negative search for Dyer; images online, *FamilySearch* (https://www.familysearch.org/ark:/61903/3:1:3QS7-9923-27W2 : accessed 5 Feb 2021). See also "Tennessee, County Marriages, 1790–1950," database with images, *FamilySearch* (https://familysearch.org : accessed 26 Sep 2020), negative search for Robert Dyer and Barsheba Tharp.

5. "Lost Records: Courthouse Fires and Disasters in Tennessee," *Tennessee Secretary of State* (https://sos.tn.gov : accessed 22 Aug 2020).

6. 1880 U.S. census, Hawkins County, Tennessee, mortality schedule, 4th District, p. 999, line 10, family 171, John R. Dyer; database with images, *Ancestry* (https://ancestry.com : accessed 22 Aug 2020); citing National Archives publication T655, roll 29. In most records of his life, John Robert Dyer went by Robert Dyer.

7. 1880 U.S. census, Hawkins County, Tennessee, pop. sch., District 4, dwelling 166, family 171, Barchebe Dyer; database with images, *Ancestry* (https://www.ancestry.com : accessed 22 Aug 2020); citing National Archives microfilm publication T9, roll 1260.

8. DeWitt, "Dyer-Tharp History," 4.

9. Negative search for death record of Barsheba Tharp in Conejos County, Colorado, email from county clerk to author, author's files. Negative search for death record in Alamosa County, Colorado, email from county clerk to author, author's files. Before 1900, some death records were kept on a county level. After 1900, they were kept by the state. See "How to Find Colorado Death Records," *FamilySearch Wiki* (https://www.family-search.org/wiki/en : last edited on 10 January 2018, at 17:03.) *Findagrave.com*, database, negative search for Barsheba Dyer, (https://findagrave.com : accessed 9 Oct 2020). *Billion Graves*, database, negative search for Barsheba Dyer, (https://billiongraves.com : accessed 9 Oct 2020). Lois Broyles, Fox Creek Cemetery records, Conejos County, Colorado, negative search for Barsheba Tharp; digitized manuscript, *FamilySearch* (http://www.familysearch.org/library/books/idurl/1/787138 : accessed 9 Oct 2020).

included himself, age 15–19, and one female, age 10–14, almost certainly Barsheba.[10] Robert and Barsheba's first son, Augustus, was born 13 December 1830 or 1831, consistent with their marriage year being about 1830.[11] Barsheba's age in 1830 means she was born about 1816 1820, probably 1816–1818 if she was age 12–14 when married. Tennessee had no law about minimum age at marriage in 1830.[12] English common law, which early Americans followed, suggested a minimum marriage age of 12 for girls with the consent of their parents.[13] Ages in later censuses conflict with the birth year range of 1816–1818 deduced from the 1830 census and marriage age. See table 1 for a comparison of Barsheba's age from census to census.

Barsheba was in a younger age category than Robert on the 1830 census, yet in 1850 the couple's ages were listed as the same. This was likely resulted from the informant's imperfect memory. Barsheba's great-granddaughter reported Barsheba's birth date as 8 September 1813 but did not cite a source.[14] The 1870 census reports Robert's age as 5 years younger than Barsheba's and gives Robert's birthplace as North Carolina. All other enumerations state he was born in Tennessee, indicating the 1870 census was an outlier.[15] No other census lists Robert as younger than Barsheba. Perhaps the enumerator inadvertently swapped their ages. Robert's birth in 1813 and Barsheba's in 1818 agrees with the other evidence. In 1860 and 1880, Barsheba was reportedly several years younger than Robert, agreeing that he was older as the 1830 census reported.

---

10. 1830 U.S. census, Hawkins County, Tennessee, p. 22, line 5, Robert Dyer; database with images, *FamilySearch* (https://www.familysearch.org : accessed 22 Aug 2020); citing National Archives microfilm publication M19, roll 178.

11. 1900 U.S. census, Hawkins County, Tennessee, 4th Civil District, E.D. 79, sheet 14A, household of Augustus W. Dyer; database with images, *FamilySearch* (https://www.familysearch.org accessed 22 Aug 2020); citing National Archives microfilm publication T623. The 1900 census states Augustus was born in December 1830. For the relationship of Augustus to his parents and the 13 Dec 1831 birthdate, see DeWitt, "John Robert Dyer and Barsheba Tharpe: Valley of The Terrapins, Slow and Steady Wins the Race."

12. John Haywood and Robert L. Cobbs, *The Statute Laws of the State of Tennessee, of a Public and General Nature, Vol. 1* (Knoxville: F.S. Heiskell, 1831) 219–220; image copy, *Google Books* (https://www.google.com/books/edition/The_Statute_Laws_of_the_State_of_Tenness/pAVOAQAAIAAJ : accessed 24 Aug 2020).

13. William Blackstone, *Commentaries on the Laws of England: Book the First* (Oxford: Clarendon Press, 1765) 424; transcript online, *Project Gutenburg* (https://www.gutenberg.org/ : accessed 5 Feb 2021).

14. DeWitt, "Dyer-Tharp History," 1.

15. 1870 U.S. census, Hawkins County, Tennessee, pop. sch., 4th District, p. 5, dwelling 31, family 31, John R. Dyer household; database with images, *FamilySearch* (https://www.familysearch.org: accessed 22 Aug 2020); citing National Archives publication M593, roll 1535.

Table 1. Birth Year of Barsheba Tharp

Census	Birth Year	Barsheba's Age	Robert's Age
1830[a]	1816-1820	10-14	15-19
1840[b]	1811-1820	20-30	20-30
1850[c]	1813	37	37
1860[d]	1814	46	50
1870[e]	1813	57	52
1880[f]	1816	64	70 in 1879 at his death[g]

For documentation of Table 1, see Appendix.

The 1830 and 1880 censuses are the most reliable sources for Barsheba's birth year range:

- Barsheba was age 10–14 (b. 1816–1820) in the 1830 enumeration, when a young teen's age is more visually obvious and less likely to have been forgotten.
- Barsheba was age 64 (b. 1816) and the head of household in 1880. She probably informed the enumerator of her age, making it somewhat more likely to be accurate.

If the 1830 and 1880 censuses were the most accurate reports of Barsheba's age, and if she was at least age twelve before her marriage in about 1830, she was born about 1816–1818.

Dyer Children

Robert and Barsheba's household included eleven children from 1840–1860. Table 2 shows their names and ages.[16]

16. 1850 U.S. census, Hawkins County, Tennessee, pop. sch., District No. 15, p. 864, dwelling 91, family 91, Robert Dyer; database with images, *FamilySearch* (https://www.familysearch.org : accessed 22 Aug 2020); citing National Archives publication M432, roll 882.

Table 2. Children in Robert and Barsheba Dyer's Households, 1840–1860

	1840[a]	1850[b]	1860[c]
1	Male, age 10-14		
2	Male, age 5-9	William Dyer, age 17	
3	Female, age 5-9	Sarah Dyer, age 15	
4	Female, age 0-4	Mary Dyer, age 13	Mary Dyer, age 23
5	Male, age 0-4	Richard Dyer, age 11	
6		Lewis Dyer, age 9	Louis Dyer, age 17
7		Louisa Dyer, age 6	Eliza Dyer, age 15
8		Francis Dyer, age 3	Bettie Dyer, age 13
9		Charles Dyer, age 1	Cha[s] Dyer, age 11
10			Ja[s] Dyer, age 9
11			Melissa Dyer, age 7

a. 1840 U.S. census, Hawkins County, Tennessee, p. 66, line 17, Robert Dyer; database with images, FamilySearch (https://familysearch.org : accessed 22 Aug 2020); citing National Archives publication M704, roll 526.

b. 1850 U.S. Census, Hawkins County, Tennessee, population schedule, District No. 15, p. 864, dwelling 91, family 91, Robert Dyer; database with images, FamilySearch (https://www.familysearch.org : accessed 22 Aug 2020); citing National Archives publication M432, roll 882.

c. 1860 U.S. Census, Hawkins County, Tennessee, population schedule, 4th District, p. 185, dwelling 1321, family 1245, John R. Dyer; database with images, FamilySearch, (https://www.familysearch.org: accessed 22 Aug 2020); citing National Archives publication M635 Roll 1255.

The oldest child in Robert's 1840 household did not appear with the family in 1850. Family records state the oldest child of Robert and Barsheba was Augustus Dyer.[17]

Augustus Dyer, age 22, lived in District 15 of Hawkins County in 1850, the same district as Robert Dyer. Augustus' household included Cinda, age 18, and Josephine, 11

---

17. DeWitt, "Dyer-Tharp History," 2.

months.[18] Augustus Dyer obtained a bond to marry Lucinda Wood in Hawkins County on 7 November 1849 with bondsman William Tharp.[19] Augustus W. Dyer witnessed William Tharp's deed in 1850.[20] William Tharp's association with Barsheba's son and proximity to the Dyer family could indicate that he was a close relative of Barsheba.

Lewis Tharp Dyer

Family records provide a clue for the name of Barsheba's father. Nancy DeWitt, a great-granddaughter of Robert and Barsheba Dyer compiled a biographical sketch of the Dyer family. She listed their son Lewis as "Lewis Tharp Dyer."[21] Lewis's name was recorded with a middle initial on his death certificate—Lewis T. Dyer.[22] Census and military records list his name as Lewis Dyer.[23] Naming patterns can provide evidence of kinship, and in this

---

18. 1850 U.S. census, Hawkins County, Tennessee, pop. sch., District No. 15, p. 869, dwelling 128, family 128, Augustus Dyer; database with images, *FamilySearch* (https://www.familysearch.org : accessed 22 Aug 2020); citing National Archives publication M432, roll 882.

19. "Tennessee, County Marriages, 1790–1950," database with images, *FamilySearch* (https://familysearch.org/ark:/61903/1:1:V5HC-3KK : 22 Aug 2020), marriage bond, Augustus Dyer and Lucinda Woods, 7 Nov 1849, Hawkins, Tennessee; citing Tennessee State Library and Archives, Nashville.

20. Hawkins County, Tennessee, Deeds 20:459, William Tharp and Nathan Vernon to Rodham Chesnut, 15 May 1850, registered 18 May 1851; image online, *FamilySearch* (https://www.familysearch.org/ark:/61903/3:1:3Q9M-CSHM-GSVP-N : accessed 10 Feb 2021).

21. DeWitt, "Dyer-Tharp Family History," p. 3.

22. "Tennessee Deaths, 1914–1966," database with images, *FamilySearch* (https://familysearch.org/ark:/61903/1:1:N9PJ-35D : 23 August 2020), Lewis T. Dyer, no. 97, 14 Apr 1916, Persia, Hawkins, Tennessee; citing Tennessee State Library and Archives, Nashville.

23. Soldier's Application for Pension, Hawkins Tennessee, no. S1283, Louis Dyer (61st Infantry), 22 May 1893, Tennessee State Library and Archives, Nashville. Compiled service record, Lewis Dyer, Pvt., Co. B, 61 Tennessee Mounted Infantry (Confederate); "Compiled Service Records of Confederate Soldiers Who Served in Organizations from the State of Tennessee," database with images, *Fold3* (https://www.fold3.com/image/83742449 : accessed 24 Aug 2020); citing Carded Records Showing Military Service of Soldiers Who Fought in Confederate Organizations, compiled 1903 - 1927, documenting the period 1861 - 1865, Record Group 109, The National Archives. 1850 U.S. census, Hawkins County, Tennessee, pop. sch., District No. 15, p. 864, dwelling 91, family 91, Robert Dyer; database with images, *FamilySearch* (https://www.familysearch.org : accessed 22 Aug 2020); citing National Archives publication M432, roll 882. 1860 U.S. census, Hawkins County, Tennessee, pop. sch., 4th District, p. 185, dwelling 1321, family 1245, John R. Dyer; database with images, *FamilySearch*, (https://www.familysearch.org: accessed 22 Aug 2020); citing National Archives publication

(note continued on following page)

case, Lewis T. Dyer's name combined with family records provide a clue that Barsheba had a relative named Lewis Tharp.

The DeWitt biography of the Dyer family states that Barsheba and Robert were orphans when they met and married each other.[24] No Dyer parental candidates were living in Hawkins in 1830, only a 20–29-year-old Ephraim Dyer.[25] Robert Dyer may have been an orphan. However, evidence points to a possible father for Barsheba who was living in 1830 when she was probably married.

Tharp Connections

In 1840, Lewis Tharp and William Tharp were the only Tharp men in Hawkins County and were enumerated on the same page as Robert Dyer.[26] If Barsheba was born about 1816–1818, her father was probably born before 1800, making him at least 18 years old if Barsheba was born. William Tharp was born about 1809.[27] He was too young to be Barsheba's father but could have been another male relative. Lewis Tharp was born about

---

M635 Roll 1255. 1870 U.S. census, Davidson County, Tennessee, pop. sch., 5th District, Tennessee Asylum for the Insane, p. 36, line 15, L. Dyer; database with images, *FamilySearch* (https://familysearch.org : 24 Aug 2020); citing National Archives publication M593, roll 1521. 1880 U.S. census, Davidson County, Tennessee, pop. sch., Civil District 5, Enumeration District (ED) 65, insane asylum, p. 30, line 15, Lewis Dyer; database with images, *FamilySearch* (https://familysearch.org : 24 Aug 2020); citing National Archives publication T9. 1900 U.S. census, Hawkins County, Tennessee, pop. sch., Civil District 4, ED 79, sheet 15A, dwelling 261, family 263, Louis Dyer in household of Polly Luster; database with images, *FamilySearch* (https://familysearch.org : 24 Aug 2020); citing National Archives publication T623. 1910 U.S. census, Hawkins Count, Tennessee, pop. sch., Civil District 6, ED 118, sheet 6B, family 118, Lewis Dyer in household of William E. Early; database with images, *FamilySearch* (https://familysearch.org : 24 Aug 2020); citing National Archives publication T624, roll 1504.

24. Dewitt, "Dyer-Tharp Family History," 1.

25. 1830 U.S. census, Hawkins County, Tennessee, p. 20, line 4, Ephraim Dyer; database with images, *FamilySearch* (https://www.familysearch.org : accessed 22 Aug 2020); citing National Archives microfilm publication M19, roll 178.

26. 1840 U.S. census, Hawkins County, Tennessee, p. 66, line 17, Robert Dyer; database with images, *FamilySearch* (https://familysearch.org : accessed 22 Aug 2020); citing National Archives publication M704, roll 526. For no other Tharp men in Hawkins in 1840, see "1840 United States Federal Census," search for "Tharp" and variants in Hawkins County, Tennessee; database, *Ancestry* (https://www.ancestry.com/search/collections/8057/ ; accessed 24 Aug 2020). The only results were William Tharp and Lewis Tharp.

27. 1850 U.S. census, Hawkins County, Tennessee, pop. sch., District 14, p. 832, dwelling/household 21, William Tharp household; database with images, *Ancestry* (https://ancestry.com : accessed 6 Feb 2021); citing NARA microfilm publication M432, roll 822.

1786.[28] Lewis Tharp's name, age, and close proximity to Robert and Barsheba Dyer make him a likely candidate for Barsheba's father.

In 1830, Robert Dyer resided in Hawkins County two households away from William Tharp.[29] Five additional Tharp/Thorp men lived in Hawkins County in 1830, shown in table 3, but only two were old enough to be likely candidates for the father of Barsheba – Lewis Tharp and Robert Tharp.

Not many records are extant prior to 1830 for Hawkins County, Tennessee to identify Robert Tharp. No 1800–1820 federal census records are available for Hawkins County; most census records prior to 1830 for Tennessee were lost.[30] No will or probate records were located for Robert Tharp.[31] Robert Tharp's heirs paid taxes in District 16 of Hawkins County in 1836 and 1837, indicating he had passed away by 1836.[32] Robert Dyer and William Tharp were taxed in District 15 in 1836.[33] Robert Tharp did not live in the same 1836 tax district as Robert and Barsheba Dyer, nor did he live in proximity to the Dyers on the 1830 census. Robert Tharp can be eliminated because there is no evidence linking him as the father of Barsheba.

Lewis Tharp was not taxed in Hawkins in 1836 or 1837.[34] Perhaps he had aged out of

---

28. 1850 U.S. census, Washington County, Arkansas, pop. sch., White River, p. 358B, dwelling/family 106, Lewis Tharp household; image, Ancestry (https://ancestry.com : accessed 25 Aug 2020); citing NARA microfilm publication M432, roll 31.

29. 1830 U.S. census, Hawkins County, Tennessee, p. 22, line 5, Robert Dyer; database with images, *FamilySearch* (https://www.familysearch.org : accessed 22 Aug 2020); citing National Archives microfilm publication M19, roll 178. Ibid., line 7, William Tharp.

30. "Tennessee Census Records," *Tennessee Secretary of State* (https://sos.tn.gov/products/tsla/tennessee-census-records : accessed 24 Aug 2020). The 1810 census was lost except Grainger and Rutherford counties. The 1820 census is incomplete and most East Tennessee counties are missing, including Hawkins.

31. Hawkins County, Tennessee, Index to Wills, 1779–1975, negative search for Robert Tharp; "Tennessee Probate Court Files, 1795–1955," DGS 4726994, *FamilySearch* (https://www.familysearch.org : accessed 23 November 2018); citing FHL microfilm 1572779, item 2.

32. "Tennessee, Early Tax List Records, 1783–1895," Hawkins County, District no. 16, p. 562, line 16, Robert Tharp's heirs, 1836; database and images, *Ancestry* (https://ancestry.com : accessed 24 Aug 2020); citing Tennessee State Library and Archives, Nashville. See also "Tennessee, Early Tax List Records, 1783–1895," Hawkins County, District no. 16 p. 490, line 22, Robert Tharp's heirs, 1837; database and images, *Ancestry* (https://ancestry.com : accessed 24 Aug 2020); citing Tennessee State Library and Archives, Nashville.

33. "Tennessee, Early Tax List Records, 1783–1895," Hawkins County, District no. 15, p. 544, line 6, Robert Dyer, 1836; database and images, *Ancestry* (https://ancestry.com : accessed 24 Aug 2020); citing Tennessee State Library and Archives, Nashville. Ibid., p. 550, line 2, Wm Tharp.

34. "Tennessee, Early Tax List Records, 1783–1895," Hawkins County, negative search for Lewis Tharp in 1836 and 1837; database with images, *Ancestry* (https://ancestry.com : accessed 24 Aug 2020); citing Tennessee State Library and Archives, Nashville..

Table 3. Dyers and Tharps in Hawkins County, 1830

Name	Page and line	Household
Lewis Tharp	p. 17, line 16	male 40-49, female 30-39, 6 children under 10
Robert (& Barsheba Tharp) Dyer	p. 22, line 5	male 15-19, female 10-14
William Tharp	p. 22, line 7	male 20-29, female age 50-59, 5 enslaved people
Robert Thorp	p. 37, line 13	male 50-59, females 50-59 and 20-29, 3 children
William Thorp	p. 54, line 23	male 20-29, female age 15-19, 1 male under 5
Wilson Thorp	p. 54, line 24	male 20-29 years
John Tharp	p. 64, line 23	male 20-29, female 20-29, 2 boys under 5

Source for table 3: 1830 U.S. census, Hawkins County, Tennessee, p. 17, line 16, Lewis Tharp; p. 22, line 5, Robert Dyer; p. 22, line 7, William Tharp; p. 37, line 13, Robert Thorp; p. 54, line 23, William Thorp; p. 54, line 24, Wilson Thorp; p. 64, line 23, John Tharp; database with images, *FamilySearch* (https://www.family-search.org : accessed 22 Aug 2020); citing National Archives microfilm publication M19, roll 178.

the poll tax. Lewis Tharp's 1840 household included a male age 50–59, female age 40–49, and six children ages 5–20.[35]

Lewis Tharp and John West of Fauquier County, Virginia

Lewis Tharp paid taxes in Hawkins County in 1810.[36] The non-alphabetized fragment of Captain Hale's 1810 company listed Lewis Tharp next to John West.[37] In 1829, Lewis Tharp

35. 1840 U.S. census, Hawkins County, Tennessee, p. 66, line 2, Lewis Tharp; database with images, *FamilySearch* (https://familysearch.org : accessed 22 Aug 2020); citing National Archives publication M704, roll 526.

36. Pollyanna Creekmore, "Early East Tennessee Taxpayers VIII., Hawkins County, 1809–1812," *The East Tennessee Historical Society Publications* (No. 32) p. 129, Hale's Company, 1810 [fragment], line 2, Lewis Tharp; image online, *Ancestry* (https://ancestry.com : accessed 24 Aug 2020) image 13 of 15; citing Tennessee State Library and Archives. The 1810, 1836, and 1837 tax lists are some of the few extant tax lists for Hawkins County.

37. Creekmore, "Early East Tennessee Taxpayers VIII., Hawkins County, 1809–1812," p. 129, Hale's Company, 1810 [fragment], line 3, John West.

and John West Sr. posted bond for John West Jr. in a murder trial in Hawkins County.[38] This proximity and association in Hawkins County indicate that Lewis Tharp and John West may have known each other before arriving in Hawkins.

Lewis Tharp and John West likely came to Hawkins County from Fauquier County, Virginia. Lewis Tharp procured a bond to marry Joanna West in Fauquier County on 14 January 1805. Permission was granted by Joanna's father, John West, the bondsman was William West, and George Tharp was a witness.[39]

Lewis first appeared on personal property tax lists in Fauquier in 1800, listed as a free white tithe over 16 years with inferred father, Jesse Tharp.[40] In Virginia, male persons 16 and over were considered tithable and chargeable for levies.[41] If Lewis was 16 years old in 1800, he was born about 1784. Lewis was listed with Jesse again in 1802 and 1803.[42]

Children of Lewis Tharp and Joanna West

William Tharp

William Tharp, the bondsman for Augustus Dyer's marriage to Lucinda Woods, and close neighbor of Robert Dyer in 1830 and 1840, was probably the son of Lewis Tharp and

---

38. Hawkins County, Tennessee circuit court minutes April 1826–1829, p. 299, 4 April 1829, State of Tennessee vs. John West; image online, *FamilySearch* (https://www.familysearch.org/ark:/61903/3:1:3QHV-D3CD-P9XL-7 : accessed 27 Feb 2021).

39. Fauquier County, Virginia, Marriage Bonds and Returns 2:370, Tharp-West marriage bond, 14 Jan 1805; images online, *FamilySearch* (https://www.familysearch.org/ark:/61903/3:1:3QS7-L9XF-6BPB : accessed 18 Aug 2020), DGS 7578972, image 451 of 688; FHL microfilm # 31633.

40. Fauquier County, Virginia, personal property tax lists, 1800, Charles Pickett District, p. 64, line 6, Lewis Tharp in household of Jessee Tharp; images, *FamilySearch* (https://www.familysearch.org/ark:/61903/3:1:3Q9M-CSQ2-W1CY : accessed 24 Aug 2020); citing FHL microfilm 2024531.

41. Shepherd, Samuel, *The Statutes at Large of Virginia, From October Session 1792, to December Session 1806, Inclusive, In Three Volumes, (New Series,) Being a Continuation of Hening, Vol. 1* (Richmond: Samuel Shepherd, 1835) 184; image online, *Hathitrust* (https://babel.hathitrust.org : accessed 25 Sep 2020).

42. Fauquier County, Virginia, personal property tax lists, 1802, Thomas Humston District, p. 45, line 15 (https://www.familysearch.org/ark:/61903/3:1:3Q9M-CSQ2-WB33). Ibid., 1803, C. Pickett District, p. 62, line 1 (https://www.familysearch.org/ark:/61903/3:1:3Q9M-CSQ2-WYP1).

Joanna West:

- William Tharp and Lewis Tharp were enumerated on the same page of the 1840 census in Hawkins County, Tennessee[43]
- William Tharp named one of his sons John Lewis Tharp.[44]
- William was born about 1809.[45] Lewis was old enough to be his father.

Both William and Lewis Tharp were associated with the Vernon family. Lewis Tharp married his second wife, Judy Vernon, on 10 September 1817.[46] William probably married the widow of Abraham Vernon, Rebecca (Pike) Vernon, who was listed as "Rebecca Thorp, formerly Varnun" in an 1837 deed between William Tharp and Rebecca's heirs.[47] After Rebecca died, her sister and nephew sold their portion of Rebecca's inheritance from Abraham Vernon to William Tharp.[48] In 1830, William's Hawkins County household included himself, a male age 20–29, a white female age 50–59, and 5 enslaved people.[49] Rebecca was probably the 50–59 year old female in William Tharp's 1830 household. She likely died after 1830 and before the 1837 deed.

---

43. 1840 U.S. census, Hawkins County, Tennessee, p. 66, line 2, Lewis Tharp and line 8, William Tharp; database with images, *FamilySearch* (https://familysearch.org : accessed 22 Aug 2020); citing National Archives publication M704, roll 526.

44. Hawkins County, Tennessee, will papers, William Tharp, signed 17 November 1869, recorded March Term 1875; images online, *FamilySearch* (https://www.familysearch.org/ark:/61903/3:1:939L-6SS2-XV : accessed 1 March 2021); citing FHL microfilm 1572795.

45. 1850 U.S. census, Hawkins county, Tennessee, pop. sch., District 14, p. 416b, family 21, William Tharp, age 41; image online, *Ancestry* (https://ancestry.com : accessed 26 Sep 2020).

46. Hawkins County, Tennessee, marriage bonds, 10 Sep 1817, Lewis Tharp – Judy Vernon; images online, *FamilySearch* (https://www.familysearch.org/ark:/61903/3:1:939Z-Y393-Q2 : accessed 25 Aug 2020); citing FHL microfilm 1572805.

47. Hawkins County, Tennessee, Deeds 16:138–140, Samuel Pike and Ruth Comstock to William Tharp, 2 Oct 1837, registered 11 Nov 1837; image online, *FamilySearch* (https://www.familysearch.org/ark:/61903/3:1:3Q9M-CSHM-PQ58-7 : accessed 17 Feb 2021).

48. Hawkins County, Tennessee, Deeds 16:138–140, Samuel Pike and Ruth Comstock to William Tharp, 2 Oct 1837, registered 11 Nov 1837; image online, *FamilySearch* (https://www.familysearch.org/ark:/61903/3:1:3Q9M-CSHM-PQ58-7 : accessed 17 Feb 2021).

49. 1830 U.S. census, Hawkins County, Tennessee, pop. sch., p. 22, line 7; database with images, FamilySearch (https://www.familysearch.org : accessed 22 Aug 2020); citing National Archives microfilm publication M19, roll 178.

No marriage records were found in Hawkins County for William Tharp before 1840.[50] However, William probably remarried by 1840 when his household included himself, age 30–40, a female age 20–30, a female age 10–15, and one enslaved person.[51] In 1850, William Tharp's household included inferred wife Elizabeth and children Sarah, John, William, and Emily.[52]

William Tharp died about 1875. His will was signed 17 November 1867 and proved March 1875. His will mentions two sons—John Lewis Tharp and William Thomas Tharp, daughter Emily Louisa Tharp, his "present wife Elizabeth," and unnamed stepchildren.[53]

Elizabeth (Tharp) Parrott

Elizabeth Parrott, wife of John Parrott, who resided in Hawkins in 1830, was probably a daughter of Lewis Tharp and Joanna West.[54] John Parrott was enumerated three households from Lewis Tharp on the 1840 Census of Hawkins County.[55] In 1850, John and Elizabeth Parrott lived in Greene County, Tennessee. Elizabeth was age 35, born about 1815 in Tennessee. Their household included a boy named John Parrott, born 1842.[56]

---

50. Hawkins County Archival Project, Marriage License and Bonds Index 1789–1844, p. 11, negative search for William Tharp; images online, *FamilySearch* (https://www.familysearch.org/ark:/61903/3:1:3QS7-9923-2W39 : accessed 5 Feb 2021). See also "Tennessee, County Marriages, 1790–1950," database with images, *FamilySearch* (https://familysearch.org : accessed 26 Sep 2020), negative search for William Tharp bef. 1840.

51. 1840 U.S. census, Hawkins County, Tennessee, pop. sch., p. 255, line 8, William Tharp; database with images, *Ancestry* (https://ancestry.com : accessed 6 Feb 2021); citing NARA microfilm publication M704, roll 526.

52. 1850 U.S. census, Hawkins County, Tennessee, pop. sch., District 14, p. 832, dwelling/household 21, William Tharp household; database with images, *Ancestry* (https://www.ancestry.com : accessed 6 Feb 2021); citing NARA microfilm publication M432, roll 822.

53. Hawkins County, Tennessee, will papers, William Tharp, signed 17 November 1869, recorded March Term 1875; images online, *FamilySearch* (https://www.familysearch.org/ark:/61903/3:1:939L-6SS2-XV : accessed 1 March 2021), images 2730–2735; citing FHL microfilm 1572795.

54. 1830 U.S. census, Hawkins County, Tennessee, pop. sch., p. 10, line 25, John Parrot; database with images, *Ancestry* (https://www.ancestry.com : accessed 26 Sep 2020); citing NARA microfilm publication M19, roll 178. The household included a male age 2–29, female age 15–19, and female under 5.

55. 1840 U.S. census, Hawkins County, Tennessee, p. 66, line 5, John Parrott; database with images, *Ancestry* (https://www.ancestry.com : accessed 22 Aug 2020); citing National Archives publication M704, roll 526.

56. 1850 U.S. census, Greene County, Tennessee, pop. sch., Division 9, p. 244A, dwelling and family 1560, John Parrott household; images online, *Ancestry* (https://ancestry.com : accessed 25 Aug 2020); citing NARA microfilm publication M432.

John L. Parrott died 21 April 1922 in Illinois. [57] His death certificate stated he was born in Hawkins, Tennessee in 1844 and his parents were Elizabeth Thorp and Thomas Parrott. No man named Thomas Parrott lived in Hawkins, Tennessee in 1840.[58] The informant on John L. Parrott's death certificate was probably mistaken about John's father's name. The parents of John L. Parrot were almost certainly the John and Elizabeth Parrott living in Greene, Tennessee in 1850 with an 8-year-old boy named John.[59] See table 4.

Onomastic evidence ties Elizabeth (Tharp) Parrott to Lewis Tharp and Joanna West. The 1850 household of John and Elizabeth Parrott included a girl named Joannah who could have been named after Elizabeth's mother, Joanna (West) Tharp. Their household also included a girl named Barsheba who was possibly named after Elizabeth's younger sister, Barsheba (Tharp) Dyer. These names provide a clue that Elizabeth (Tharp) Parrott was the daughter of Lewis Tharp and Joanna West as well as a sister to Barsheba Tharp.

John and Elizabeth (Tharp) Parrott probably moved from Hawkins County before 1850 when they were enumerated in Green County, Tennessee.[60] No marriage record exists for John Parrott and Elizabeth Tharp in Hawkins County.[61] They were probably married just before John Parrott's enumeration on the 1830 census, when his household included one female age 15–19 (likely his wife Elizabeth) and one female under age 5.[62] This young female born before the 1830 enumeration was not included in the John Parrott 1850 census enumeration. By 1850, this inferred eldest daughter may have married. The 1848 marriage of Martha Ann Parrott to Richard Campbell in Hawkins County provides a likely candidate.[63]

---

57. "Illinois Deaths and Stillbirths, 1916–1947," database, *FamilySearch* (https://familysearch.org/ ark:/61903/1:1:N3XR-TYZ : 20 Aug 2020), indexed entry for John L. Parrott, 21 Apr 1922, died Lawrenceville, Lawrence county, Illinois; Public Board of Health, Archives, Springfield; citing FHL microfilm 1,556,731.

58. "1840 United States Federal Census," negative search for Thomas Parrott in Hawkins, Tennessee, *Ancestry* (https://www.ancestry.com/search/collections/8057/ : accessed 6 Feb 2021); citing NARA microfilm publication M704.

59. 1850 U.S. census, Greene County, Tennessee, pop. sch., Division 9, p. 244A, dwelling and family 1560, John Parrott household; images online, *Ancestry* (https://ancestry.com : accessed 25 Aug 2020); citing NARA microfilm publication M432.

60. Ibid.

61. "Tennessee, County Marriages, 1790–1950," database with images, *FamilySearch* (https://familysearch. org : accessed 26 Sep 2020), negative search for Elizabeth Tharp.

62. 1830 U.S. census, Hawkins County, Tennessee, pop. sch., p. 10, line 25, John Parrot; database with images, *Ancestry* (https://www.ancestry.com : accessed 26 Sep 2020); citing NARA microfilm publication M19, roll 178.

63. "Tennessee, Marriage Records, 1780–2002," database with images, Richard Campbell and Martha Ann Parrott, 21 Sept 1848, *Ancestry* (https://www.ancestry.com : accessed 25 Sep 2020).

Table 4. 1850 U.S. Census, Greene County, Tennessee, John Parrott Household

Name	Age	Birth year	Birthplace
John Parrott	44	1806	North Carolina
Elizabeth	35	1815	Tennessee
Rebecca	17	1833	Tennessee
Joannah	16	1834	Tennessee
Barsheba	12	1838	Tennessee
Reuben	10	1840	Tennessee
John	8	1842	Tennessee
William	6	1844	Tennessee
Robert	2	1848	Tennessee
Frances	1	1849	Tennessee

1850 U.S. census, Greene County, Tennessee, population schedule, Division 9, p. 244A, dwelling and family 1560, John Parrott household; images online, *Ancestry* (https://ancestry.com : accessed 25 Aug 2020); citing NARA microfilm publication M432.

If Elizabeth (Tharp) Parrott was born in 1815, she was almost certainly a daughter of Lewis Tharp's first wife, Joanna West. The 1860 and 1880 censuses agree that Elizabeth was born in 1815.[64] The 1870 census states that Elizabeth was born in 1810, which is still within the time of Lewis Tharp's marriage to Joanna West.[65]

Another possibility is that Elizabeth (Tharp) Parrot was the daughter of Robert Tharp who lived in Hawkins County and was deceased by 1836, where his heirs were taxed

64. 1860 U.S. census, Alexander County, Illinois, pop. sch., Clear Creek Post Office, p. 96, dwelling/family 650, Elizabeth Parrott in John Parrott household; image online, *Ancestry* (https://ancestry.com : accessed 25 Aug 2020); citing NARA microfilm publication M653. See also 1880 U.S. census, Union County, Illinois, pop. sch., Dongola, E.D. 118, p. 112B, dwelling 194, Elizabeth Parrott household; image online, *Ancestry* (https://ancestry.com : accessed 25 Aug 2020); citing NARA microfilm publication T9, roll 254.

65. 1870 U.S. census, Alexander County, Illinois, pop. sch., Clear Creek, p. 121B, Elizabeth Parrott in household of James Wallace; image online, *Ancestry* (https://ancestry.com : accessed 25 Aug 2020); citing NARA microfilm publication M593, roll 188.

in District 16.[66] In 1836, John Parrott was taxed in District 3, which did not include any Tharps.[67] No evidence points to Robert Tharp as Elizabeth (Tharp) Parrot's father, except possibly the naming of a son Robert. Evidence does point to Lewis Tharp:

■ Elizabeth's husband John Parrott resided four households from Lewis Tharp in 1840
■ Elizabeth's daughters were named Joannah and Barsheba, possibly after Elizabeth's mother and younger sister. Elizabeth named a son John L. Parrott, and his middle initial could have been Lewis.
■ Elizabeth's oldest daughter, Martha Ann Parrott, lived near William Tharp in 1850[68]
■ Martha Ann Parrott's husband, Richard H. Campbell, witnessed William Tharp's deed[69]

DNA matches between descendants of Elizabeth Tharp and Barsheba Tharp also add evidence that the women were sisters – with Lewis Tharp as the most likely father.

DNA Study

Autosomal DNA (atDNA) is passed from parent to child and can reveal information about ancestors up to 5–7 generations back, if many test takers' results are analyzed.[70] Autosomal

---

66. "Tennessee, Early Tax List Records, 1783–1895," Hawkins County, District no. 16, p. 562, line 16, Robert Tharp's heirs, 1836.

67. "Tennessee, Early Tax List Records, 1783–1895," Hawkins County, District no. 3, p. 437, line 16, John Parrott, 1836.

68. 1850 U.S. census, Hawkins County, Tennessee, pop. sch., District 14, p. 832, dwelling/family 19, Richard Campbell household; image online, *Ancestry* (https://www.ancestry.com : accessed 6 Feb 2021); citing NARA microfilm M432, roll 882. For William Tharp, see dwelling/household 21. For Martha as a daughter of Elizabeth, see Nicole Dyer, "Parents of Martha Ann Parrott," *Family Locket* (https://familylocket.com/barsheba-tharp-proof-argument/ : accessed 2 March 2021).

69. Hawkins County, Tennessee, Deeds 20:459, William Tharp and Nathan Vernon to Rodham Chesnut, 15 May 1850, registered 18 May 1851; image online, *FamilySearch* (https://www.familysearch.org/ark:/61903/3:1:3Q9M-CSHM-GSVP-N : accessed 10 Feb 2021).

70. Michelle Leonard, Alasdair F. Macdonald, Graham S. Holton, "Why use DNA Testing for Genealogy?" in Graham S. Holton, ed., *Tracing Your Ancestors Using DNA* (South Yorkshire, England: Pen & Sword Family History, 2019) 2.

DNA tests look at genetic data from the 22 chromosome pairs, one copy received from the father, one copy received from the mother. The 23rd chromosome pair are the sex chromosomes, X and Y, and atDNA sometimes includes matches on the X-chromosome, but not the Y-chromosome. The parent-child relationship is the only one that shares an exact amount of DNA. Other relationships must be compared with additional records to determine the relationship.[71] Close family, first cousins, and second cousins will always share DNA.[72] Third cousins and beyond may not be a genetic match to each other because of the random recombination of DNA during meiosis.[73] Children share 50% of their DNA with each parent, but not an even 25% with each grandparent. They may have inherited 20% from their maternal grandmother and 30% from their maternal grandfather. Because of this, amounts of shared DNA between two individuals can indicate several relationships.

Methodology

Autosomal DNA results were compared at GEDmatch, AncestryDNA, MyHeritage DNA, and 23andMe. To reduce the odds of including matching segments that are not identical by descent, the following strategies were used:

- Segments smaller than 7 cM were not included in the comparisons.
- All matching segments included have over 700 SNPs.
- Total shared DNA amounts were compared against statistical norms using the Shared cM project tool

To reduce the odds of attributing shared DNA to the wrong ancestor, these strategies were used:

- The kits that were uploaded to GEDmatch were checked with the "Are Your Parents Related" tool
- Pedigree evaluations were completed to check for more than one common ancestor

---

71. Michelle Leonard, "Understanding the Principles of DNA Testing for Genealogy," in Graham S. Holton, ed., *Tracing Your Ancestors Using DNA* (South Yorkshire, England: Pen & Sword Family History, 2019) 38.

72. "Cousin Statistics," *International Society of Genetic Genealogy Wiki* (https://isogg.org/wiki/Cousin_statistics : last edited on 4 August 2020, at 20:49).

73. Michelle Leonard, "Understanding the Principles of DNA Testing for Genealogy," in Graham S. Holton, ed., *Tracing Your Ancestors Using DNA* (South Yorkshire, England: Pen & Sword Family History, 2019) 38.

DNA Testers

Each DNA tester gave consent to be included in this study. Their names have been anonymized for privacy. Fourteen documented descendants of Barsheba Tharp are included in Group A shown in figure 1.[74]

Five documented descendants of Lewis Tharp and Joanna West are in Group B, shown in figure 2. Additional DNA matches who descend from Lewis Tharp and Joanna West were located but did not respond to requests to be included in this study. Table 5 compares the shared DNA between descendants of Lewis and his first wife Joanna and the descendants of Barsheba Tharp. The shared DNA indicates a genetic relationship between descendants of Elizabeth Tharp and descendants of Barsheba Tharp, providing confirmation of the hypothesis presented that both were daughters of Lewis Tharp.

Lewis Tharp's Second Marriage

Joanna (West) Tharp died sometime before his second marriage in 1817. No death record has been located for Joanna West.[75] Lewis Tharp signed a marriage bond to marry Judy Vernon in Hawkins County, Tennessee on 10 September 1817.[76] The bondsman was Nathan Vernon, probably Judy's father, witnessed by Willie B. Mitchell. Lewis Tharp's marriage to Judy Vernon occurred within the years that Barsheba Tharp was born, about 1816–1818. Future research will be required to determine which wife of Lewis Tharp was the mother of Barsheba.

74. The test takers and matches gave permission for their name and DNA match details to be included in this report. Some test takers agreed to be included but declined to include their full names.

75. *Findagrave*, database, negative search for Joanna/Joanna Tharp, d. before 1817, (https://findagrave.com : accessed 26 Sep 2020). See also *Cemeteries of Hawkins County, Tennessee* Vols. 1–3 (Rogersville, TN: Hawkins County Genealogy Society, 1985–1991), negative search for Joanna Tharp; images online, *FamilySearch* (https://www.familysearch.org/search/catalog/433504 : accessed 26 Sep 2020).

76. Hawkins County, Tennessee, marriage bonds, 10 Sep 1817, Lewis Tharp – Judy Vernon; images online, *FamilySearch* (https://www.familysearch.org/ark:/61903/3:1:939Z-Y393-Q2?i=688&cc=1619127 : accessed 25 Aug 2020); citing FHL microfilm 1572805.

Children of Lewis Tharp and Judy Vernon

Lewis Tharp and Judy Vernon had eight children in their household from 1830–1850, as shown in table 6.

Lewis, Judy, and six of their children migrated to White River, Washington County, Arkansas before 1846 when Jesse Tharp married Eliza Robinson.[77] Lewis and Judy were enumerated with their youngest daughter Lucy in 1850.[78] Married children Anna, Mary, Matilda, and Jesse were all enumerated with their inferred spouses and children families on the same page as each other on the 1850 census.[79] Joanna [Tharp] Farris lived in neighboring Madison County.[80] Probable son Nathan Tharp was married in White River in 1847, but died in 1849 on his way to California.[81]

Lewis Tharp died 25 October 1853 and was buried in Reese Cemetery, Hicks, Washington County, Arkansas.[82] The courthouse in Washington County burned in 1862.[83] No will or probate records were found for Lewis Tharp.[84] Judy continued to reside in

---

77. "Arkansas, Washington County Marriage Records, 1845–1941," Jesse Tharp and Eliza Robinson, 17 Sep 1846.

78. 1850 U.S. census, Washington County, Arkansas, pop. sch., White River, p. 358B, dwelling/family 106, Lewis Tharp household; image online, *Ancestry* (https://ancestry.com : accessed 25 Aug 2020); citing NARA microfilm publication M432, roll 31.

79. Ibid., p. 355a, dwelling/family 54, Anna in household of Wiley Roberts. Ibid., dwelling/family 56, Mary Woods in William H Woods household. Ibid., dwelling/family 59, Matilda in Robert Robison household. Ibid., dwelling /family 60, Jesse Tharp household; (https://ancestry.com).

80. 1850 U.S. census, Madison County, Arkansas, pop. sch., War Eagle, p. 301b, dwelling/family 740, Joanna in Anderson J. Farris household; https://www.ancestry.com).

81. "Arkansas, Washington County Marriage Records, 1845–1941," Nathan Tharp and Mary Van Hoose, 24 Sep 1848. For Nathan's death, see "Thirty-six Years Ago," *Fayetteville (Arkansas) Weekly Democrat*, 16 Apr 1885, p. 3, col. 5; image online, *Newspapers* (https://www.newspapers.com/image/273399454# : accessed 26 Sep 2020).

82. *Find a Grave*, database and images (https://www.findagrave.com/memorial/41677826/lewis-tharp : accessed 25 August 2020), memorial page for Lewis Tharp (1783–25 Oct 1853), Find a Grave Memorial no. 41677826, citing Reese Cemetery, Hicks, Washington County, Arkansas, USA; Maintained by ctwardo (contributor 47093149), headstone photo by S Barger (contributor 47414911).

83. "History of the Historic Washington County Court House," *Washington County Arkansas* (https://www.washingtoncountyar.gov : accessed 26 Sep 2020).

84. Washington County, Arkansas probate, Will Records A-B, negative search for Lewis Tharp; images, *FamilySearch* (https://www.familysearch.org/search/catalog/23513 : accessed 26 Sep 2020).

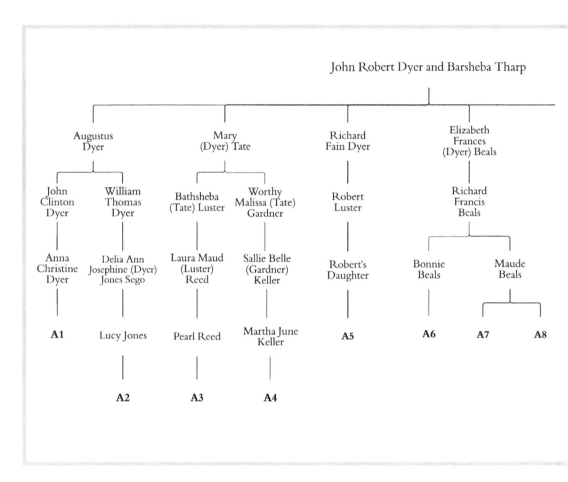

Figure 1. Descendants of John Robert Dyer and Barsheba Tharp (Group A)

For documentation of parent-child links in Figure 1, see appendix.

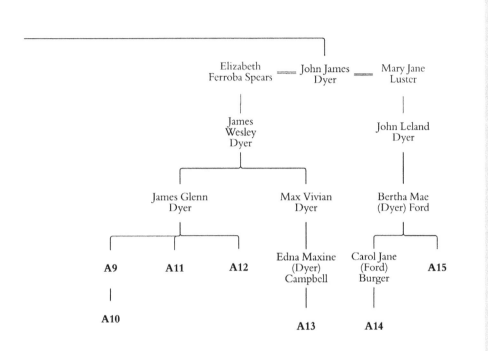

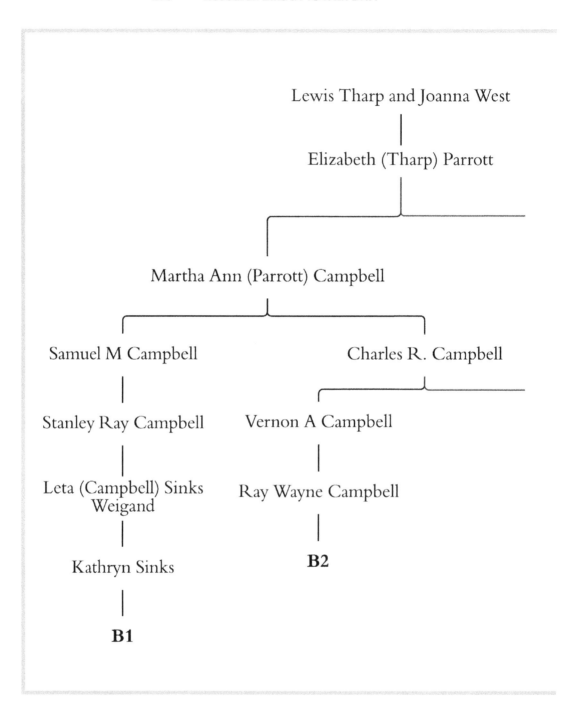

Figure 2. Descendants of Lewis Tharp and Joanna West (Group B)

For documentation of parent-child links in Figure 2, see appendix.

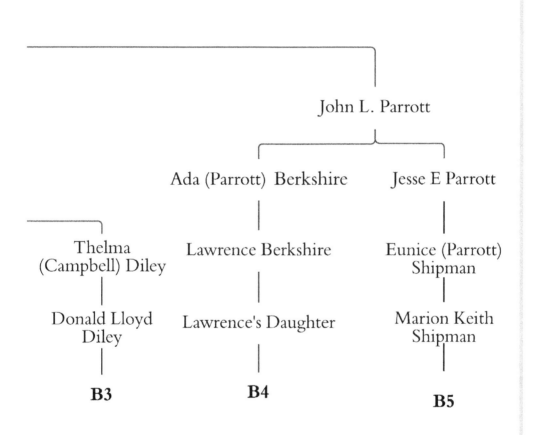

Table 5. Shared DNA between Group B and Group A

Lewis / Joanna Descendant	Barsheba Descendant	Total Shared DNA (cM)	Hypothesized Relationships	Predicted Shared cM Range - Full	Predicted Shared cM Range - Half
B1	A3	11	Full or Half 5C1R	0-80	No data
B1	A9	18	Full or Half 4C2R	0-93	No data
B1	A11	30	Full or Half 4C2R	0-93	No data
B1	A12	29	Full or Half 4C2R	0-93	No data
B2	A9	16.3	Full or Half 4C1R	0-126	No data
B2	A13	34	Full or Half 5C	0-117	No data
B2	A4	10.9	Full or Half 5C	0-117	No data
B2	A7	13.3	Full or Half 4C1R	0-126	No data
B2	A6	15	Full or Half 4C1R	0-126	No data
B3	A9	10	Full or Half 4C1R	0-126	No data
B3	A6	13	Full or Half 4C1R	0-126	No data
B3	A13	14	Full or Half 5C	0-117	No data
B3	A5	11	Full or Half 4C1R	0-126	No data
B3	A12	11	Full or Half 4C1R	0-126	No data
B3	A7	10	Full or Half 4C1R	0-126	No data
B4	A1	17	Full or Half 4C1R	0-126	No data
B4	A9	8	Full or Half 4C1R	0-126	No data
B5	A9	16	Full or Half 4C1R	0-126	No data
B5	A6	20	Full or Half 4C1R	0-126	No data
B5	A7	28	Full or Half 4C1R	0-126	No data

Sources for Table 5: "One-to-One Autosomal DNA Comparison" *GEDmatch* (https://www.gedmatch. com), kits A188998 (B2), A534458 (A9), NT5439655 (A11), PA1661722 (A12), ZM3328588 (A13), A024243 (A4), A260471 (A7); default options (Build 37) with "Prevent Hard Breaks" selected. The kits of A3, A6, B1, B3, B4, and B5 were not uploaded to GEDmatch. Their matches were analyzed using AncestryDNA tools. "DNA Matches," *AncestryDNA* (https://ancestry.com/dna/ : accessed 23 Sep 2020).

Table 6. Children Lewis Tharp's Households, 1830–1850

	1830[a]	1840[b]	185[c]	Name
1	Female, age 5-9			Anna Tharp, b. 1820, md. abt. 1837[d]
2	Female, age 5-9			Joanna Tharp, b. 1821, md. 1837[e]
3	Male, age 5-9	Male, age 15-19		*unknown*
4	Male, age 5-9	Male, age 15-19		Jesse Tharp, b. 1825, md. 1846[f]
5	Male, age 0-4	Male, age 10-14		Nathan Tharp, b. 1825, md. 1848[g]
6	Female, age 0-4	Female, age 15-19		Matilda Tharp, b. 1826, md. 1847[h]
7		Female, age 5-9		Mary Tharp, b. 1830-31, md. 1847[i]
8		Female, age 5-9	Lucy Tharp, age 17	Lucy Tharp, b. 1833 [j]

For documentation of Table 6, see Appendix.

Washington County in 1860 and 1870.[85] Census records indicate that she was born in 1795 in North Carolina. She died 4 September 1879 and was buried in Reese Cemetery next to Lewis Tharp.[86]

Descendants of Lewis Tharp and Judy Vernon

Figure 3 shows eight documented descendants of Lewis Tharp and Judy Vernon. Table 7 compares the shared DNA between Lewis and Judy's descendants and the descendants of Barsheba Tharp. The amount of shared DNA is consistent with both half and full fourth cousin relationships. The Shared cM project reports that the fourth cousin (4C) relationship typically shares 0–139 cM and an average of 35. The fourth cousin once removed (4C1R) relationship typically shares 0–126 cM and an average of 28 cM.[87]

---

85. 1860 U.S. census, Washington County, Arkansas, pop. sch., White River, p. 790, dwelling 2114, family 183, Judia Tharp, age 66, servant in household of Clark Mason; images, *Ancestry* (https://www.ancestry.com : accessed 26 Sep 2020). 1870 U.S. census, Washington County, Arkansas, pop. sch., Prairie, p. 39, dwelling 269, family 271, Juda Tharp, age 76, in Annie Roberts household; images, *Ancestry* (https://www.ancestry.com : accessed 26 Sep 2020); citing NARA microfilm publication M593, roll 66.

86. *Find a Grave*, database and images (https://www.findagrave.com/memorial/41677838/judieth-tharp : accessed 26 September 2020), memorial page for Judieth "Judy" Vernon Tharp (1795–4 Sep 1879), Find a Grave Memorial no. 41677838, citing Reese Cemetery, Hicks, Washington County, Arkansas, USA; Maintained by ctwardo (contributor 47093149), headstone photo by S Barger (contributor 47414911).

87. Blaine Bettinger, The Shared cM Project Version 4.0 (March 2020), PDF online, The Genetic Genealogist (https://thegeneticgenealogist.com : accessed 26 Aug 2020) p. 38.

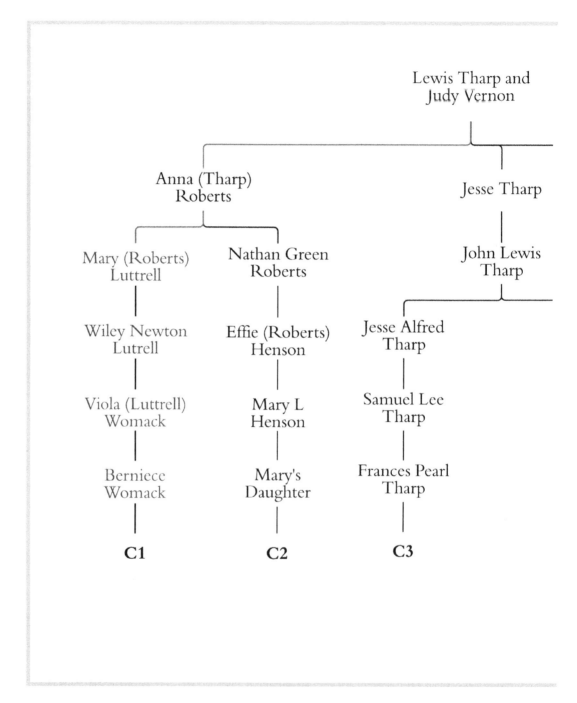

Figure 3. Descendants of Lewis Tharp and Judy Vernon (Group C)

For documentation of parent-child links in Figure 3, see appendix.

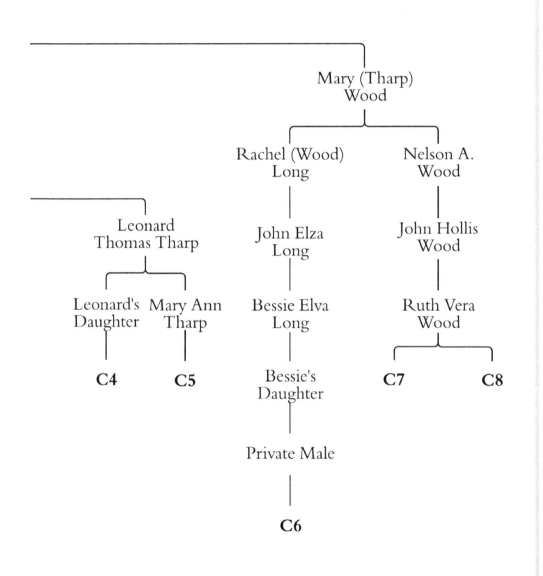

If Judy was not Barsheba's mother, many of the relationships in table 6 would be half fourth cousin (H4C) and half fourth cousin once removed (H4C1R) relationships. Only eighty-nine submissions were included in the Shared cM Project for the H4C relationship, with a range of 0–74 and an average of 30. No data is provided in the Shared cM Project for the H4C1R relationship. The H4C relationship includes the same number of separating meioses as 4C1R. The Shared cM Project groups these relationships into meiosis grouping ten, which includes 2,633 submissions. For meiosis grouping ten, the range of shared DNA is 0–126 with an average of 28 cM.

The total shared cM for each of the hypothesized full or half fourth cousin relationships in table 7 fits within the predicted ranges for the full fourth cousins or the relationships in meiosis grouping ten.[88]

Pedigree Completeness

Two people may share an inflated amount of DNA if they have more than one ancestor in common. Pedigree analysis was performed for the match between C7 and A5, who share 106 cM, and the match between C5 and A15, who share 95.1 cM. No additional common ancestors were found. Their pedigrees are almost complete to the 3rd great grandparent level, which is the generation of the hypothesized parents of Barsheba Tharp. Another generation was reviewed to check for common ancestors in the 4th great grandparent range. The trees were less complete at that level. A15's paternal side is from Buckinghamshire, England, and is not complete beyond the 2nd great grandparent level. A15's ancestors whose parents are unknown were from Buckinghamshire, England. This reduces the chance that A15 will share an unknown ancestor with C5, whose known ancestors were all from United States (see table 8).

Jesse and Lucy Tharp Family

Jesse and Lucy Tharp of Fauquier, Virginia were probably the parents of Lewis Tharp. Jesse Tharp was taxed in Fauquier beginning in 1782.[89] In 1810, Jesse was over age 45, born before 1765.[90] He was old enough to be Lewis' father. Jesse Tharp witnessed William

---

88. Ibid.

89. Fauquier County, Virginia, personal property tax lists, 1782, p. 34, line 2, Jesse Tharp; images, *FamilySearch* (https://www.familysearch.org/ark:/61903/3:1:3Q9M-CSQ2-Q3TS-G?i=29: accessed 25 Aug 2020); citing FHL microfilm 2024530.

90. 1810 U.S. census, Fauquier County, Virginia, p. 408, line 11, Jesse Tharp; images online, *Ancestry* (https://ancestry.com : accessed 25 Aug 2020); citing NARA microfilm publication M252.

Table 7. Shared DNA between Group C and Group A

Lewis/Judy Descendant	Barsheba Descendant	Total Shared DNA (cM)	Hypothesized relationships	Predicted Shared cM Range—Full	Predicted Shared cM Range—Half
C2	A9	38	Full or half 4C1R	0-126	No data
C2	A11	31	Full or half 4C1R	0-126	No data
C2	A7	15	Full or half 4C1R	0-126	No data
C4	A1	13	Full or half 4C	0-139	0-126 (MG10)*
C4	A3	30	Full or half 4C1R	0-126	No data
C4	A5	18	Full or half 4C	0-139	0-126 (MG10)
C4	A9	40	Full or half 4C	0-139	0-126 (MG10)
C4	A11	24	Full or half 4C	0-139	0-126 (MG10)
C4	A7	17	Full or half 4C	0-139	0-126 (MG10)
C4	A14	66	Full or half 4C1R	0-126	No data
C5	A9	64	Full or half 4C	0-139	0-126 (MG10)
C5	A12	33	Full or half 4C	0-139	0-126 (MG10)
C5	A4	21	Full or half 4C1R	0-126	No data
C5	A7	73	Full or half 4C	0-139	0-126 (MG10)
C5	A10	64.5	Full or half 4C1R	0-126	No data
C5	A14	92.3	Full or half 4C1R	0-126	No data
C5	A15	**95.1**	Full or half 4C	0-139	0-126 (MG10)
C3	A9	30	Full or half 4C1R	0-126	No data
C3	A12	31	Full or half 4C1R	0-126	No data
C3	A4	17	Full or half 5C	0-117	No data
C3	A7	36.7	Full or half 4C1R	0-126	No data
C3	A8	11.5	Full or half 4C1R	0-126	No data
C3	A10	45	Full or half 5C	0-117	No data
C3	A14	17.7	Full or half 5C	0-117	No data
C1	A9	26	Full or half 4C1R	0-126	No data
C1	A7	19.7	Full or half 4C1R	0-126	No data
C6	A9	15	Full or half 4C2R	0-93	No data
C7	A3	11	Full or half 4C1R	0-126	No data
C7	A5	**106**	Full or half 4C	0-139	0-126 (MG10)
C7	A9	50	Full or half 4C	0-139	0-126 (MG10)
C7	A12	47	Full or half 4C	0-139	0-126 (MG10)
C7	A7	53	Full or half 4C	0-139	0-126 (MG10)
C8	A3	10	Full or half 4C1R	0-126	No data

Lewis/Judy Descendant	Barsheba Descendant	Total Shared DNA (cM)	Hypothesized relationships	Predicted Shared cM Range—Full	Predicted Shared cM Range—Half
C8	A5	83	Full or half 4C	0-139	0-126 (MG10)
C8	A0	62	Full or half 4C	0-139	0-126 (MG10)
C8	A12	43	Full or half 4C	0-139	0-126 (MG10)
C8	A7	53	Full or half 4C	0-139	0-126 (MG10)

Sources for Table 7: "One-to-One Autosomal DNA Comparison" *GEDmatch* (https://www.gedmatch.com), kits TU6039253 (C5), M767887 (C3), T422844 (C1), A534458 (A9), NT5439655 (A11), PA1661722 (A12), A024243 (A4), A260471 (A7), A965888 (A8); default options (Build 37) with "Prevent Hard Breaks" selected. The kits of C2, C4, C6, C7, C8, A3, A5, A10, A14, and A15 were not uploaded to GEDmatch. Their matches were analyzed using AncestryDNA, MyHeritageDNA, and 23andMe tools. C2, C4, C6, C7, and C8 were compared with A1, A3, A4, A5, A7, A9, A11, A12 at *Ancestry* "DNA Matches" (https://ancestry.com/dna/ : accessed 23 Sep 2020). C3, C4, and C5 were compared with A10 and A14 at *23andMe* "Advanced DNA Comparison" (https://you.23andme.com/tools/relatives/dna/ : accessed 24 Sep 2020). A15 and C5 were compared at *MyHeritageDNA,* "DNA Matches" (https://www.myheritage.com/dna/matches/ : accessed 24 Sep 2020). *MG10 stands for Meiosis Grouping 10 in the shared cM Project, which includes the Half 3CR, 3C3R, Half 4C, and 4C1R relationships, which all have the same number of separating meioses.

Burke's will in 1803, but no will or probate record remains for Jesse.[91] Jesse and Lucy Tharp witnessed their daughter Elizabeth's marriage in 1801. They jointly stated they were "willing to give her up."[92]

In 1804, Lewis was a free white tithe in the household of George Tharp.[93] George was first listed as a tithable in Jesse's household in 1795, so was probably born 16 years prior in about 1779.[94] George was likely a son of Jesse, and older brother to Lewis.

---

91. Fauquier County, Virginia, Wills 3:481–2, William Burke, 17 May 1803; images online, *FamilySearch* (https://www.familysearch.org/ark:/61903/3:1:3Q9M-C9TC-X3SR-W : accessed 25 Aug 2020); citing FHL microfilm 31567. Ibid., books 3–14, negative search for Jesse Tharp.

92. Fauquier County, Virginia, Marriage Bonds and Returns 2:229, Elizabeth Tharp – Thornton Golden marriage bond, 19 Jan 1801; images online, *FamilySearch* (https://www.familysearch.org/ark:/61903/3:1:3QSQ-G9XF-61F9?i=379 : accessed 25 Sep 2020), DGS 7578972, image 380 of 688; FHL microfilm # 31633.

93. Fauquier County, Virginia, personal property tax lists, 1804, Simon Morgan District, p. 52, line 14, George Tharp (https://www.familysearch.org/ark:/61903/3:1:3Q9M-CSQ2-WY2R).

94. Ibid., 1795, Edward Humston District, p. 43, line 10, Jessey and George Tharp; images, *FamilySearch* (https://www.familysearch.org/ark:/61903/3:1:3Q9M-CSQ2-Q3TN-H : accessed 25 Aug 2020); citing FHL microfilm 2024530.

Table 8. Pedigree Completeness

Name	Percentage Complete to 3rd Great Grandparents	Percentage Complete to 4th Great Grandparents
A5	87.5%	75%
A15	75%	71%
C5	81%	67%
C7	100%	89%

For the pedigrees, see "Public Member Trees," *Ancestry,* user Nicole Dyer, "Dyer Family Tree,"
for A5, https://www.ancestry.com/family-tree/tree/71135853/family?cfpid=432218691946,
for A15, https://www.ancestry.com/family-tree/tree/71135853/family?cfpid=432218693768,
for C5, https://www.ancestry.com/family-tree/tree/71135853/family?cfpid=432218428172,
for C7, see https://www.ancestry.com/family-tree/tree/71135853/family?cfpid=432218433590.

Martin Tharp, likely younger brother of Lewis, lived in Fauquier County in 1820.[95] An older woman, over 45 years of age was included in his household, almost certainly his mother, Lucy Tharp. Martin resided in Fauquier in 1830, age 30–39, born 1791–1800.[96] He may have been included as one of the unnamed tithables in Jesse Tharp's household in 1814, indicating he had turned 16 that year.[97] Lucy Tharp was taxed in 1815, probably because Jesse died.[98] She was taxed for 1 male over 16, probably her youngest son Martin. In 1816, Lucy was not taxed for any males over 16, but for 2 horses only.[99] Thomas Tharp,

---

95. 1820 U.S. census, Fauquier County, Virginia, p. 90, line 3, Martin Thorp; image online, *Ancestry* (https://www.ancestry.com : accessed 26 Sep 2020); citing NARA microfilm publication M33, roll 136.

96. 1830 U.S. census, Fauquier County, Virginia, p. 467, line 16, Martin Tharp; image online, *Ancestry* (https://www.ancestry.com : accessed 26 Sep 2020); citing NARA microfilm publication M19, roll 194.

97. Fauquier County, Virginia, personal property tax lists, 1814, Stephen Chilton District, p. 21, line 31, Jesse Tharp; images, *FamilySearch* (https://www.familysearch.org/ark:/61903/3:1:3Q9M-CSQ2-M2N8?i=412&cat=775969 : accessed 25 Sep 2020); citing FHL microfilm 2024530. Jesse Tharp was only taxed for one male over 16 the year previous.

98. Fauquier County, Virginia, personal property tax lists, 1815, Stephen Chilton District, p. 39, line 14, Lucy Tharp; images, *FamilySearch* (https://www.familysearch.org/ark:/61903/3:1:3Q9M-CSQ2-M2F2?i=493&cat=775969 : accessed 25 Sep 2020); citing FHL microfilm 2024530.

99. Fauquier County, Virginia, personal property tax lists, 1816, Stephen Chilton District, p. 45, line 11, Lucy Tharp; images, *FamilySearch* (https://www.familysearch.org/ark:/61903/3:1:3Q9M-CSQ2-MLPS?cat=775969 : accessed 25 Sep 2020); citing FHL microfilm 2024530.

who was taxed for 2 males over 16, may have housed his brother Martin that year.[100] In 1817, Martin Tharp was listed for the first time by name on the tax list. [101] Lucy was not listed, implying that Martin had reached an age to be considered the head of household for tax purposes. In 1830, Lucy Tharp was listed as the head of her own household on the federal census.[102] She also headed her own household in 1840 census, at age 80–90.[103]

The children of Jesse and Lucy Tharp of Fauquier County, Virginia, include:

1. John Tharp, b. abt 1778, first taxed in 1794,[104] a tithable in Jesse's household in 1795[105]
2. George Tharp, b. abt 1779, a tithable in Jesse's household in 1795[106]
3. Elizabeth Tharp, b. abt 1780, of age to marry in 1801 to Thornton Golden, parents Jesse and Lucy Tharp were willing to give her up to Mr. Golden[107]
4. Thomas Tharp, b. abt 1781, a tithable in Jesse's household in 1797[108]

---

100. Fauquier County, Virginia, personal property tax lists, 1816, Stephen Chilton District, p. 45, line 10, Thomas Tharp; images, *FamilySearch* (https://www.familysearch.org/ark:/61903/3:1:3Q9M-CSQ2-MLPS?i=620&cat=775969 : accessed 25 Sep 2020); citing FHL microfilm 2024530.

101. Fauquier County, Virginia, personal property tax lists, 1817, Stephen Chilton District, p. 33, line 11, Martin Tharp; images, *FamilySearch* (https://www.familysearch.org/ark:/61903/3:1:3Q9M-CSQ2-ML-LY?cat=775969 : accessed 25 Sep 2020); citing FHL microfilm 2024532.

102. 1830 U.S. census, Fauquier County, Virginia, p. 467, line 15, Lucy Tharp; image online, *Ancestry* (https://www.ancestry.com : accessed 26 Sep 2020); citing NARA microfilm publication M19, roll 194.

103. 1840 U.S. census, Fauquier county, Virginia, Leeds, p. 230, Lucy Tharpe; image online, *Ancestry* (https://www.ancestry.com : accessed 26 Sep 2020); citing NARA microfilm publication M704, roll 558.

104. Fauquier County, Virginia, personal property tax lists, 1704, Edward Humston District, p. 46, line 7, John Tharp; images, *FamilySearch* (https://www.familysearch.org/ark:/61903/3:1:3Q9M-CSQ2-Q3TG-P : accessed 25 Sep 2020); citing FHL microfilm 2024531. Birth years of the males were estimated by subtracting 16 from the first year they were taxed.

105. Fauquier County, Virginia, personal property tax lists, 1795, Edward Humston District, p. 43, lines 10–11, Jessey and John Tharp; images, *FamilySearch* (https://www.familysearch.org/ark:/61903/3:1:3Q9M-CSQ2-Q3TN-H : accessed 25 Sep 2020); citing FHL microfilm 2024531.

106. Ibid., line 10, George Tharp in Jessey Tharp household.

107. Fauquier County, Virginia, Marriage Bonds and Returns 2:229, Elizabeth Tharp – Thornton Golden marriage bond, 19 Jan 1801. The birth year of Elizabeth was estimated by subtracting 21 years from the year of her marriage.

108. Fauquier County, Virginia, personal property tax lists, 1797, Joseph Withers District, p. 42, line 22, Thomas Tharp in household of Jesse Tharp; images, *FamilySearch* (https://www.familysearch.org/ark:/61903/3:1:3Q9M-CSQ2-W9MX-3 : accessed 25 Sep 2020).

5. William Tharp, b. abt 1783, a tithable in Jesse's household in 1799[109]
6. Lewis Tharp, b. abt 1784, a tithable in Jesse's household in 1800[110]
7. Tilman Tharp, b. abt 1790, a tithable in Jesse's household in 1806[111]
8. Mary Tharp, b. abt 1792, md. Samuel Lawrence 2 Jan 1812, Jesse gave consent[112]
9. Martin Tharp, b. abt 1798, probable tithable in Jesse's household in 1814[113]

Lewis Tharp's father-in-law, John West, associated with the Tharp family in more than one way. John West was taxed in Fauquier from 1800–1804. [114] In 1800, John West's taxes included tithable George Tharp, who may have worked for him. John West was the bondsman for George Tharp's marriage to Polly Noland in 1801 in Fauquier.[115]

The tax list for the district that would probably have included the Tharps and John

109. Ibid., 1799, Thornton Buckner District, p. 47, line 22, Wm Tharpe in household of Jesse Tharpe; images, *FamilySearch* (https://www.familysearch.org/ark:/61903/3:1:3Q9M-CSQ2-W1PG : accessed 25 Sep 2020).

110. Fauquier County, Virginia, personal property tax lists, 1800, Charles Pickett District, p. 64, line 6, Lewis Tharp in household of Jessee Tharp.

111. Ibid., 1806, Thomas Robinson District, p. 48, line 6, Tilman Tharp in household of Jesse Tharp; images, *FamilySearch* (https://www.familysearch.org/ark:/61903/3:1:3Q9M-CSQ2-W99W-B : accessed 25 Sep 2020); citing FHL microfilm 2024531.

112. Fauquier County, Virginia, Marriage Bonds and Returns 3:182, Mary Tharp – Samuel Lawrence marriage bond, 2 Jan 1812; images online, *FamilySearch* (https://www.familysearch.org/ark:/61903/3:1:3QSQ-G9XF-6BTX : accessed 25 Sep 2020), DGS 7578972, image 563 of 688; FHL microfilm # 31633. Mary's age was estimated assuming she was under age 21 at her marriage, since her father gave consent for the marriage license, but about 20 years old.

113. Fauquier County, Virginia, personal property tax lists, 1814, Stephen Chilton District, p. 21, line 31, Jesse Tharp.

114. Fauquier County, Virginia, personal property tax lists, 1800, Charles Pickett District, p. 68, line 10, John West; images, *FamilySearch* (https://www.familysearch.org/ark:/61903/3:1:3Q9M-CSQ2-W1MB : accessed 24 Aug 2020); citing FHL microfilm 2024531. Ibid., 1801, Chs Pickett District, p. 71, line 12 (https://www.familysearch.org/ark:/61903/3:1:3Q9M-CSQ2-W1S3). Ibid., 1802, Thomas Humston District, p. 52, line 10 (https://www.familysearch.org/ark:/61903/3:1:3Q9M-CSQ2-WBQQ). Ibid., 1803, C. Pickett District, p. 71 line 4 (https://www.familysearch.org/ark:/61903/3:1:3Q9M-CSQ2-WYTZ). Ibid., 1804, Simon Morgan District, p. 57, line 4 (https://www.familysearch.org/ark:/61903/3:1:3Q9M-CSQ2-WYHF).

115. Fauquier County, Virginia, Marriage Bonds and Returns 2:227, bond, George Tharp - Polly Noland, 12 January 1801; images online, *FamilySearch* (https://www.familysearch.org/ark:/61903/3:1:3QS7-99XF-6182 : accessed 25 Aug 2020); citing FHL microfilm 31633.

West seems to have been lost for 1805.[116] In 1806, John West and Lewis Tharp were not taxed in Fauquier, but Jesse Tharp was.[117] John West and Lewis Tharp likely left Fauquier County about 1806, soon after John West and his wife Sarah sold 165 acres of land to Samuel Fisher on 7 December 1805.[118]

Other descendants of Jesse Tharp may have followed Lewis Tharp and John West to Hawkins. A man named John Tharp enlisted in the army on 10 May 1829 in Louisville and stated he was born in Fauquier, Virginia in 1809. He died 1 September 1832.[119] This could be John Tharp who lived in Hawkins County, Tennessee in 1830.[120]

Descendants of Jesse and Lucy Tharp

Table 9 compares the DNA of Jesse and Lucy Tharp's descendants with Barsheba Tharp's descendants. The amount of shared DNA is consistent with the hypothesized relationships.[121] Figure 4 shows 4 documented descendants of Jesse and Lucy Tharp.

Additional documentation for lines of descent in Figures 1–4 is available at the author's Ancestry public member tree.[122]

Descendants of Lewis Tharp share a Triangulated Segment

Table 10 shows a triangulated segment between 3 descendants of Lewis Tharp. Elizabeth

---

116. Fauquier County, Virginia, personal property tax lists, 1805, negative search for Tharp and West (https://www.familysearch.org/ark:/61903/3:1:3Q9M-CSQ2-W99G-K : accessed 25 Aug 2020). Only two of the three typical lists were included in the digitized images for 1805.

117. Ibid., 1806, Thomas Robinson District, p. 48, line 6, Jesse Tharp (https://www.familysearch.org/ark:/61903/3:1:3Q9M-CSQ2-W99W-B). Ibid., negative search for Lewis Tharp and John West.

118. Fauquier County, Virginia, Deeds 16:312-3, West-Fisher, 7 December 1805, recorded 18 January 1809; images online (https://www.familysearch.org/ark:/61903/3:1:3Q9M-CSKJ-92V8 : accessed 25 Aug 2020).

119. "U.S. Army, Register of Enlistments, 1798–1914," 1828 Jan - 1835, p. 186, line 70, John Tharp, enlisted 10 May 1829; database with images, *Ancestry* (https://ancestry.com : accessed 24 Aug 2020), image 184 of 440; citing National Archives Microfilm Publication M233.

120. 1830 U.S. census, Hawkins County, Tennessee, p. 64, line 23, John Tharp; database with images, *FamilySearch* (https://www.familysearch.org : accessed 22 Aug 2020); citing National Archives microfilm publication M19, roll 178.

121. Blaine Bettinger, Shared cM Project, v.4, interactive version by Jonny Perl, *DNA Painter* (https://dnapainter.com/tools/sharedcmv4: last updated 26 March 2020).

122. Nicole Dyer, "Dyer Family Tree," Public Member Tree, *Ancestry* (https://www.ancestry.com/family-tree/tree/71135853/family/familyview).

Tharp was the daughter of Lewis Tharp and his first wife, Joanna West. Anna Tharp was the daughter of Lewis Tharp's second wife, Judy Vernon. The triangulated segment strengthens the case that Barsheba is the daughter of Lewis Tharp.

Naming Patterns

At least five grandchildren of Lewis Tharp may have been named after him, providing onomastic evidence tying the children of Lewis Tharp to him:

- John Lewis Tharp, b. 1842, son of William Tharp[123]
- John L. Parrott, b. 1844, son of John and Elizabeth (Tharp) Parrott[124]
- Lewis Tharp Farris, son of Anderson J and Joanna (Tharp) Farris[125]
- Lewis Roberts, son of Wiley and Anna (Tharp) Roberts[126]
- John Lewis Tharp, b. 1849, son of Jesse and Eliza (Roberson) Tharp[127]

Barsheba Tharp was almost certainly also the daughter of Lewis Tharp, adding a sixth grandchild to the list, Lewis T. Dyer.[128]

---

123. Hawkins County, Tennessee, will papers, William Tharp, signed 17 November 1869, recorded March Term 1875; images online, *FamilySearch* (https://www.familysearch.org/ark:/61903/3:1:939L-6SS2-XV : accessed 1 March 2021); citing FHL microfilm 1572795.

124. "Illinois Deaths and Stillbirths, 1916–1947," database, *FamilySearch*, indexed entry for John L. Parrott, 21 Apr 1922.

125. *Find a Grave*, database and images (https://www.findagrave.com : accessed 26 September 2020), memorial page for Lewis Tharp Farris (28 Jun 1839–17 Mar 1912), Find a Grave Memorial no. 120006145, citing Lockwood Cemetery, Lockwood, Dade County, Missouri, USA ; Maintained by Dan McEver (contributor 48409053), headstone photo by Judy K. Roberts (contributor 47187185). The headstone says Lewis T. Farris.

126. 1850 U.S. census, Washington County, Arkansas, pop. sch., White River, p. 355a, dwelling/family , dwelling/family 54, Lewis in household of Wiley Roberts.

127. 1850 U.S. census, Washington County, Arkansas, pop. sch., White River, p. 355a, dwelling/family 60, John Tharp in Jesse Tharp household. For middle initial, see 1870 U.S. census, Washington County, Arkansas, pop. sch., White River, p. 273a, dwelling 4, family 5, J.L. Tharp in Jesse Tharp household; images, *Ancestry* (https://www.ancestry.com : accessed 26 Sep 2020); citing NARA microfilm publication M593, roll 66. For name Lewis, see his son's death certificate: "Texas, Death Certificates, 1903–1982," John Wesley Tharp, son of Louis Tharp and Annie Lou Watson, certificate no. 16546, died 25 Mar 1975; images, *Ancestry* (https://www. ancestry.com : accessed 26 Sep 2020).

128. "Tennessee Deaths, 1914–1966," database with images, *FamilySearch,* Lewis T. Dyer, no. 97, 14 Apr 1916, Persia, Hawkins, Tennessee.

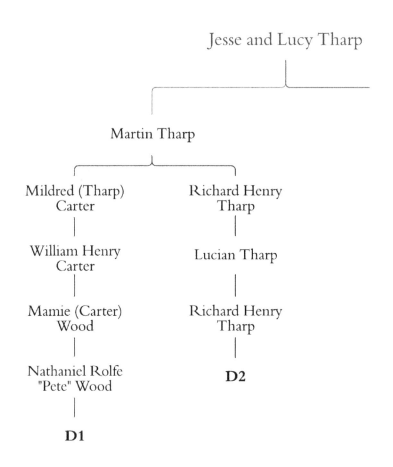

Figure 4. Descendants of Jesse and Lucy Tharp (Group D)

For documentation of parent-child links in Figure 4, see appendix.

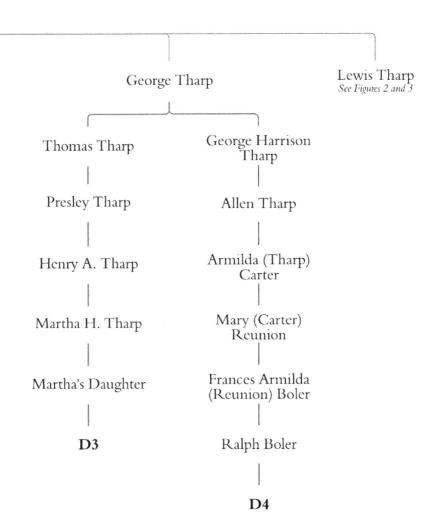

Table 9. Shared DNA between Group D and Group A

Jesse/ Lucy Descendant	Barsheba Descendant	Total Shared DNA (cM)	Hypothesized relationship	Predicted Shared cM Range
D1	A2	31	5C1R	0-80
D1	A9	46.6	5C	0-117
D1	A11	14.3	5C	0-117
D1	A12	15.7	5C	0-117
D1	A7	19.8	5C	0-117
D1	A15	39.6	5C	0-117
D2	A1	11	4C1R	0-126
D2	A2	34.7	4C2R	0-93
D2	A9	43.4	4C1R	0-126
D2	A11	14.8	4C1R	0-126
D2	A15	81.1	4C1R	0-126
D4	A9	26	5C2R	0-65
D4	A11	13	5C2R	0-65
D4	A12	12	5C2R	0-65
D3	A5	12	5C1R	0-80
D3	A9	20.4	5C1R	0-80
D3	A11	9.6	5C1R	0-80
D3	A7	9.7	5C1R	0-80
D3	A8	10.2	5C1R	0-80

Sources for Table 7: "One-to-One Autosomal DNA Comparison" *GEDmatch* (https://www.gedmatch.com), kits WK5599087 (D1), A454562 (D3), A534458 (A9), NT5439655 (A11), PA1661722 (A12), A260471 (A7), A965888 (A8); default options (Build 37) with "Prevent Hard Breaks" selected. The kits of D2, D4, A2, A5, and A15 were not uploaded to GEDmatch. Their matches were analyzed using AncestryDNA and MyHeritageDNA tools. D3 and D4 were compared with A5, A9, A11, and A12 at *Ancestry* "DNA Matches" (https://ancestry.com/dna/ : accessed 23 Sep 2020). D1 and D2 were compared A1, A2, A9, A11 and A15, at *MyHeritageDNA,* "DNA Matches" (https://www.myheritage.com/dna/matches/ : accessed 24 Sep 2020). For the predicted shared cM range Blaine Bettinger, Shared cM Project, v.4, interactive version by Jonny Perl, DNA Painter (https://dnapainter.com/tools/sharedcmv4: last updated 26 March 2020).

Table 10. Triangulated Segment on Chromosome 14 among descendants of Lewis Tharp

Test Takers (Ancestor)	Start	Stop	Shared Cm	SNPs
B2 (Elizabeth Tharp) and A9 (Barsheba Tharp)	22,498,019	32,390,458	16.3 cM	1,653
C1 (Anna Tharp) and B2 (Elizabeth Tharp)	24,200,567	32,438,586	12.4 cM	1,205
A9 (Barsheba Tharp) and C1 (Anna Tharp)	24,200,567	40,903,327	26 cM	3,846

Source: "GEDmatch ® Autosomal One-to-one Comparison – V1.0," GEDmatch (https://www.gedmatch. com), kits A188998 (B2), T422844 (C1), A534458 (A9); default options (Build 37) with "Prevent Hard Breaks" selected.

Conclusion

Evidence points to Lewis Tharp as the father of Barsheba Tharp. Family records, proximity in Hawkins County and naming patterns provide clues to a familial relationship. A DNA study tested the hypothesis that descendants of Barsheba Tharp would share DNA with descendants of Lewis Tharp and confirmed that Lewis Tharp was the father of Barsheba. Barsheba's descendants also share DNA with descendants of Lewis's parents, Jesse and Lucy Tharp. More research is required to determine which wife of Lewis Tharp was Barsheba's mother.

Appendix

Sources for Table 1

a. 1830 U.S. census, Hawkins County, Tennessee, p. 22, line 5, Robert Dyer; database with images, *FamilySearch* (https://www.familysearch.org : accessed 22 Aug 2020); citing National Archives microfilm publication M19, roll 178.

b. 1840 U.S. census, Hawkins County, Tennessee, p. 66, line 17, Robert Dyer; database with images, *FamilySearch* (https://familysearch.org : accessed 22 Aug 2020); citing National Archives publication M704, roll 526.

c. 1850 U.S. census, Hawkins County, Tennessee, population schedule, District No. 15, p. 864, dwelling 91, family 91, Robert Dyer; database with images, *FamilySearch* (https://www.familysearch.org : accessed 22 Aug 2020); citing National Archives publication M432, roll 882.

   d. 1860 U.S. census, Hawkins County, Tennessee, population schedule, 4th District, p. 185, dwelling 1321, family 1245, John R. Dyer; database with images, *FamilySearch*, (https://www.familysearch.org: accessed 22 Aug 2020); citing National Archives publication M635 Roll 1255.

   e. 1870 U.S. census, Hawkins County, Tennessee, population schedule, 4th District, p. 5, dwelling 31, family 31, John R. Dyer household; database with images, *FamilySearch* (https://www.familysearch.org: accessed 22 Aug 2020); citing National Archives publication M593, roll 1535.

   f. 1880 U.S. census, Hawkins County, Tennessee, District 4, dwelling 166, family 171, Barchebe Dyer; database with images, *Ancestry* (https://www.ancestry.com : accessed 20 Aug 2020); citing National Archives microfilm publication T9, roll 1260.

   g. 1880 U.S. census, Hawkins County, Tennessee, mortality schedule, 4th District, p. 999, line 10, family 171, John R. Dyer; database with images, *Ancestry* (https://ancestry.com : accessed 22 Aug 2020); citing National Archives publication T655, roll 29.

Sources for Figure 1

For Augustus Dyer's parents, see the text.

   For Mary (Dyer) Tate and Elizabeth Frances (Dyer) Beals, see 1850 U.S. census, Hawkins Co., Tennessee, pop. sch., p. 864, dwell./fam. 91, Mary and Francis in Robert Dyer household.

   For Richard Fain Dyer, see "Tennessee Deaths, 1914–1966," Richard F. Dyer, 3 Feb 1921.

   For John James Dyer, see 1880 U.S. census, Hawkins Co., Tennessee, pop. Sch., dwell. 166, fam. 171, household of Barchebe Dyer.

   For John Clinton Dyer and William Thomas Dyer, see 1870 U.S. census, Hawkins County, Tennessee, population schedule, District 4, p. 34B, dwelling/family 29, Augustus Dyer household; image, *Ancestry* (https://ancestry.com : accessed 13 October 2020); citing National Archives publication M593, roll 1535. Also 1880 U.S. census, Hawkins County, Tennessee, population schedule, District 4, ED 77, p. 209B, dwelling 176, family 181, Augustus Dyer household; image, *Ancestry* (https://ancestry.com : accessed 13 October 2020); citing National Archives publication T9, roll 1260.

   For Anna see "Tennessee, Delayed Birth Records, 1869–1909," file no. D-416078, Anna Christine Dyer, Hawkins, Tennessee, 10 Sep 1893; image, *Ancestry* (https://ancestry. com : accessed 13 Oct 2020).

   For Delia, see "Pennsylvania, Death Certificates, 1906–1968," Washington County, no. 39357, Delia Ann Josephine Sego, 17 April 1953; image, *Ancestry* (https://ancestry.com : accessed 13 Oct 2020).

For Lucy, see 1920 U.S. census, McLean County, Illinois, population schedule, Bloomington Precinct 3, ED 93, p. 4B, Lucy in Henry Jones household; image, *Ancestry* (https://ancestry.com : accessed 13 Oct 2020); citing National Archives publication T625, roll 386.

For Bathsheba and Worthy, 1870 U.S. census, Hawkins County, Tennessee, population schedule, District 4, p. 35A, Mary Tate household; image, *Ancestry* (https://ancestry.com : accessed 13 Oct 2020); citing National Archives publication M593, roll 1535. Also "Tennessee, Death Records, 1908–1965," Sullivan County, no. 50-14493, Worthy Malissa Gardner, 20 Jan 1950; image, *Ancestry* (https://ancestry.com : accessed 13 Oct 2020).

For Laura, "Arizona, Death Records, 1887–1960,"Graham County, no. 2979, Laura Maud Reed, 30 May 1953; image, *Ancestry* (https://ancestry.com : accessed 13 Oct 2020).

For Pearl, 1910 U.S. census, Graham County, Arizona, population schedule, Pima, ED 47, dwelling 340, family 350, Robert E. Reed household; image, *Ancestry* (https://ancestry.com : accessed 13 Oct 2020); citing National Archives microfilm publication T624, roll 39.

For Sallie, 1900 U.S. census, Greene County, Tennessee, population schedule, Civil District 11, ED 39, dwelling/family 219, Gilbert Gardner household; image, *Ancestry* (https://ancestry.com : accessed 13 Oct 2020); citing National Archives microfilm publication T623.

For Martha, 1920 U.S. census, Greene County, Tennessee, population schedule, Civil District 16, ED 85, dwelling 137, family 139, Sallie B. Keller household; image, *Ancestry* (https://ancestry.com : accessed 13 Oct 2020); citing National Archives microfilm publication T625, roll 1741.

For Robert Luster, 1900 U.S. census, Hawkins County, Tennessee, population schedule, New Hope, ED 79, p. 14, dwelling 244, family 246, Richard Dyer household; image, *Ancestry* (https://ancestry.com : accessed 16 Oct 2020); citing National Archives microfilm publication T623. Robert Luster was listed as a boarder in the household of Richard Dyer and his wife Hiley, probably hiding the relationship. Richard was a polygamist and had another wife named Sallie Luster, according to descendants. See Darla Shawcroft Crowther to Nicole Dyer, 14 October 2020, Ancestry Messenger, *Ancestry* (ancestry.com /messaging), files of author. Robert Luster was enumerated twice in 1900, the other time with his mother Sallie. See 1900 U.S. census, Hawkins County, Tennessee, population schedule, Dosons Crux, ED 91, p. 5, household/dwelling 76, Sallie Luster household; image, *Ancestry* (https://ancestry.com : accessed 16 Oct 2020); citing National Archives microfilm publication T623. In 1910, Robert Luster was listed as a son of Richard F. Dyer and his surname Luster had been partially erased and crossed out. See also 1910 U.S. census, Hawkins County, Tennessee, population schedule, Civil District 6, ED 118, p. 7A, family 131, Richard F. Dyer household; image, *Ancestry* (https://ancestry.com : accessed 16 Oct 2020; citing National Archives microfilm publication T624, roll 1504.

For Robert's daughter, living, private sources in author's files.

For Richard Francis Beals, 1900 U.S. census, Graham County, Arizona, population schedule, ED 21, p. 39, dwelling 678, family 687, John S. Beals household; image, *Ancestry* (https://ancestry.com : accessed 16 Oct 2020); citing National Archives microfilm publication T623.

For Maude Beals, see 1920 U.S. census, Otero County, New Mexico, population schedule, Weed, ED 125, p. 3A, family 54, Richard F. Beals Household; image, *Ancestry* (https://ancestry.com : accessed 16 Oct 2020); citing National Archives publication T625, roll 1077.

For James Wesley Dyer, see "Utah, Death and Military Death Certificates, 1904–1961," Salt Lake County, no. 56181022, James Wesley Dyer, 15 May 1956; image, *Ancestry* (https://ancestry.com : accessed 16 Oct 2020).

For James Glenn and Max Vivian Dyer, see 1910 U.S. census, Conejos County, Colorado, population schedule, Rio Grand, ED 16, p. 1B, dwelling/family 16, James W. Dyer household; image, *Ancestry* (https://ancestry.com : accessed 16 Oct 2020); citing National Archives microfilm publication T624, roll 113.

For Edna Maxine Dyer, see "Deaths," *The (Washington D.C.) Evening Star*, 28 Aug 1967, p. B-5, col. 5, Dyer, Max V. obituary; image, *GenealogyBank* (https://www.genealogybank.com : accessed 16 Oct 2020).

For John Leland Dyer, see 1900 U.S. census, Conejos County, Colorado, population schedule, Sanford, ED 9, p. 24, house/family 103, Mary J. Dyer; image, *Ancestry* (https://ancestry.com : accessed 16 Oct 2020); citing National Archives microfilm publication T623. See also "Tennessee, Marriage Records, 1780–2002," John J. Dyer – Mary Jane Luster, 20 Feb 1887, Hawkins, Tennessee; image, *Ancestry* (https://ancestry.com : accessed 16 Oct 2020). See also "U.S., Social Security Applications and Claims Index, 1936–2007," John Leland Dyer, SSN 700015230; database, *Ancestry* (https://ancestry.com : accessed 16 Oct 2020).

For Bertha Mae (Dyer) Ford, see 1920 U.S. census, Alamosa County, Colorado, population schedule, Alamosa, ED 2, p. 7A, John L. Dyer household; image, *Ancestry* (https://ancestry.com : accessed 16 Oct 2020); citing National Archives publication T625, roll 155.

For Carol Jane (Ford) Burger, see *Sun Advocate (Price, Utah)* 27 July 2006, Carol Burger obituary, *GenealogyBank* (https://www.genealogybank.com : accessed 16 October 2020).

Sources for Figure 2

For Elizabeth's parents, see text.

For Martha and **John's** parents, see text.

For Samuel, Illinois Department of Public Health, certificate of death no. 113 (1939), Samuel Marshall Campbell; Division of Vital Statistics, Springfield.

For Stanley, 1910 U.S. census, Alexander County, Illinois, population schedule, Thebes, ED 177, sheet 6A, dwelling 65, household 69, Stanley R. Campbell in Samuel M. Campbell household; image online, *Ancestry* (https://ancestry.com : accessed 10 Feb 2021); citing NARA microfilm publication T624, roll 230.

For Leta, 1930 U.S. census, Alexander County, Illinois, population schedule, Tamms, ED 20, sheet 2B, dwelling/family 44, Leta Campbell in Stanley R. Campbell household; image online, *Ancestry* (https://ancestry.com : accessed 10 Feb 2021); citing NARA microfilm publication T626, roll 406.

For Kathryn, "Leta Weigand," newspaper clipping, 28 Jan 2005; image online, Donna King, "King Family Tree," attached to Leta Myrl Campbell (1927–2005), "Public Member Trees," database, *Ancestry* (https://ancestry.com : accessed 10 Feb 2021).

For Charles, see 1880 U.S. census, Wayne County, Illinois, population schedule, Massillon, ED 143, p. 12, dwelling 82, family 86, Charles R. Campbell in Richard Campbell household; image online, *Ancestry* (https://ancestry.com : accessed 10 Feb 2021); citing NARA microfilm publication T9, roll 257.

For Vernon, 1900 U.S. census, Barton County, Kansas, population schedule, Great Bend, ED 19, sheet 21, dwelling 447, family 467, Vernie in Charles Campbell household; image online, *Ancestry* (https://ancestry.com : accessed 20 Feb 2021); citing NARA microfilm publication T623, roll 471.

For Ray, 1930 U.S. census, Spokane County, Washington, population schedule, Spokane, ED 32-13, sheet 3A, Dalke Street, Ray W. Campbell in Vernon A. Campbell household; image online, *Ancestry* (https://ancestry.com : accessed 11 Feb 2021); citing NARA microfilm publication T626, roll 2515.

For Thelma, 1910 U.S. census, Ripley County, Missouri, population schedule, Harris, ED 157, sheet 14A, dwelling 261, family 263, Thelma Campbell in Charles R. Campbell household; image online, *Ancestry* (https://ancestry.com : accessed 11 Feb 2021); citing NARA microfilm publication T624, roll 805.

For Donald, 1930 U.S. census, Douglas County, Washington, population schedule, Valley, ED 9–29, sheet 3A, household 58, family 65, Donald D. Dilley in Jess L. Dilley household; image online, *Ancestry* (https://ancestry.com : accessed 11 Feb 2021); citing NARA microfilm publication T626, roll 2486.

For Ada see 1880 U.S. census, Lawrence County, Illinois, population schedule, Petty, ED 193, p. 28, dwelling 48, family 49, Ada Parrott in John Parrott household; image online, *Ancestry* (https://ancestry.com : accessed 21 Feb 2021); citing NARA microfilm publication T9, roll 224.

For Lawrence see 1900 U.S. census, Lawrence County, Illinois, population schedule, Petty, ED 116, sheet 1, dwelling/family 4, Laurence in Elmer Berkshire household; image online, *Ancestry* (https://ancestry.com : accessed 11 Feb 2021); citing NARA microfilm publication T623, roll 317.

Lawrence's Daughter is living; documentation for her parents is privately held by Nicole Dyer. For **Jesse**, 1900 U.S. census, Lawrence County, Illinois, population schedule, Petty, ED 116, sheet 8, dwelling 150, family 151, Jesse Perrot in John Perrot household; image online, *Ancestry* (https://ancestry.com : accessed 10 Feb 2021); citing NARA microfilm publication T623, roll 317.

For Eunice, 1910 U.S. census, Union County, New Mexico, population schedule, Alamosa, ED 282, Sheet 7A, dwelling 140, family 160, Eunice Parrott in Jesse Parrot household; image online, *Ancestry* (https://ancestry.com : accessed 11 Feb 2021); citing NARA microfilm publication T624, roll 919.

For Marion, 1930 U.S. census, Seminole County, Oklahoma, population schedule, Wolf, ED 67–35, sheet 2A, dwelling/family 22, Marion Shipman in Fred Shipman household; image online, *Ancestry* (https://ancestry.com : accessed 11 Feb 2021); citing NARA microfilm publication T626, roll 1931.

Sources for Figure 3

For the parents of Anna Tharp, Jesse Tharp, and **Mary Tharp,** see text.

For Mary (Roberts) Luttrell and **Wiley** see Nicole Dyer, "Parents of Mollie Roberts and Wiley Newton Luttrell," 15 Feb 2021, *Family Locket* (https://familylocket.com/barsheba-tharp-proof-argument/ : accessed 15 Feb 2021).

For Nathan Green Roberts see Arkansas Board of Health, certificate of death, 1935, no. 1313, Nathan Green Roberts, Washington County; database with images, "Arkansas, Death Certificates, 1914–1969," *Ancestry* (https://ancestry.com : accessed 11 Feb 2021).

For Viola (Luttrell) Womack, 1910 U.S. census, Wheeler county, Texas, population schedule, Precinct 1, ED 218, sheet 4A, dwelling 54, family 55, Viola Luttrell in Newt Luttrell household; database with images, *FamilySearch* (https://ancestry.com : accessed 11 Feb 2021); citing NARA microfilm publication T624, roll 1600.

For Berniece, 1940 U.S. census, Marshall County, Oklahoma, population schedule, Odell, ED 48-7, sheets 10A-10B, household 182, Berneece in Jim H. Womack household; database with images, *Ancestry* (https://ancestry.com : accessed 15 Feb 2021); citing NARA microfilm T627, roll 3311.

For Effie, 1900 U.S. census, Washington County, Arkansas, population schedule, Wyman, ED 115, sheet 13, Effie M. in Nathan G. Roberts household; database with images, *Ancestry* (https://ancestry.com : accessed 15 Feb 2021); citing NARA microfilm T623, roll 79.

For Mary L. Henson, 1930 U.S. census Washington County, Arkansas, population schedule, Prairie, ED 72-25, sheet 5B, dwelling 114, household 117, Mary L. Henson in Malcolm Y. Henson household; database with images, *Ancestry* (https://ancestry.com : accessed 15 Feb 2021); citing NARA microfilm T626, roll 97.

Mary's Daughter is living; documentation for her parents is privately held by Nicole Dyer.

For John Lewis Tharp, Nicole Dyer, "Parents of John Lewis Tharp of Washington County, Arkansas," 16 February 2021, *Family Locket* (https://familylocket.com/barsheba-tharp-proof-argument/ : accessed 16 Feb 2021).

For Jesse Alfred Tharp, 1880 U.S. census, Washington County, Arkansas, population schedule, White River, ED 208, p. 22, dwelling 197, family 204, Jesse A. Thorp in John L. Thorp household; database with images, *Ancestry* (https://www.ancestry.com/imageviewer/collections/6742/images/4239970-00675 : accessed 16 Feb 2021); citing NARA microfilm T9, roll 58.

For Leonard, 1900 U.S. census, Milam County, Texas, population schedule, Justice Precinct 5, ED 77, sheet 21A, dwelling/family 330, Leonard in John Tharp household; database with images, *Ancestry* (https://ancestry.com : accessed 16 Feb 2021); citing NARA microfilm T623, roll 1659.

Leonard's Daughter is living; documentation for her parents is privately held by Nicole Dyer.

For Mary Ann Tharp, 1940 U.S. census, Leon County, Texas, population schedule, Justice Precinct 2, ED 145-5, sheet 1B, household 15, Mary A in Leonard Thorp household; database with images, *Ancestry* (https://ancestry.com : accessed 16 Feb 2021); citing NARA microfilm T627, roll 4093.

For Samuel Lee Tharp, 1910 U.S. census, Milam County, Texas, population schedule, Justice Precinct 6, ED 69, sheet 10B, dwelling/family 178, Sam in Jesse A. Tharp household; database with images, *Ancestry* (https://ancestry.com : accessed 16 Feb 2021); citing NARA microfilm T624, roll 1578. For **Frances,** 1940 U.S. census, Bell County, Texas, population schedule, Justice Precinct 4, ED 14-18, sheet 3A, household 49, Francis in Sam Tharp household; database with images, *Ancestry* (https://ancestry.com : accessed 16 Feb 2021); citing NARA microfilm T627, roll 3983.

For Rachel and **Nelson,** Nicole Dyer, "Mary (Tharp) Wood's Children," 16 February 2021, *Family Locket* (https://familylocket.com/barsheba-tharp-proof-argument/ : accessed 16 February 2021).

For John Elza Long, 1900 U.S. census, Collin County, Texas, population schedule, Justice Precinct 5, ED 18, sheet 5A, dwelling/family 80, William K. Long household; database with images, *Ancestry* (https://ancestry.com : accessed 16 Feb 2021); citing NARA microfilm T623, roll 1621.

For Bessie, 1930 U.S. census, Pottawatomie County, Oklahoma, population schedule, Forest, ED 63-27, sheet 1A, dwelling/household 9, Elsie Long household; database with images, *Ancestry* (https://ancestry.com : accessed 16 February 2021); citing NARA microfilm T626, roll 1928.

Bessie's Daughter and Private Male are living; documentation for their parents is privately held by Nicole Dyer.

For John Hollis Wood, 1900 U.S. census, Fannin County, Texas, population schedule, Justice Precinct 1, ED 63, sheet 16A, dwelling 306, family 313, Hollis Wood in Jane Wood household; database with images, *Ancestry* (https://ancestry.com : accessed 16 Feb 2021); citing NARA microfilm T623, roll 1633. Jane Wood was widowed in 1900. For the marriage of John Hollis Wood's parents, see Arkansas, Washington County Marriage Records, 1845–1941," Nelson Wood and Jane Ballard, 22 Oct 1874, image, *Ancestry* (https://ancestry.com : accessed 16 Feb 2021).

For Ruth Vera Wood, 1930 U.S. census, Pottawatomie County, Oklahoma, population schedule, Shawnee, ED 63-48, sheet 16A and 16B, dwelling 341, family 394, Hollis Wood household; database with images, *Ancestry* (https://ancestry.com : accessed 16 Feb 2021); citing NARA microfilm T626, roll 1928.

Sources for Figure 4

For the parents of **Martin, George, and Lewis Tharp**, see the text.

For Mildred Jane Tharpe, Fauquier County, Virginia, Marriage Bonds and Returns 5:211, Nathaniel G. Carter - Mildred Jane Tharpe, daughter of Martin Tharp, marriage bond, 2 Nov 1840; images online, FamilySearch (https://ancestry.com : accessed 16 Feb 2021) DGS 7578973, image 337 of 445; FHL microfilm 31633.

For William Henry Carter, "Virginia, U.S., Select Marriages, 1785–1940," Bettie Tarman - Wm. H. Carter, son of Nathaniel and Mildred J., 15 Feb 1877; index, *Ancestry* (https://ancestry.com : accessed 16 Feb 2021). F

For Mamie, 1900 U.S. census, Fauquier County, Virginia, population schedule, Marshall, ED 33, sheet 12B, dwelling 216, family 218, William Carter household; database with images, *Ancestry* (https://ancestry.com : accessed 16 Feb 2021); citing NARA microfilm T623, roll 1708.

For Nathaniel Wood, 1930 U.S. census, Fauquier County, Virginia, population schedule, Marshall, ED 31-12, sheet 18A, dwelling 345, family 366, Nathaniel in Daniel Wood household; database with images, *Ancestry* (https://ancestry.com : accessed 16 Feb 2021); citing NARA microfilm T626, roll 2443.

For Richard Henry Tharp, Virginia Board of Health, Bureau of Vital Statistics, certificate of death, 26 Dec 1919, file no. 28680, Richard Henry Thorp, Fauquier County; database with images, *Ancestry* (https://ancestry.com : accessed 16 Feb 2021).

For Lucian, 1880 U.S. census, Fauquier County, Virginia, population schedule, Marshall, ED 40, sheet 52D, dwelling 315, family 322, Lucian in R.H. Tharp household; database with images, *Ancestry* (https://ancestry.com : accessed 16 Feb 2021); citing NARA microfilm T9, roll 1364.

For Richard Henry Tharp, Virginia Board of Health, Bureau of Vital Statistics, certificate of death, 22 Feb 1945, file no. 4105, Richard Henry Thorpe, Fauquier County; database with images, *Ancestry* (https://ancestry.com : accessed 16 Feb 2021).

For Thomas Tharp and George Harrison Tharp, Nicole Dyer, "Parents of Thomas Tharp and George Harrison Tharp," 17 February 2021, *Family Locket* (https://familylocket.com/barsheba-tharp-proof-argument/ : accessed 17 Feb 2021).

For Presley Tharp, see Nicole Dyer, "Parents of Presley Tharp of Carroll County, Kentucky," 17 February 2021, *Family Locket* (https://familylocket.com/barsheba-tharp-proof-argument/ : accessed 17 Feb 2021). For **Henry A. Tharp,** 1880 U.S. census, Carroll County, Kentucky, population schedule, Mill Creek, ED 36, dwelling/family 48, Henry A. in Presley Tharp's household; database with images, *Ancestry* (https://ancestry.com : accessed 16 Feb 2021); citing NARA Microfilm T9, roll 408.

For Martha Helen Tharp, 1920 U.S. census, Carroll County, Kentucky, population schedule, Worthville, ED 65, sheet 1B, dwelling/family 14, Martha H. in Henry A. Tharp household; database with images, *Ancestry* (https://ancestry.com : accessed 17 Feb 2021); citing NARA microfilm T625, roll 561.

Martha's daughter is living; documentation for her parents is privately held by Nicole Dyer.

For Allen D. Tharp, see Nicole Dyer, "Parents of Allen D. Tharp of Henry County, Kentucky," 17 February 2021, *Family Locket* (https://ancestry.com : accessed 17 Feb 2021).

For Armilda (Tharp) Carter, Indiana State Board of Health, certificate of death, 7 Nov 1907, no. 38, Armilda Carter, Hendricks County; image online, *Ancestry* (https://ancestry.com : accessed 17 Feb 2021).

For Mary (Carter) Reunion, 1880 U.S. census, Hendricks County, Indiana, population schedule, Union, ED 131, sheet 462C, dwelling/family 294, Mary E. in Enoch Carter household; database with images, *Ancestry* (https://ancestry.com : accessed 17 Feb 2021); citing NARA microfilm T9, roll 283.

For Frances Armilda (Reunion) Boler, Indiana State Board of Health, certificate of death, 23 Apr 1936, no. 14202, Armilda Francis Boler; database with images, *Ancestry* (https://ancestry.com : accessed 17 Feb 2021).

For Ralph Boler, 1930 U.S. census, Hendricks County, Indiana, population schedule, Brownsburg, ED 32-16, sheet 3A, dwelling 70, family 71, Ralph J. in Joseph W. Boler household; database with images, *Ancestry* (https://ancestry.com : accessed 17 Feb 2021); citing NARA microfilm T626, roll 591.

Sources for Figure 6

a. 1830 U.S. census, Hawkins County, Tennessee, p. 17, line 16, Lewis Tharp; image, *Ancestry* (https://www.ancestry.com : accessed 22 Aug 2020); citing National Archives microfilm publication M19, roll 178.

b. 1840 U.S. census, Hawkins County, Tennessee, p. 66, line 2, Lewis Tharp; image, *Ancestry* (https://www.ancestry.com : accessed 22 Aug 2020); citing National Archives publication M704, roll 526.

c. 1850 U.S. census, Washington County, Arkansas, population schedule, White River, p. 358B, dwelling/family 106, Lewis Tharp household; image, *Ancestry* (https://www.ancestry.com : accessed 25 Aug 2020); citing NARA microfilm publication M432, roll 31.

d. 1850 U.S. census, Washington County, Arkansas, population schedule, White River, p. 355a, dwelling 54, Anna, age 30, in household of Wiley Roberts; image, *Ancestry* (https://www.ancestry.com : accessed 26 Sep 2020); citing NARA microfilm publication M432, roll 31. Marriage estimate is based on birth of oldest child in 1838.

e. 1860 U.S. census, Washington County, Arkansas, population schedule, White River, dwelling 2029, family 102, Joannah Faries household; image, *Ancestry* (https://www.ancestry.com : accessed 26 Sep 2020), citing NARA microfilm publication M653. "Tennessee, Marriage Records, 1780–2002," Janna Tharp and Anderson Farris, 31 Aug 1837, image, *Ancestry* (https://www.ancestry.com : accessed 26 Sep 2020).

f. "Arkansas, Washington County Marriage Records, 1845–1941," Jesse Tharp, age 22 and Eliza Robinson, age 17, 17 Sep 1846, image, *Ancestry* (https://www.ancestry.com : accessed 26 Sep 2020).

g. "Arkansas, Washington County Marriage Records, 1845–1941," Nathan Tharp, age 23 and Mary Van Hoose, age 27, 24 Sep 1848, image, *Ancestry* (https://www.ancestry.com : accessed 26 Sep 2020).

h. "Arkansas, Washington County Marriage Records, 1845–1941," Matilda Tharp, age 21 and Robert J Roberson, age 17, 29 Jul 1847, image, *Ancestry* (https://www.ancestry.com : accessed 26 Sep 2020).

i. Ibid., Mary Tharp, age 18 and Wm Wood, age 18, 29 Jul 1847. For birth in 1830, see 1850 U.S. census, Washington County, Arkansas, population schedule, White River, dwelling/family 56, Mary Woods, age 19, in William H Woods household; image, *Ancestry* (https://ancestry.com : accessed 26 Sep 2020); citing NARA microfilm publication M432, roll 31.

j. 1850 U.S. census, Washington County, Arkansas, population schedule, White River, p. 358B, dwelling/family 106, Lucy Tharp, age 17, in Lewis Tharp household; image, *Ancestry* (https://www.ancestry.com : accessed 25 Aug 2020); citing NARA microfilm publication M432, roll 31.

Sample 3: Using DNA and Documentary Research to Identify the Biological Parents of Fern Smith Tischer

Prepared by Robin Wirthlin, 9 January 2021

TO: The Family of Fern Smith Tischer

Research Objective

Use DNA and documentary research to identify Fern Charlotte Smith Tischer's biological parents. Fern was born on 11 December 1911 in Chicago, Cook, Illinois, and died 1 June 2005 in Lake Odessa, Ionia, Michigan.

Limitations

- DNA tests were taken at AncestryDNA, but not transferred to other DNA testing companies.
- DNA segment analysis could not be employed in this project because AncestryDNA does not provide DNA segment information or a chromosome browser to help prove kinship. However, AncestryDNA has the most user-submitted family trees of any DNA testing company. Therefore, pedigree triangulation (comparing family trees of 2 or more matches in the same shared match group and amount of shared DNA to identify ancestors) was the best technique for discovering ancestors shared with DNA matches.

Background Summary

The following was known when the search started in 1998:

1. Fern Smith Tischer was born on 11 December 1911 in Chicago, Cook, Illinois.[1]
2. Ruth Brady went with Bessie Green (original adoptive mother) to pick up the newborn baby, Fern. Bessie was scared, so Fern was given to Ruth Brady (friend of Bessie) when she was less than one hour old.[2]
3. Fern lived with Ruth and John Brady until she was six weeks old when she was suddenly taken away from them and given to Bessie and Elmer Green.[3]
4. When Fern was between 6 and 8 years old, she was given to Bessie's parents, Mabel and John F. "Jack" Smith, to do housework and care for them in their old age.[4]
5. When Fern was about ten years old, she overheard Bessie and Mabel talking. She had recently learned that she was adopted and was curious about the conversation. Bessie and Mabel said, "If only Fern knew that the doctor that delivered her just lives up the street on [Fern couldn't remember the street during the interview]."[5] Fern walked to the doctor's home office at either 329 S. Ashland bl. or 3229 Washington Ave. and wrote down the address.[6] She was satisfied with just this information until 1930.

---

1. Probate Court of the County of Barry, Michigan, Certificate of Determination of Time and Place of Birth, Fern Hull, filed 14 June 1944, birth date 11 December 1911, Chicago, Cook, Illinois, Father William Hull, mother unknown, legitimate, foster mother Ruth Brady Ripstra verified the birth date.

2. Ruth Brady Ripstra, (Villa Park, Illinois) to Fern Smith Tischer, greeting card, December 1983, privately held by Fern's family, [ADDRESS FOR PRIVATE USE], Michigan, 2021; also Fern Smith Tischer, (Lake Odessa, Michigan), telephone interview by Robin Wirthlin, November 1998, transcript privately held, Robin Wirthlin, Robin@FamilyLocket.com, 2021.

3. Fern Smith Tischer, interview, November 1998.

4. Fern Smith Tischer, interview, November 1998; also 1920 U.S. census, Barry County, Michigan, population schedule, Yankee Springs Township, p. 312 (stamped), Enumeration District (E.D.) 66, sheet 4-B, dwelling 93, family 95, John F. Smith household; image, *Ancestry* (http://www.ancestry.com : accessed 8 January 2021), citing National Archives microfilm T625, roll 756. Eight-year-old Fern is listed as John F. and Mabel Smith's daughter.

5. Fern Smith Tischer, interview, November 1998.

6. "U.S., City Directories, 1822–1995," *Ancestry* (https://www.ancestry.com/imageviewer/collections/2469/images/4730907?pId=1234398855 : accessed 5 February 2021), 1917, James A Stough, physician, 329 Ashland bl, image 870 of 1130, p. 1738; also 1910 U.S. census, Cook County, Illinois, population schedule, Chicago, p. 64 (stamped), Enumeration District (ED) 881, sheet 7A, dwelling 65, family 122, James A. Stough household, citing National Archives microfilm T624, roll 263, FHL microfilm 1374276; address 329 Ashland Boulevard; also 1920 U.S. census, Cook County, Illinois, population schedule, Chicago, p. 123 (stamped), Enumeration District (ED) 757, sheet 6-A, dwelling 69, family 144, James A. Stough household, citing National Archives microfilm T625, roll 322; address 3229 Washington Ave., Chicago, original access date on microfilm 7 April 2001.

6. Fern wrote to the doctor in 1930, asking if she was illegitimate.[7]
7. James Austin Stough, MD, replied on 10 January 1930.[8]

"Miss Fern Smith (Hull) . . . You are not an Illegitimate child. You was born about 4 months after your parents were married. Your fathers name was or is William Hull. Your mothers name I don't know that I ever knew. Your parents left Chicago about 6 years after you were born, they then had three more children. Your parents were attending Oberlin College at Oberlin Ohio when the trouble happened."

Research undertaken before 2005 included extensive research conducted between 1998–2005 in census records, city directories, Oberlin College Archives, birth records, name change records, marriage records, death records, probate records, obituaries, online searches, and draft registration cards.[9] No records for William Hull or a child born on 11 December 1911 were located that identified Fern's biological parents. Dr. James Austin Stough (1861–1934) delivered Fern.[10] None of his medical records or logbooks are known to exist.[11] Fern Smith Tischer passed away on 1 June 2005 without learning the identity of her biological parents.[12]

Summary of Research Findings

▪ Analyzed autosomal DNA test results for Fern Smith Tischer's son Corwin Tischer, daughter LT, and daughter Janet Tischer Okrei. Fern's biological parents were not

---

7. Fern Smith Tischer, interview, November 1998.

8. J.A. Stough, (West Palm Beach, Florida) to Miss Fern Smith (Hull), letter, 10 January 1930; privately held by Fern's family [ADDRESS FOR PRIVATE USE], Michigan, 2021.

9. Research findings, Fern Smith Tischer file, Robin Wirthlin, Robin@FamilyLocket.com, 2021.

10. Fern Smith Tischer, interview, November 1998; also *Find a Grave*, database and images, (https://www.findagrave.com : accessed 28 January 2021), memorial 27933530, Dr. James A. Stough (1861–1934), Greenwood Cemetery, Lagrange, LaGrange, Indiana; also "Dr. J.A. Stough of first L.H.S. Class Dies Here Tuesday," LaGrange Standard, (LaGrange, Indiana), 12 July 1934, p. 1.

11. Juin Whipple Foresman, San Juan Capistrano, California, to Robin Wirthlin, letter, 1 February 2002, memories of Dr. James Austin Stough, Personal Correspondence, privately held by Wirthlin, 2021.

12. *Find a Grave*, database and images (https://www.findagrave.com : accessed 04 February 2021), memorial 80495682, Fern Charlotte Smith Tischer (1911–1 June 2005), Lakeside Cemetery, Lake Odessa, Ionia County, Michigan, USA.

identified until DNA results were utilized.[13]

▨ Separated the DNA matches of Fern's children into groups comprised of people descended from families with surnames Hunt, Lawrence, Miller, Mueller, Blomeyer, and Krull.

▨ Used the pedigree triangulation method to discern that Fern's biological maternal great-grandparents were Henry Blomeyer and Henrietta Krull. Her maternal grandparents were George Adam Miller and Amelia Minna Louisa Blomeyer. Fern's paternal grandparents were Giles Hunt and Ann Lowrance.

▨ Learned that the surname of Fern's biological father, William, was Hunt, not Hull.

▨ **Discovered through DNA research that Fern Smith Tischer's biological parents were William Luther Hunt and Elizabeth Amanda Miller.**

▨ Located records for the marriage of William L. Hunt and Elizabeth Amanda Miller. They married on 2 September 1911 in St. Louis, Missouri.[14] This verifies the marriage information provided in the 1930 letter from Dr. Stough to Fern that she was born four months after her parents married.

▨ Identified four additional children who were born to William and Elizabeth Hunt:
   ◦ Robert Miller Hunt (born 24 April 1913, Chicago, Illinois).[15]
   ◦ Cyril Bernard Hunt (born 28 Aug 1914, Chicago, Illinois.)[16]
   ◦ Elizabeth Ann Hunt (born 8 Aug 1916, Chicago, Illinois).[17]

---

13. 1920 U.S. census, Cook County, Illinois, population schedule, Chicago, p. 123 (stamped), Enumeration District (ED) 757, sheet 6-A, dwelling 69, family 144, James A. Stough household; image, *Ancestry* (http://www.ancestry.com : accessed 5 February 2021), citing National Archives microfilm T625, roll 322.

14. St. Louis, Missouri, Office of Recorder of Deeds, Marriage License, Wm. L. Hunt and Elizabeth Miller, 2 September 1911; also "Missouri, County Marriage, Naturalization, and Court Records, 1800–1991," database with images, *FamilySearch* (https://familysearch.org/ark:/61903/3:1:3QS7-8989-9N27 : accessed 8 January 2021), no. 167303, image 298 of 697, p. 575; Missouri State Archives, Jefferson City, citing FHL film #7513845; also "William Luther Hunt." Obituary, unknown newspaper, *Mackley Genealogy* (http://mackleygenealogy.com/~mackley/Obit_Display.php?pid=HU_000927.jpg : accessed 18 June 2018).

15. *Find a Grave*, database and images (https://www.findagrave.com : accessed 9 January 2021), memorial 49209556, Robert Miller Hunt (24 April 1913–18 September 1962), Arlington National Cemetery, Arlington, Arlington, Virginia, USA.

16. *Find a Grave*, database and images (https://www.findagrave.com : accessed 9 January 2021), memorial 59845982, Capt Bernard Cyril Hunt (28 August 1914–5 February 1990), Arlington National Cemetery, Arlington, Arlington, Virginia, USA.

17. "Elizabeth Ann Hunt Gardner (Age 98) "Betty," *The Washington Post* (Washington, D.C.), 28-November - 30 November 2014; database with images, *Legacy* (https://www.legacy.com/obituaries/washingtonpost/obituary.aspx?n=elizabeth-a-gardner&pid=173302614&fhid=16998 : accessed 8 January 2021).

- William Luther Hunt, Jr. (born 6 Oct 1918, Washington, D.C.).[18] This piece of evidence verifies additional information in the letter from Dr. Stough to Fern. He wrote that Fern's parents had three more children before moving away from Chicago, Illinois.
- Discovered that William Luther Hunt was born on 2 June 1886 in Farmington, St. Francois, Missouri.[19] He died on 18 November 1971 in Baltimore, Maryland, and was buried in Friendship United Methodist Church Cemetery, located in Friendship, Anne Arundel, Maryland.[20]
- Established that Elizabeth Amanda Miller was born on 17 February 1892 in Farmington, St. Francois County, Missouri, and died on 15 March 1985 in Annandale, Fairfax, Virginia.[21] Elizabeth Amanda Miller was buried in Friendship United Methodist Church Cemetery in Friendship, Maryland.[22]
- Learned that William L. Hunt attended Carleton College.[23]
- Created a timeline of the important people and events surrounding Fern's birth.
- Built a biological family tree for Fern Charlotte Smith Tischer.

Itemized Research Findings

DNA Inheritance

Since extensive documentary research was unsuccessful in identifying Fern Smith Tischer's biological parents, the next step was to use DNA research to identify them.[24]

---

18. "Obituary of William L. Hunt," *David C. Gross Funeral Homes & Cremation Centers* (https://davidcgross.com/tribute/details/136702/William-Hunt/obituary.html#tribute-start : accessed 9 January 2021).

19. "Missouri, Birth Registers, 1847–1919," database with images, *Ancestry* (https://www.ancestry.com/imageviewer/collections/1170/images/vrmmo1833_c6028-0087?pId=3017955 : accessed 8 January 2021), June 4, 1886, Male Hunt, entry 634, image 60 of 115, unpaginated.

20. *Find a Grave*, database and images (https://www.findagrave.com : accessed 04 February 2021), memorial 115255793, William Luther "Buck" Hunt (2 June 1886–15 November 1971), Friendship United Methodist Church Cemetery, Friendship, Anne Arundel County, Maryland, USA.

21. "Virginia, Death Records, 1912–2014, database and images, *Ancestry* (https://www.ancestry.com : accessed January 2018), Elizabeth M. Hunt, (17 February 1892 – 15 March 1985), image 41 of 499.

22. *Find a Grave*, database and images (https://www.findagrave.com : accessed 04 February 2021), memorial 115255792, Elizabeth Amanda Miller Hunt (17 February 1892–15 March 1985), Friendship United Methodist Church Cemetery, Friendship, Anne Arundel County, Maryland, USA.

23. Robert Louis Hunt, "William "Buck" Hunt," *Geni* (https://www.geni.com/people/William-Buck-Hunt/366147133680011694#/tab/overview : accessed 23 December 2017).

24. Wirthlin, Fern Smith Tischer file, 2021.

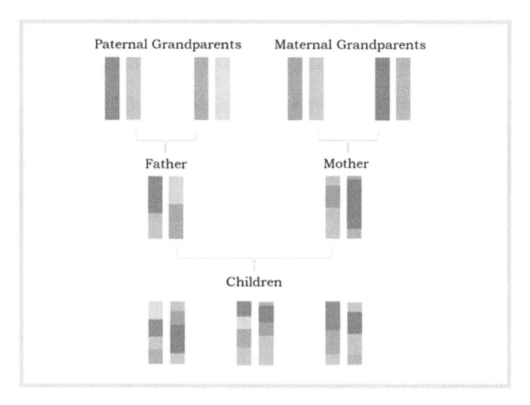

Figure 1. DNA segments are recombined and passed on to children, grandchildren, and so on through the generations.

Although Fern passed away in 2005, she passed 50% of her DNA on to each of her children, and each of them received a little different 50%. Three of Fern's children, Corwin Tischer, Janet Tischer Okrei, and LT, took AncestryDNA tests in late 2017 and early 2018. Results from the three DNA tests could be used to identify Fern's living biological family members, and possibly Fern's parents could be identified. The DNA match list for Fern's three children indicated that they had some close biological relatives—from first to third cousins.

The following information will lay a foundation for understanding DNA inheritance and testing results. Parents pass 50% of their DNA on to their children. These children become parents and, in turn, pass on 50% of their DNA to their children. The DNA that the second generation inherits is a mixture of about 25% of each grandparents' DNA (see Figure 1). As the generations continue, DNA recombines and is passed on randomly but is generally cut in half with each generation. DNA matches can help verify ancestors 6–8 generations back in time.

The amount of DNA shared between two relatives is given in centimorgans (cM) in DNA test results. A centimorgan is a measurement of the likelihood that DNA will recombine. Generally speaking, the larger the cM amount, the closer the two people are related.

DNA itself cannot confirm family connections and must be used with genealogical information about family relationships to be meaningful. Therefore, historical records are critical to the success of DNA analysis.

The primary concept in DNA analysis is that DNA testers and their DNA matches share a common ancestor or common ancestral couple. When the relationship between two DNA testers is estimated or definitively learned via analyzing shared DNA and documentary research, the shared ancestor(s) can be determined. If one of the DNA matches knows who the shared ancestor was, the other DNA match can learn more about their family history, even if they didn't know who their ancestor(s) were at the beginning of the research. Frequently, DNA testers identify their ancestors by linking a family tree to their DNA account. Researchers can view the related family trees or search other online family trees to see or build connections between DNA matches and the ancestors they share in common with the DNA tester.

DNA Research Findings

AncestryDNA reported a long list of people in their database who shared DNA with Fern's children. The first research step was to use the "Shared Matches" feature in AncestryDNA to create two genetic networks or groups of DNA matches related to Corwin and LT and each other. Janet Okrei's DNA results were available four months after Corwin and LT's results. The amount of shared DNA with each of Janet's DNA matches confirmed the family relationships.

The first genetic network was made of DNA matches related to the three children's father, Gerald Tischer. The second genetic network comprised the rest of the matches – who by default were related to their mother, Fern. Information about the amount of shared DNA and family trees linked to the DNA matches' profiles had the potential to achieve the research objective and identify Fern's biological parents.

Table 1 lists Fern's children, and the amount of DNA they share listed in centimorgans (cM) with their close DNA matches from genetic network 2. cM Range values are from the Shared cM Project Version 3.0 because the initial DNA analysis was done between December 2017 and July 2018.[25]

---

25. Blaine Bettinger and Jonny Perl, "The Shared cM Project 3.0 tool v3," *DNA Painter* (https://dnapainter. com/tools/sharedcmv3 : updated 12 October 2017).

Table 1. DNA comparison showing the amount of DNA that Fern's children share with their biological cousins

Tester	Corwin Shared DNA[a]	LT Shared DNA[b]	Janet Shared DNA[c]	Relation	Shared DNA in cM for the Relationship	Most Recent Common Ancestor
Tester 1	451 cM	393 cM	394 cM	1C1R	102-980, avg. 433 cM	William Hunt/ Elizabeth Miller
Tester 2	1062 cM	788 cM	794 cM	1C	396-1397, avg. 866 cM	William Hunt/ Elizabeth Miller
Tester 3	1032 cM	625 cM	841 cM	1C	396-1397, avg. 866 cM	William Hunt/ Elizabeth Miller
Tester 4	510 cM	652 cM	562 cM	1C	396-1397, avg. 866 cM	William Hunt/ Elizabeth Miller
Tester 5	863 cM	678 cM	643 cM	1C	396-1397, avg. 866 cM	William Hunt/ Elizabeth Miller
Tester 6	154 cM	300 cM	205 cM	2C	41-592, avg. 229 cM	Giles Hunt/Ann Lowrance
Tester 7	530 cM	557 cM	697 cM	1C1R	102-980, avg. 433 cM	Giles Hunt/Ann Lowrance
Tester 8	141 cM	198 cM	139 cM	2C	41-592, avg. 229 cM	George Miller/ Amelia Blomeyer
Tester 9	194 cM	234 cM	190 cM	2C	41-592, avg. 229 cM	George Miller/ Amelia Blomeyer
Tester 10	320 cM	207 cM	190 cM	2C	41-592, avg. 229 cM	George Miller/ Amelia Blomeyer
Tester 11	210 cM	209 cM	145 cM	2C	41-592, avg. 229 cM	Henry Blomeyer/ Henrietta Krull

a. AncestryDNA matches for Corwin Tischer, database report, *AncestryDNA* (https://www.ancestry.com : accessed December 2017-July 2018) DNA match results for testers 1-11.

b. AncestryDNA matches for LT, database report, *AncestryDNA* (https://www.ancestry.com : accessed December 2017-July 2018) DNA match results for testers 1-11.

c. AncestryDNA matches for Janet Okrei, database report, *AncestryDNA* (https://www.ancestry.com : accessed April-July 2018) DNA match results for testers 1-11.

The amount of shared DNA between Corwin Tischer, LT, and Janet Okrei and Testers 1–11 was used to estimate relationships using the Shared cM Project tool.[26] The Shared

26. Perl and Bettinger, "The Shared cM Project 3.0 tool v3," *DNA Painter*, October 2017).

cM Project is the industry accepted standard for evaluating family relationships based on the amount of shared DNA. Version 3.0 used the data from 25,000 DNA testers who reported the amount of DNA they shared with their known relatives.[27] All amounts of shared DNA between Fern's children and DNA matches called Testers 1–11, fit within the observed range and high probability for specific relationships in the Shared cM Project. This information meant that the relationships were probable, and genealogical records were needed to confirm the relationships and the shared ancestors.

The DNA matches in genetic network 2 were examined to learn if they had a linked or unlinked family tree or no tree at all. If a family tree was available, it was compared with others in genetic network 2 to identify ancestors and locations found in multiple DNA matches' trees. The DNA matches and their ancestors were added to a chart to illustrate their family connections. The amount of DNA shared with the closest DNA matches was used to place the matches into specific relationships in the family tree. As the chart grew, it became apparent that many of the close DNA matches shared the same ancestors (see figure 2).

Not all of the close DNA matches had family trees associated with their DNA profiles, especially those with higher amounts of shared DNA. An in-depth comparison of shared DNA and estimated relationships was correlated with hints from online family trees. Some "quick trees" were built for DNA matches with no tree or small family trees to connect to ancestors recorded in multiple DNA matches' family trees. Reasonably exhaustive research was not performed while building the quick trees, but strong evidence was obtained to verify each parent-to-child link.

Fern's parents were identified when people in the family trees of multiple DNA matches connected in both time and location. First, the connection between the Hunt and Lawrence families was established and confirmed with Giles Hunt and Ann Lowrance's 3 February 1875 marriage record.[28] Census records list family members and others living in the same household and were the most accessible records to identify their children. The census records may contain errors and are only as correct as the informant's memory and the census taker's understanding. The 1880, 1900, and 1910 U.S. census listed Giles Hunt

27. Blaine Bettinger, *The Shared cM Project—Version 3.0* (August 2017), (https://thegeneticgenealogist.com/wp-content/uploads/2017/08/Shared_cM_Project_2017.pdf : accessed December 2017).

28. "Missouri, U.S., Marriage Records, 1805–2002," database and images, *Ancestry* (https://www.ancestry.com/imageviewer/collections/1171/images/vrmmo1833_c6017-0321?pId=9612005 : accessed 1 February 2021), St Francois > Record images for St. Francois > 1836–1876, Giles Hunt and Annie Lawrance, 3 February 1875, p. 367, image 287 of 304, citing Missouri State Archives; Jefferson City, MO, USA; Missouri Marriage Records.

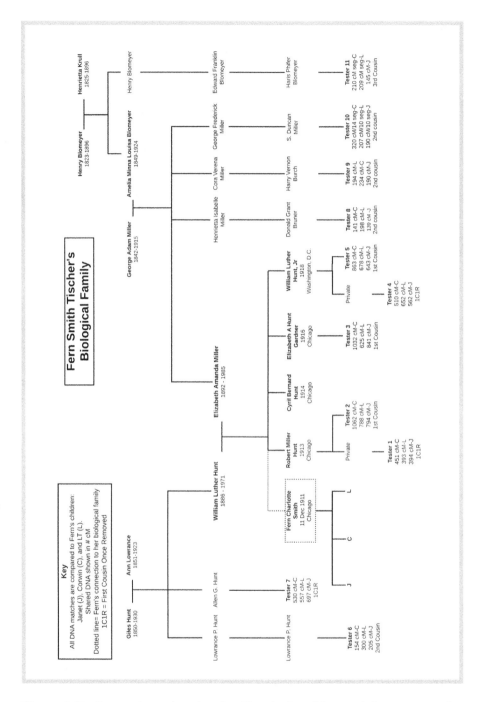

Figure 2. Pedigree chart showing family relationships and the amount of DNA that verifies the DNA tester's locations in the family tree

and Ann Lowrance's children as Lucinda/Eliza L., John W., Bertha L., Parkhurst L., **William M./William L**, Allen G., Carmen, and Bonnie D. Hunt.[29] Because similar family information was listed in the three censuses in St. Francois, St. Francois, Missouri, there was evidence that the correct family had been identified. William Hunt was named with different middle initials in the 1900 and 1910 census, and further research was needed to learn William Hunt's correct middle initial.

The relationship between the Millers and the Blomeyers was established through family tree comparison. The connection was verified with the 29 March 1868 marriage record for George Adam Miller and Amelia Minna Louisa Blomeyer.[30] The 1880, 1900, and 1910 U.S. census listed their children as Emma, Daniel, Etty, Mancy, Coral/Cora, George/Geo/George F., Millie, Smith V., Henry B., **Lizzie/Elizabeth M.**, Waldon, Arthur W. The Find A Grave record for George Adam Miller listed the following children: Emma Theresa Miller Cleve, Daniel Adam Miller, Henrietta Isabelle Miller Bruner, Mary Alice Miller Smith, Cora Verena Miller McCoy, George Fredrick Miller, Lydia Elizabeth "Lizzie" Miller, Amelia Louisa Miller Strobel, Harry Smith Victor Miller, Henry Blomeyer Miller, **Elizabeth Amanda Miller Hunt**, and Arthur Waldo Miller.[31] When comparing census and Find A Grave records, it was noted that some of the Miller children had different names on the census, and not all of the children in the Find A Grave record were recorded on the censuses. Lydia Elizabeth "Lizzie" Miller was born and died between the 1880 and 1900 census, which explains why she is not recorded with the family but is

---

29. 1880 U.S. census, St. Francois County, Missouri, population schedule, St. Francois, p. 422D (stamped), Enumeration District (ED) 118, dwelling 134, family 134, John C. Hunt household; image, *Ancestry* (http://www.ancestry.com : accessed 3 February 2021), citing National Archives microfilm T9, roll 714; also 1900 U.S. census, St. Francois County, Missouri, population schedule, St. Francois, p. 191 (stamped), Enumeration District (ED) 98, sheet 19-B, dwelling 133, family 133, Giles Hunt household; image, *Ancestry* (http://www.ancestry.com : accessed 3 February 2021), citing National Archives microfilm T623, 1854 rolls; also 1910 U.S. census, St. Francois County, Missouri, population schedule, St. Francois Township, p. 244 (stamped), Enumeration District (ED) 95, sheet 13A, dwelling 223, family 235, Jiles Hunt household; image, *Ancestry* (http://www.ancestry.com : accessed 20 January 2021), citing National Archives microfilm T624, roll 808.

30. "Missouri, U.S., Marriage Records, 1805–2002," database and images, *Ancestry* (https://www.ancestry.com/imageviewer/collections/1171/images/vrmmo1833_c6017-0237?usePUB=true&usePUB-Js=true&pId=9611311 : accessed 1 February 2021), St Francois > Record images for St. Francois > 1836–1876, George A. Miller and Emily L. M. Blomeyer, 29 March 1868, p. 209, image 203 of 304; citing Missouri State Archives, Jefferson City, MO, USA, Missouri Marriage Records.

31. *Find A Grave* , database and images (https://www.findagrave.com : accessed 3 February 2021), memorial 104148343, George Adam Miller (2 February 1842–24 March 1915), Copenhagen Cemetery, Farmington, St. Francois County, Missouri, USA.

recorded in Find A Grave.[32] It appears that Elizabeth Amanda Miller was named after her sister, who had passed away. The marriage and census records established the connection between George A. Hunt and Amelia Blomeyer and gave a list of children who were possible parent candidates for Fern S. Tischer.

Next, the intersection between the Hunts and the Millers was sought. At first, the DNA tests showed that the primary matches with family trees were Testers 1, 4, 7, 10, and 11. Tester 3 had no family tree connected with his DNA account. When he replied to a message one year later, he shared that he was adopted and didn't know [the identity of] any birth family members. As time went on, more of Fern's close relatives tested their DNA. Each of the newer testers, 2, 5, and 8, added DNA evidence that the family structure shown in the chart was correct.

The high amounts of DNA that Janet, Corwin, and LT shared with testers 1, 2, 4, and 5 indicated that the relationships were first cousins, or first cousins once removed. If the testers were first cousins, then their parents were full siblings to Fern! This discovery meant that at least some of the information Dr. James A. Stough wrote to Fern was correct - that Fern's parents had more children (three) before they moved away from Chicago.

Records of Fern's siblings and parents were sought to confirm the DNA connections. It was discovered that Fern's sibling's parents were William Hunt and Elizabeth Miller. The relationships were verified when family trees and genealogical documents showed how the DNA testers fit into the larger family structure. The following timeline was established with records and corresponded with the information provided by Fern at the beginning of the research in 1998.

Fern's four full siblings were

- Robert Miller Hunt (born 24 April 1913, Chicago, Illinois).[33]
- Cyril Bernard Hunt (born 28 Aug 1914, Chicago, Illinois.)[34]

---

32. *Find A Grave* , database and images (https://www.findagrave.com : accessed 3 February 2021), memorial 178353425, Lydia Elizabeth "Lizzie" Miller, (July 1882–16 October 1883), Copenhagen Cemetery, Farmington, St. Francois County, Missouri, USA.

33. *Find a Grave*, database and images (https://www.findagrave.com : accessed 9 January 2021), memorial 49209556, Robert Miller Hunt (24 April 1913–18 September 1962), Arlington National Cemetery, Arlington, Arlington, Virginia, USA.

34. *Find a Grave*, database and images (https://www.findagrave.com : accessed 9 January 2021), memorial 59845982, Capt Bernard Cyril Hunt (28 August 1914–5 February 1990), Arlington National Cemetery, Arlington, Arlington, Virginia, USA.

- ■ Elizabeth Ann Hunt (born 8 Aug 1916, Chicago, Illinois).[35]
- ■ William Luther Hunt, Jr. (born 6 Oct 1918, Washington, D.C.).[36]

Dr. James Austin Stough told Fern that her father's name was William Hull. DNA connections revealed that Fern was related to the Hunt family. Dr. Stough misremembered Fern's parent's surname. The difference in the names could be due to the length of time—nineteen years—between 1911 when Fern was born and 1930 when Dr. Stough wrote to her and stated that her father's name was William Hull.

It is unknown how Dr. Stough knew William Hunt and the specific information that the Hunts had three more children before moving away from Chicago. Why didn't Dr. Stough know Elizabeth's name? Further research could discover if the Stoughs and the Hunts attended church together.

The obituaries of both men may give clues about how they knew each other. William Hunt's obituary stated that he was a 50-year member of Candida Lodge A.F. and F.M. of Chicago [Ancient Free and Accepted Masons].[37] Dr. James A. Stough's obituary reported that he was a Chicago Masonic and Odd Fellows Lodges member. Were the two men members of the same Masonic lodge? Further research could uncover the connection.

Dr. Hull also wrote that Fern's parents attended Oberlin College in Oberlin, Ohio, "when the trouble happened." A life sketch of William Hunt stated that he had attended Carleton College in Farmington, Missouri.[38] William was listed with his parents in the 1910 census for St. Francois, St. Francois, Missouri.[39] Elizabeth Miller lived in Farmington, St. Francois, Missouri, in 1910, where Carleton College was located.[40] While the time cannot

---

35. "Elizabeth Ann Hunt Gardner (Age 98) "Betty," The Washington Post (Washington, D.C.), 28-November - 30 November 2014; database with images, *Legacy* (https://www.legacy.com/obituaries/washingtonpost/obituary.aspx?n=elizabeth-a-gardner&pid=173302614&fhid=16998 : accessed 8 January 2021).

36. "Obituary of William L. Hunt," *David C. Gross Funeral Homes & Cremation Centers* (https://davidcgross.com/tribute/details/136702/William-Hunt/obituary.html#tribute-start : accessed 9 January 2021).

37. "William Luther Hunt." Obituary, unknown newspaper, *Mackley Genealogy* (http://mackleygenealogy.com/~mackley/Obit_Display.php?pid=HU_000927.jpg : accessed 18 June 2018).

38. Robert Louis Hunt, "William "Buck" Hunt," *Geni*.

39. 1910 U.S. census, St. Francois Co., MO, St. Francois Township, p. 244 (stamped), ED 95, sheet 13A, dwell. 223, family 235, Jiles Hunt.

40. 1910 U.S. census, St. Francois Co., MO, Farmington, p. 253 (stamped), ED 96, sheet 1-B, dwell. 12, fam. 13, George A. Miller; also Robert Louis Hunt, "William "Buck" Hunt," *Geni*; also Paul Batesel, "Carleton College Farmington, Missouri 1854–1916," *America's Lost Colleges,* (https://www.lostcolleges.com/carleton-college : accessed 5 February 2021).

Table 2. Timeline of events and locations of important people in
Fern S. Tischer's life

Event	Date	Location	Source
Elizabeth Miller residence	15 April 1910	Farmington, St. Francois, Missouri	1910 U.S. census, St. Francois Co., Missouri, Farmington, p. 253 (stamped), ED 96, sheet 1B, dwell. 12, fam. 13, George A. Miller.
William L. Hunt residence	11 May 1910	St. Francois Twp., St. Francois, Missouri	1910 U.S. census, St. Francois County, Missouri, population schedule, St. Francois Township, p. 244 (stamped), ED 95, sheet 13A, dwell. 223, family 235, Jiles Hunt.
Wm Hunt residence	1911	4015 W. Vanburen, Chicago, Cook, Illinois	"U.S., City Directories, 1822-1995," *Ancestry* (https://www.ancestry.com/imageviewer/collections/2469/images/4715285?pId=1233755832 : accessed 3 February 2021), 1911, The Lakeside City Directory, Chicago, Illinois, Wm Hunt, image 178 of 761, p. 657.
William L. Hunt married Elizabeth Miller	2 September 1911	St. Louis, Missouri	"Missouri, County Marriage, Naturalization, and Court Records, 1800-1991," database with images, *FamilySearch* (https://familysearch.org : accessed 8 January 2021), St. Louis>Marriage licenses 1911-1912, no. 167303, image 298 of 697, p. 575; Missouri State Archives, Jefferson City.
Fern Charlotte Smith Born	11 December 1911	Chicago, Cook, Illinois	Delayed birth certificate; Interview with Fern Charlotte Smith Tischer 1998
Ruth Brady took Fern home	11 December 1911	Chicago, Cook, Illinois	Ruth Brady Ripstra to Fern Smith Tischer, December 1983; also Fern Smith Tischer, interview, November 1998.

Wm L. Hunt residence	1913	3977 Drexel bl, Chicago, Cook, Illinois	"U.S., City Directories, 1822-1995," *Ancestry* (https://www.ancestry.com/imageviewer/collections/2469/images/4719782?pId=1233755832 : accessed 4 February 2021), 1913, Lakeside Annual Directory of the City of Chicago, image 333 of 911, p. 652, Wm L Hunt.
Robert Miller Hunt born	24 April 1913	Not directly stated	*Find a Grave*, memorial 49209556, Robert Miller Hunt (24 Apr 1913–18 Sep 1962).
Wm L. Hunt residence	1914	2456 Diana ct, Chicago, Cook, Illinois	U.S., City Directories, 1822-1995, *Ancestry* (https://www.ancestry.com/imageviewer/collections/2469/images/4724251?pId=1233755832 : accessed 4 February 2021), 1914, Lakeside Guide of Chicago, Chicago Directory Co., Wm L Hunt, clk, image 335 of 1002, p. 760.
Cyril Bernard Hunt	28 August 1914	Chicago, Cook, Illinois	*Find a Grave*, memorial 59845982, Capt Bernard Cyril Hunt (28 Aug 1914–5 Feb 1990); also "Illinois, Cook County, Birth Certificates, 1871-1949," index, *FamilySearch* (https://familysearch.org/ark:/61903/1:1:Q23S-3HVV : accessed 20 January 2021), Cyril Bernard Hunt, Certificate No. 43197, 28 August 1814, Chicago, Reg Date 15 February 1960.
Wm L. Hunt residence	1915-17	2456 Geneva ter[race], Chicago, Cook, Illinois	"U.S., City Directories, 1822-1995," *Ancestry* (https://www.ancestry.com/imageviewer/collections/2469/images/4729061?pId=1233755832 : accessed 4 February 2021), 1915, Lakeside Annual Directory of the City of Chicago, Wm L Hunt, clk, image 385 of 1063, p. 774.

Elizabeth Ann Hunt	8 August 1916	Chicago, Cook, Illinois	"Elizabeth Ann Hunt Gardner (Age 98) "Betty," The Washington Post (Washington, D.C.), (28-November - 30 November 2014); database Legacy. com.
William Luther Hunt, Jr	6 October 1918	Washington, D.C.	"Obituary of William L. Hunt," David C. Gross Funeral Homes & Cremation Centers, 6 October 1918.
Residence of William L. & Elizabeth Miller and children Robert M., Cyril B., Elizabeth A., William L. Hunt	10 January 1920	Washington, D.C.	1920 U.S. census, District Of Columbia, Washington, population schedule, Washington, D.C., p. 112 (stamped), Enumeration District (ED) 124, sheet 10-A, dwelling 152, family 239, William L. Hunt household; image, Ancestry (http://www. ancestry.com : accessed 3 February 2021), citing National Archives microfilm T625, roll 208.
Residence of Fern Smith in 1920	24 January 1920	Yankee Springs, Barry, Michigan	1920 U.S. census, Barry Co., Michigan, Yankee Springs Township, p. 312 (stamped), ED 66, sheet 4-B, dwell. 93, fam 95, John F. Smith.

be pinpointed, the location and opportunity for acquaintance allowed for their first child's conception (see table 2).

Dr. Stough also told Fern that her parents were married four months before she was born. A marriage license and return record certified that William L. Hunt and Elizabeth Miller were married in St. Louis, Missouri, on 2 September 1911.[41] They obtained a marriage license on the same day that the marriage was performed.

The marriage license (Figure 3) stated that William lived in Chicago, implying that he already lived in Chicago before the marriage was performed. The marriage license also noted that Elizabeth lived in Farmington, Missouri, at the marriage time. Additionally, a 5 September 1911 newspaper article from the St. Louis Post-Dispatch informed the

41. "Missouri, County Marriage, Naturalization, and Court Records, 1800–1991," database with images, FamilySearch (https://familysearch.org/ark:/61903/3:1:3QS7-8989-9N27? : accessed 8 January 2021), no. 167303, image 298 of 697, p. 575; Missouri State Archives, Jefferson City, citing FHL film 7513845.

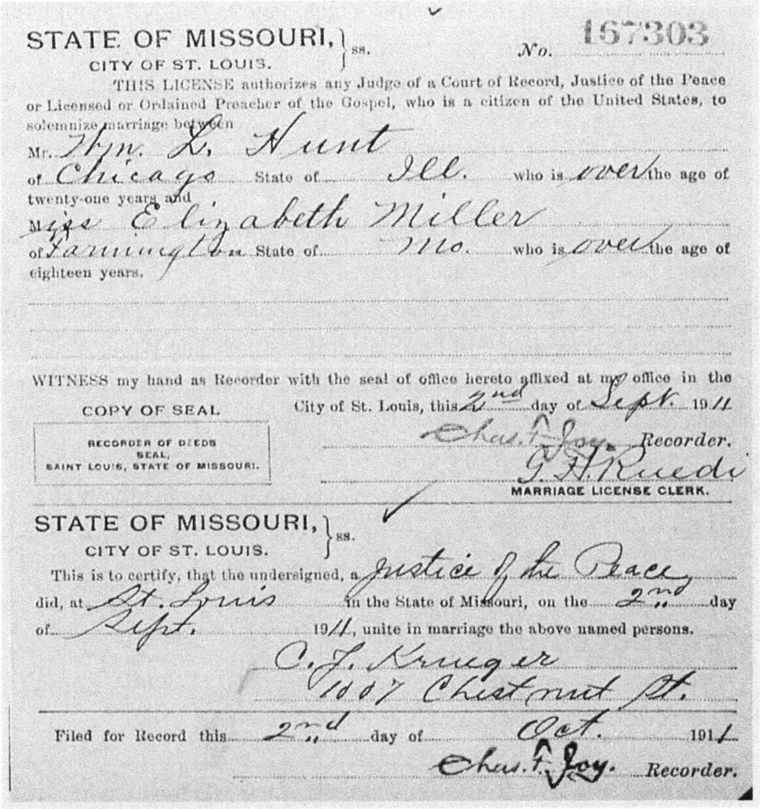

STATE OF MISSOURI, } ss. No. 167303
CITY OF ST. LOUIS.

THIS LICENSE authorizes any Judge of a Court of Record, Justice of the Peace or Licensed or Ordained Preacher of the Gospel, who is a citizen of the United States, to solemnize marriage between

Mr. Wm. L. Hunt of Chicago State of Ill. who is over the age of twenty-one years and

Miss Elizabeth Miller of Farmington State of Mo. who is over the age of eighteen years.

WITNESS my hand as Recorder with the seal of office hereto affixed at my office in the City of St. Louis, this 2nd day of Sept. 1911

COPY OF SEAL

RECORDER OF DEEDS SEAL, SAINT LOUIS, STATE OF MISSOURI.

Chas. F. Joy. Recorder.

G. H. Ruedi
MARRIAGE LICENSE CLERK.

STATE OF MISSOURI, } ss.
CITY OF ST. LOUIS.

This is to certify, that the undersigned, a Justice of the Peace did, at St. Louis in the State of Missouri, on the 2nd day of Sept. 1911, unite in marriage the above named persons.

C. J. Krueger
1407 Chestnut St.

Filed for Record this 2nd day of Oct. 1911

Chas. F. Joy. Recorder.

Figure 3. Marriage License and Return for Wm. L. Hunt of Chicago, Ill. and Elizabeth Miller of Farmington, Mo.

public that William L. Hunt of Chicago, IL and Amanda Elizabeth Hunt of Farmington, MO obtained a marriage license.[42] The marriage records further validated the connection between the Hunt and Miller DNA matches and Fern's biological parents.

Another confirmation of the marriage was William Luther Hunt's obituary, which referred to his and Elizabeth's 60th wedding anniversary taking place two months before November 1971, which was calculated as September 1911.[43] When the information from the marriage license, newspaper notice, and obituary was correlated, there was no doubt

42. "Marriage Licenses," *St. Louis Post-Dispatch*, (St. Louis, Missouri), 5 September 1911, William L. Hunt, Chicago, Ill., and Elizabeth Miller, Farmington, Mo., p. 9, col 3; *Newspapers.com* (www.newspapers.com : accessed 8 January 2021).

43. "William Luther Hunt." Obituary, unknown newspaper, *Mackley Genealogy* (http://mackleygenealogy.com/~mackley/Obit_Display.php?pid=HU_000927.jpg : accessed 18 June 2018).

that William Hunt and Elizabeth Miller fit the description given by Dr. James A. Stough that they were married four months before Fern was born.

Conclusion

DNA evidence was the breakthrough needed in the search for Fern Charlotte Smith Tischer's biological parents. After DNA evidence pointed to William Hunt and Elizabeth Miller as Fern's parents, obituaries, birth, marriage, death records, census records, and city directories gave documentary evidence of family relationships. The family relationships were verified when documents were considered along with the amount of shared DNA, and a genetic connection was verified.

Fern's posterity has been given peace and closure to a long personal quest to identify her birth parents. While not always the case, Fern's biological family has positively reacted and embraced Fern's posterity.

Further Research Suggestions

Search Carleton College records for William Hunt and Elizabeth Miller:

> "Folder 3: Printed material, 1875–1913. House publications, including the first issue of The Exponent (February 1875), published by Carleton Institute, and seven issues of The Carletonian (1909–1913), published by Carleton College."

> "The Carletonian" yearbook or newspaper was published from 1909–1913—in the key timeframe for William Hunt and Elizabeth Miller to be students.

Locate church records for William Hunt and Elizabeth Miller in Farmington, St Francois, Missouri, St. Francois, St. Francois, Missouri, Chicago, Cook, Illinois, Washington, D.C.

Locate birth or christening records for Elizabeth Miller from Farmington, St. Francois, Missouri.

Glossary

Autosomal DNA (atDNA): Autosomal DNA is the DNA found in human chromosomes and is composed of 22 pairs of autosomes, numbered 1 to 22. One copy of each chromosome is inherited from the mother, and one copy from the father. This type of DNA isuseful in helping identify relatives who share common ancestors up to 6–8 generations.

AutoClusters: AutoClusters are computer-generated groupings of DNA matches that share DNA with you and with some of your DNA matches. People in the clusters most likely share common ancestors. See www.geneticaffairs.com.

Base Test Takers: Individuals who have taken a DNA test and given you access to their results as part of a research project to discover more about a specific objective.

Chromosome Browser: Tool that illustrates the chromosomes and segments of DNA shared between two or more DNA matches.

Centimorgan (cM): Measurement of the likelihood that DNA will recombine where the larger the number, the more closely related the DNA matches are.

DNA: Deoxyribonucleic acid; a molecule in each cell that carries genetic information and is passed from parents to children.

DNA Match: Person with whom you share DNA; a DNA testing company has found that the values at specific locations (alleles), which are recorded as A, G, T, C, match others in the DNA companies' database.

DNA Match List: List of people with whom you share DNA which includes the amount of DNA shared, an estimated relationship the tester shares with the DNA matches, and sometimes their family tree.

Endogamy: Occurs among some geographically isolated populations or populations who choose to marry primarily within the population. As a result of this, the children inherit DNA from the founders of the population in multiple ways.

GEDCOM File: Genealogy Data Communication; a universal family tree program file that can be moved between different types of genealogy software.

Genetic Distance (GD): The number of mutations differentiating two individuals' Y-DNA or mtDNA test results; the lower the genetic distance (GD), the closer the people are related.

Genetic Network: Groups or clusters of shared matches; people in a cluster often share at least one common ancestor or ancestral couple.

Haplogroup: Group of genetically related people who share a similar mitochondrial DNA (males and females) or Y-DNA (males) haplotypes and who share a common ancestor somewhere back in time.

Haplotype: Group of marker values for a DNA test taker; the markers are frequently inherited together and are useful in genealogy to compare how a test taker is related to others.

Nucleotide: Compound molecule made of a phosphate, a sugar, and a nitrogenous base that bond together to make DNA including adenine, guanine, thymine, and cytosine abbreviated in a raw DNA report as A, G, T, and C.

Marker: Locations in DNA that are tested to determine the SNP or STR values.

Meiosis: A two-step process of genetic mixing and cell division that produces four gametes—sperm for males and eggs for females. Each sperm or egg holds one copy of each chromosome 1–22. Sperm hold Y-DNA or X-DNA, and eggs hold X-DNA.

Mitochondrial DNA (mtDNA): DNA found in mitochondria, which are organelles in each cell; inherited by both men and women from their mothers; inherited along matrilineal lines and may remain unchanged for thousands of years.

Most Recent Common Ancestors (MRCA): the couple from whom you and your DNA match descend who lived most recently in time; could be just one ancestor if the match descends from a different spouse than you.

Misattributed Parentage Event (MPE): situation where the biological parents are not the same as those identified in genealogical records.

Non-Paternal Event (NPE): also known as "Not the Parent Expected;" see MPE

Pedigree Triangulation: Method of comparing the family trees of three or more DNA matches to identify common ancestors shared by the tester and the DNA matches.

Pedigree Collapse: This happens when related individuals have children. These children have fewer unique ancestors than expected because their parents have some ancestors in common.

Phasing: Assigning alleles to maternal or paternal chromosomes in atDNA test results.

Proof Arguments: Written proof that includes conflicting evidence or a case built on indirect evidence and requires more than a summary of evidence.

Quick Trees: family tree built for DNA matches by finding some records, but not doing reasonably exhaustive research; sometimes called "quick and dirty trees."

Segment Triangulation: A method of comparing specific segments of DNA from three people. If all three have inherited the same DNA segment on the same chromosome, then they likely share a common ancestor.

Sex Chromosomes: X and Y chromosomes; females inherit one X from their father and one X from their mother; males inherit a Y chromosome from their father and an X chromosome from their mother.

Short Tandem Repeats (STRs): Regions of DNA where a small motif is repeated several times in a consecutive sequence in the genetic code; for genetic genealogy purposes, Y-DNA is tested for STRs.

Single Nucleotide Polymorphisms (SNPs): Variations in DNA code at a single location; DNA companies test around 700,000 locations in a person's DNA, where the DNA code is more likely to vary.

Traced Relationship: Relationship of two people based on evidence in documentary research.

Y-DNA: DNA that is passed down in males virtually intact from father to son along the patrilineal line.

Index

About the Authors

Diana Elder, AG

Diana Elder AG® is a professional genealogist accredited in the Gulf South region of the United States. She serves as a Commissioner for The International Commission for the Accreditation of Professional Genealogists (ICAPGen). Diana first used Y-DNA in 2009 to connect her Texas Royston family to the descendants of John Royston, born 1610 of Virginia. Since then Diana has continued adding to her DNA knowledge and experience, completing the advanced DNA course, "A Practical Approach: Establishing Genealogical Proof with DNA" in 2018 and the "All-DNA Advanced Evidence Analysis Practicum" in 2020 (both through the Salt Lake Institute of Genealogy). Diana regularly uses DNA in her client work as well as her own family history research. Diana is the author of the bestselling book, *Research Like a Pro: A Genealogist's Guide* and the creator of the Research Like a Pro study group and e-Course. Diana and her daughter, Nicole Dyer are the hosts of the Research Like a Pro Genealogy Podcast and share research tips on their website, FamilyLocket.com.

Nicole Dyer

Nicole Dyer is a professional genealogist, lecturer, and creator of FamilyLocket.com and The Research Like a Pro Genealogy Podcast. She is the co-author of *Research Like a Pro: A Genealogist's Guide*. Nicole has spoken at many genealogy conferences and events including RootsTech and the National Genealogy Society Conference. She specializes in Southern United States research and enjoys incorporating DNA evidence into her research. She is an instructor in the Research Like a Pro study group and Research Like a Pro with DNA study group. She has completed the following Salt Lake Institute of

Genealogy (SLIG) courses: Intermediate Foundations, Introduction to Genetic Genealogy, Meeting Standards Using DNA Evidence—Research Strategies, and All-DNA Advanced Evidence Analysis Practicum. Nicole is a member of the Pima County Genealogy Society, the National Genealogical Society and the Association of Professional Genealogists.

Robin Wirthlin

Robin Wirthlin is a professional genealogist, educator, and consultant specializing in using DNA to solve complex genealogy research problems. She enjoys solving family history mysteries and breaking through "brick walls" of documentary dead-ends with DNA. Her client work includes identification of unknown or misattributed parentage and other traditional genealogy research. An avid student of emerging DNA tools and technology, Robin has taken courses in DNA, forensic genealogy, and historical documentary topics at SLIG, GRIP, and numerous conferences. Robin helped develop and is an instructor in the Research Like a Pro with DNA method. She has also created two DNA Process Tree Charts outlining concise steps through a DNA research project (available at FamilyLocket.com). Robin has a B.S. in Molecular Biology from BYU, a Certificate in Genealogical Research from Boston University, and is a member of the International Society of Genetic Genealogy (ISOGG), Association of Professional Genealogists, and the National Genealogical Society. She also blogs about DNA at FamilyLocket.com.

Made in the USA
Las Vegas, NV
09 January 2022

40836824R00190